A World Geography of Irrigation
Leonard M. Cantor

The use of water for irrigation is essential to the survival of many people in many parts of the world. Unlike other uses of water, irrigation is highly consumptive. Thus, the efficient use and effective conservation of irrigation water are of crucial importance if nations are to cope with mounting food shortages and expanding populations. The significance of this book is underscored by the fact that it is the first study to give on a world scale a synoptic picture of irrigation. Based, in part, on recent field work and research in the United States, the book examines the key geographical factors that impinge on the successful extension of irrigation.

The first part of the book, a systematic study of the geography of irrigation, includes chapters on the history of irrigation and the use of primitive methods of irrigation, past and present; modern perennial irrigation based on the use of surface and ground waters; the operational aspects of irrigation, together with associated problems such as sedimentation, salination, and waterlogging; a detailed examination of specific irrigated landscapes in different parts of the world; and a survey of the broad economic and social aspects of irrigation.

The second part consists of an up-to-date regional survey of the development of irrigation throughout the world and includes chapters on Monsoon Asia, Southwest Asia, Europe, Africa, North America, Latin America, and Australia.

THE AUTHOR: Leonard M. Cantor was born in London, where he was later educated at King's College. After teaching for several years, he joined the faculty of Keele University, England, where he now lectures in education and geography. He spent the years 1964–65 as a visiting lecturer at Reed College, Portland, Oregon, and was able to do field work on irrigation in the western part of the United States.

A World Geography of
Irrigation

FRONTISPIECE:
A Murcian huerta showing the intensive nature of irrigated agriculture along the southern coastlands of Spain, with their characteristically well-tilled soil and hand labour. The palm trees in the background give this particular part of Spain a subtropical appearance.

A World Geography of
Irrigation

Leonard M. Cantor

PRAEGER PUBLISHERS
New York · Washington

BOOKS THAT MATTER
Published in the United States of America in 1970
by Praeger Publishers, Inc., 111 Fourth Avenue,
New York, N.Y. 10003

Library of Congress Catalog Card Number: 78–101639

Printed in Great Britain

PREFACE

The study of irrigation is of particular interest to geographers. At present, when there are rapidly growing populations and a world food shortage, the expansion of irrigated agriculture to increase food production is of crucial importance. During the last twenty years the area under irrigation in the world has approximately doubled, but there has not been a corresponding increase in agricultural production. This is partly because in many countries the areas most suited to irrigation have already been developed. But it is also partly the result of a general failure to understand the complexity of the problems involved. The successful extension of irrigated agriculture is not simply a question of the construction of dams and canal networks; it also demands careful social planning and mastery of a sophisticated type of farming which is quite foreign to many farmers, especially those in developing countries. I hope that this book will help to promote an understanding of the complex geographical factors, physical, economic and human, that underlie the successful development of irrigated agriculture.

Geographers are also concerned with the contribution of irrigated agriculture to the landscapes of large areas of the world's land surface, including Monsoon Asia, the Mediterranean lands, and the arid and semi-arid lands. In these regions, its influence on land use and settlement patterns has been profound.

The book is arranged in two main sections. The first includes a systematic outline of the history of irrigation and describes the methods, both traditional and modern, by which water is applied to the land. It examines the operational problems brought about by the large-scale development of irrigation, the landscapes it creates, and the social and economic problems following in its wake. The second section describes the present condition of irrigated agriculture in the various regions of the world and is arranged on a regional basis. Here I have drawn freely upon a wide variety of standard works of regional geography to whose authors I owe an obvious debt. Where appropriate, I have included details of recent developments, based wherever possible on reliable

v

and tested information. When such information is unreliable and should be treated with caution – this is particularly true of governmental statistics of areas under irrigation – I have so indicated in the text.

My aim has been to gather information from a variety of sources, some not easily accessible in this country, and to provide for the student of geography a synoptic picture of world irrigated agriculture. The book is based partly on personal inquiry and observation in North America and Western Europe, but draws very largely from secondary sources, particularly from the United States, where there is more detailed knowledge of irrigation in all its aspects and a greater volume of literature on the subject than perhaps anywhere else in the world.

Finally, although the conclusions I draw and any errors and omissions I have made are my own, I am indebted to many who have allowed me to make use of their knowledge and who have, in a variety of ways, helped me to write this book: to Professor Emrys Jones and Mr. R. R. Rawson of the London School of Economics, who read the preliminary drafts and who have made many helpful and pertinent suggestions; to Dr. James N. Wilson of Long Beach State College, California; to Dr. R. C. Ward of the University of Hull; to the Librarians and their staffs of Reed College, Portland, Oregon, and Keele University; to Mr. Geoffrey Barber, who drew the maps and diagrams; and above all to my wife, who so tolerantly and encouragingly endured the protracted labours associated with the writing of this book.

March 1969   KEELE

CONTENTS

Section 1

IRRIGATION IN PERSPECTIVE

1 The Supply of Water 3
2 Traditional Irrigation 10
3 Modern Perennial Surface Irrigation 22
4 Modern Irrigation Based on Ground Water 40
5 Storage and Conservation 47
6 The Human Landscape of Irrigation 62
7 Economic Aspects of Irrigation 83

Section 2

THE REGIONAL GEOGRAPHY OF IRRIGATION

Introduction 99
8 Monsoon Asia 102
9 South-west Asia 131
10 Europe and Russia 150
11 Africa 178
12 North America 207
13 Latin America 222
14 Australasia 235

vii

LIST OF MAPS AND DIAGRAMS

Figure		*Page*
1	The hydrologic cycle	3
2	A kanat	18
3	The Columbia Basin project: Main irrigation works	24
4	A typical modern irrigation system (simplified)	27
5	The application of irrigation water	31
6	A well (simplified) showing the effects of continuous pumping	41
7	The Aoulef Oasis, Tidikelt, Algeria	63
8	Irrigation in the Gezira, Sudan	66
9	Ricelands of the Red River delta, North Vietnam	71
10	Tank irrigation in Ceylon	72
11	Canal and well irrigation, Uttar Pradesh, India	74
12	Irrigation on the Chenab Doab, West Pakistan	75
13	The Las Torres irrigation settlement, Guadalquivir Valley, Spain	80
14	The San Men project, China	104
15	Major irrigated areas in Indochina	110
16	Major irrigation projects in Thailand	114
17	Major irrigation areas in Java	115
18	Major irrigated areas and irrigation projects in India	119
19	The Indus Basin Plan	125
20	Irrigation in the Helmand Basin, Afghanistan	133
21	Major dams in Iran	135
22	Major irrigation works in Iraq	137
23	Irrigated areas in Syria and Lebanon	139
24	The Israel National Water Carrier and Jordan Valley Plan	143
25	The water resources of Turkey	147
26	Fontanili in the North Italian Plain	152
27	Irrigation in the lower Rhône Valley, France	154
28	Major irrigation projects in Spain	161
29	The Badajoz Plan	162
30	The Alentejo Irrigation Plan, Portugal	164
31	Major irrigation projects in Greece	165

Figure		Page
32	Major irrigated areas in Soviet Central Asia	171
33	Major irrigated areas in Caucasia	175
34	Major control structures in the Nile Basin	182
35	The Jonglei scheme	184
36	The Aswan High Dam project	186
37	Irrigated areas between the White and Blue Niles, Sudan	189
38	Water resources in North-west Africa	190
39	Main irrigated areas in Libya	193
40	The Niger River project, Mali	194
41	The Richard Toll project, Senegal	195
42	The Sabi and Lundi valleys, Rhodesia	199
43	The major irrigated areas of South Africa	201
44	The Orange River project	202
45	Irrigation schemes in Swaziland	204
46	The major irrigated areas of the western United States	208
47	The California Water Plan	211
48	The Colorado River Storage Project	214
49	The major control works of the Missouri Basin project	217
50	Major irrigated areas in Canada	219
51	Major irrigated areas in Mexico	223
52	The Papaloapan project	224
53	Irrigated areas in Peru	229
54	Major irrigation centres in north-west Argentina	230
55	Major irrigation projects in Venezuela	232
56	Irrigation in the south-east interior lowlands of Australia	237
57	The Snowy Mountains scheme	239
58	The Menindee Lakes project	241
59	The Ord River project	242
60	Irrigation schemes in South Island, New Zealand	244

LIST OF PLATES

A Murcian huerta   *Frontispiece*

(between pages 130 and 131)

1 Traditional Methods of Irrigation I
    A The shaduf, denkli or picottah
    B The sakia or Persian wheel
2 Traditional Methods of Irrigation II
    A Archimedes' screw or tambour
    B Water-wheels or norias
3 Traditional Methods of Irrigation III
    A Treadmill in China
    B Terrace irrigation in Japan
4 The Columbia Basin Project
    A Grand Coulee Dam
    B The West Canal and project area
5 The Distribution of Irrigation Water
    A Chu River, Soviet Central Asia
    B Central Valley of California
6 The Application of Irrigation Water I
    A Contour ditch irrigation
    B Border irrigation
7 The Application of Irrigation Water II
    A Furrow irrigation
    B Sprinkler irrigation
8 The Drainage of Irrigation Water
    A Waterlogging
    B Salination
9A The Transpiration of Irrigation Water:
    Water hyacinths in East Pakistan
9B The Desedimentation of Irrigation Water:
    Imperial Dam on the Colorado River

10 Irrigated Landscapes I
    A Plain of the Chao Phraya River, Thailand
    B Tank landscape in Ceylon
11 Irrigated Landscapes II
    A Nile Delta, Egypt
    B The Tunisian Sahara
12 Irrigated Landscapes III:
    The Imperial Valley of southern California
13 Monsoon Asia, India
    A The Malabar Coast of southern India
    B The Nagarjunarsagar Dam in Andhra Pradesh
14 Monsoon Asia, Pakistan
    A The Sukkur Barrage on the Indus River
    B The Mangla Dam on the Jhelum River
15 Contrasting Canal Systems in South-west Asia
    A Inundation canals, Iraq
    B Canals of the Israel National Water Carrier
16 Modern Colonisation Schemes in Europe
    A Languedoc, France
    B Badajoz Plan, Spain
17 Africa
    A Nile Delta, Egypt
    B The Jonzini Dam, Republic of South Africa
18 North America
    A St. Mary's Dam, Canada
    B The Friant-Kern Canal, United States
19 Latin America
    A Rimac Valley, Peru
    B Vineyards in central Chile
20 Australasia
    A Vineyards near Mildura, Australia
    B Canterbury Plains, New Zealand

ACKNOWLEDGEMENTS

We wish to thank the following sources who have kindly given permission for their photographs to appear in this book:

Frontispiece, plates 1A, 2A, 2B, 3A, 11B, 15A, 19A: Paul Popper Ltd.

Plates 1B, 11A, 13A, 19B: J. Allan Cash

Plate 3B: Japan Information Centre

Plates 4A, 4B, 5B, 9B, 18B: United States Bureau of Reclamation

Plate 5A: Society for Cultural Relations with the U.S.S.R.

Plate 6A, 6B: United States Department of Agriculture—Soil Conservation Service

Plates 7A, 17A: United States Information Service

Plate 7B: Wright Rain Ltd.

Plates 8A, 8B: Hunting Surveys Ltd.

Plate 9A: United Nations Food and Agriculture Organisation

Plates 10A, 10B, 20B: Aerofilms Limited

Plate 12: United States Geological Survey

Plate 13B: Camera Press Limited (photograph by David Channer)

Plates 14A, 14B: Pakistan Government

Plate 15B: Embassy of Israel, London

Plate 16A: French Government

Plate 16B: Trabajos Aéreos Fotográficos

Plate 17B: Republic of South Africa Government

Plate 18A: Province of Alberta Government

Plate 20A: Australian News and Information Bureau

We would also like to thank Faber and Faber Ltd. for permission to reproduce the extract on pages 35 and 36 from *The World Bank: A Prospect* by James Morris.

IRRIGATION IN PERSPECTIVE

CHAPTER I
THE SUPPLY OF WATER

The total amount of water contained in our planet is constant and invariable and can neither be increased nor diminished. It assumes a variety of forms, such as the oceans, moisture vapour, fresh water, lake water of varying degrees of salinity, and ice. As most of this water is locked away in the oceans, in snowfields, ice caps and glaciers, only a small proportion is available in a form readily usable by man. Moreover, a great deal of the water in and on the land is polluted by minerals or by industrial waste and so frequently rendered unusable.

Of the water contained in the oceans, a very small proportion daily changes its form and composition and is moved to the land, where it can be used by man and from where it returns to the oceans. This process, which has no beginning and no end, is known as the hydrologic cycle (Fig. 1). It comprises a gigantic system operating in and on the land and oceans of the earth and in the atmosphere surrounding it. It is estimated that something like 80,000 cubic miles of water are evaporated each year from the

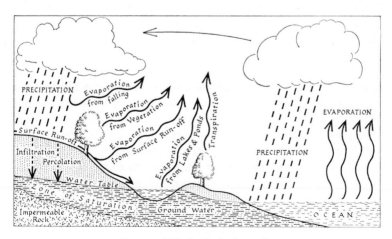

Fig. 1. The hydrologic cycle.

oceans, together with approximately 15,000 cubic miles of water evaporated from the lakes, rivers, canals and land surfaces of the continents. This total global evaporation is exactly balanced by the total precipitation, of which approximately 24,000 cubic miles in the form of water fall on the land surfaces and the rest on the oceans.[1] This cyclical movement of water is divisible into three main stages. Firstly, solar radiation, acting upon the surface of the oceans, heats the surface layers and causes evaporation and the diffusion of water vapour upwards into the atmosphere. The water vapour, which at this stage is pure, is then transported great distances by the winds. During its movement across the oceans and over the land, it may become polluted in a variety of ways: by atmospheric dust, by particles of radioactive material or by industrial and domestic smoke and soot.

In the second stage of the cycle, the air masses containing the water vapour are suddenly cooled. This cooling, which may occur for a number of reasons, though primarily as a result of the air masses being forced to rise over high ground, causes condensation to take place and rain or snow to be precipitated. Of this precipitation, some falls directly into the oceans, out of man's reach, and some is too heavily polluted to be usable.

The third and final stage is that in which the water moves back, over and under the land, into the oceans from which it came. Of the water which falls upon the land, some flows over the surface, some sinks into the soil, and some is taken up by the roots of vegetation to be used by plants and subsequently released into the atmosphere by transpiration. If, for example, an average of thirty inches of rainfall reaches the land surface each year, approximately twenty-one inches will evaporate directly or be transpired by vegetation. Of the remaining nine inches, most will run directly to the oceans as surface run-off or permeate the rock materials beneath the surface to form underground water and, at a later stage, indirectly reach the oceans. It will be seen, therefore, that the hydrologic cycle is completed in these ways; water which began in the oceans sooner or later returns to them. The only stage in the cycle at which man can, at present, intervene and make use of the water on a large scale is the third, and only then if the water is comparatively pure.

SOURCES OF WATER

In practice, there are four general sources of water available to man: surface water, ground water, atmospheric water and the oceans. By far the most important of these is surface water in the form of rivers, streams and lakes, and the greater part of this book is concerned with a description of its utilisation in the form of irrigation. Of the other three sources, ground water is increasing rapidly in importance, particularly in those areas which lack surface drainage. The use of pure water derived artificially from the atmosphere and the oceans may become significant if and when technological advances make it available on a sufficiently large scale and at an economic cost.

Ground water or, as it is sometimes called, underground water occurs below the surface of the ground in a zone of saturation, that is, the zone in which permeable rocks are saturated with water under hydrostatic pressure. Water moves down from the surface by gravity to enter this zone, the upper surface of which is called the water table or phreatic surface; for this reason, ground water is sometimes called phreatic, subsurface or subterranean water.[2] All the pores and spaces within the zone of saturation are filled with water, and its depth depends upon local geology. The lower limit of the zone is the point at which the underlying rock formation becomes so dense that water cannot penetrate it. It may vary in depth from a few feet to hundreds of feet and there are isolated examples of porous rock having been found at depths of more than a mile. The zone of saturation is very important because it supplies all wells and maintains the normal, relatively uniform flow of streams. It acts as a gigantic reservoir which retains water during wet periods, causing a rise in the water table. In this way it stores large quantities of water, which because of the slowness of movement through the zone are, under normal conditions, discharged at a fairly uniform rate.

Ground water has been laid down very unevenly beneath the surface and moves towards the oceans like surface water, only much more slowly. It flows through cracks or fissures in rocks or through water-bearing strata called aquifers. On occasions it may be trapped in aquifers by underlying impermeable rocks to form great reservoirs such as those which lie deep under the Sahara Desert. These contain pure fossil water, that is, ground water which has accumulated under past conditions over thousands of years and is no longer subject to natural recharge. In a similar category is connate water, which was trapped in the interstices of sedimentary rocks at the time they were deposited and thus differs from normal ground water, which is atmospheric in origin. Connate water may be released by subsequent igneous activity in the form of juvenile water, but both are relatively small sources of usable water. The chief uses of ground water are for irrigation and domestic purposes. It is of no direct importance for the generation of hydroelectricity but is of considerable indirect importance in that the flow of streams is primarily sustained by it. Consequently, a depletion in the supply of ground water may result in a depletion of stream flow and a diminution of water power.

Atmospheric water, or water vapour, has two major advantages over water contained in the oceans: it is to be found everywhere above the land surface and it is free of salt. For these reasons, it has been said that 'he who finds the key to precipitating water from the atmosphere solves part of one of the most difficult tasks in supplying water to needy areas, that of transportation and distribution'.[3] Unfortunately, no large-scale, successful, economic method has yet been devised to tap this water supply and direct it to places where it is most needed. One serious initial obstacle lies in the fact that clouds are not necessarily water-bearing and may be 'dry'. If, however, they do contain appreciable amounts of water vapour, this may either dry out or condense and fall as rain or snow. The most that we have been able to do is to cause a particular humid cloud—one that would almost certainly sooner or later have precipitated—to shed its moisture at a time and place of our choosing.

This is achieved in one of two ways. The first method involves the 'seeding' of clouds from aeroplanes or rockets with small particles of various chemicals, which under auspicious circumstances cause water droplets to form and precipitation to take place. The second method is to create artificial convection currents by heating a large air mass near the ground. The air thereupon rises rapidly into the cloud, upsets the equilibrium, and causes precipitation. Some local successes have been achieved by these methods, but both are expensive and both depend upon the presence of water-filled clouds, something which cannot, as yet, be ensured. Other, more widely applicable methods of bringing about artificial precipitation may one day be devised, but that day is still distant.[4]

The oceans remain by far the largest potential source of water and together with the inland seas contain 92·7 per cent of the earth's water. This water could be made potable if its saline content were reduced from about 35,000 parts per million to 500 parts per million or less. We have known for a long time that it is possible to produce fresh water by heating salt water and so promoting distillation. It is only recently, however, that such processes have been developed on anything like a large scale. A number of processes are currently in use, of which the most promising are 'flash' distillation and reverse osmosis. The former is based on the heating of brine and the reduction of pressure, which causes the liquid to 'flash' into steam. This process has been developed by British scientists, using gas-cooled nuclear reactors to supply the power, and it is generally agreed that for some time to come it will be the most economic source of desalted water.[5] Reverse osmosis, a process in which the Americans have specialised, uses semi-permeable membranes which permit the passage of water but do not allow salt ions to pass through.

Each of these processes depends upon the use of energy, which may be thermal, mechanical or solar. They each suffer from the disadvantage that the cost of desalination is very high; it has been estimated that at present in the western part of the United States, desalinated water costs between fifteen and twenty-five times more than irrigation water obtained from rivers and wells.[6] Because it is still costly to produce desalinated water, it is used almost exclusively for drinking rather than for irrigation. Exceptionally, it may be put to the latter use. In Aruba and Guernsey, for example, desalinated water is used to grow vegetables and tomatoes respectively, in the former because of local high prices and in the latter during times of drought.[7]

Because of growing world pressure on water resources, more and more stress is being laid on the need to find an economic method of producing desalinated water. In November 1964, for example, the United States and the Soviet Union signed a two-year agreement to undertake joint research into the possibilities of using atomic energy to desalinate salt water.

If, by this or other means, costs can be greatly reduced, desalinated water may have a use in improving the quality of irrigation water for crops of high value. In basins of inland drainage, the salt content of ground water is sometimes liable to increase following the deposition of fertilisers and other salts leached out of the soil. Under such conditions, the addition of desalinated water to the aquifer could help both to increase the quantity of fresh water available and to decrease its salt concentration, so that smaller quantities of water would be required on a given area of irrigated crop. There seems little doubt that the use of desalinated water opens up new and interesting possibilities in the field of water quality control. In the words of a recent United Nations report on the use of desalinated water in developing countries, 'It is possible to be cautiously optimistic concerning the role of water desalination in assisting water-short areas of developing countries to meet their water needs'.[8]

It is clear therefore that although a great deal of water is available for use by man, the supply is not infinite. While it is likely that the quantity of usable water will be increased by such technological developments as desalination and the creation of artificial precipitation, it is certain that for some time to come by far the greater proportion of our water supplies will be derived primarily from surface run-off and to a lesser extent from subterranean sources. In a complex society, water is put to a great variety of uses: for irrigating crops, for the generation of hydroelectricity, for recreation, for canals and waterways, for controlling pollution and as a source of food. In one way or another, all these uses are interdependent. For example, the construction of a modern dam promotes irrigation, the generation of hydroelectricity, flood control and recreation. Frequently, however, the uses of such natural resources as water may be to some degree competitive and mutually exclusive. Thus a choice must sometimes be made between one use and another.[9] The diversion of water from a stream for irrigation or for drinking may impair navigation and power uses downstream by decreasing stream level and flow, and may create pollution problems. Individual excessive pumping of underground water supplies may cause a general lowering of the water table with inhibiting effects on other uses of water, while the storage of water in reservoirs may cause considerable losses through evaporation.

Of all these competing uses, water for irrigation is perhaps the most important, as it is essential for the survival of many people in many parts of the world. Unlike the other uses of water, it tends to be very consumptive. That is to say, it interferes substantially with the hydrologic cycle of evaporation, rainfall and run-off; this effect is mainly due to heavy losses by evaporation. In addition, the return flow of irrigation water to rivers and canals after use does not contain the same quality of water which was originally applied to the field. It is almost always altered by varying degrees of mineral concentration and organic matter and may be unfit for some uses without ameliorating treatment.[10] For these reasons, efficient use and effective conservation of irrigation waters are of growing and crucial importance.

Bibliographical References

1. *Water* (U.S. Department of Agriculture Yearbook, 1955), p. 41.
2. *Large-Scale Ground Water Development* (United Nations, New York), 1960 (ST/ECA/65), p. 84.
3. *A Place to Live* (U.S. Department of Argiculture Yearbook, 1963), p. 95.
4. *Science and Technology for Development, II* (United Nations, New York), 1963 (E/CONF.39/1), p. 70.
5. Kronberger, H., 'Fresh Water by Nuclear Power', *New Scientist*, Oct. 7, 1965, pp. 31-33.
6. *A Place to Live, op. cit.*, p. 96.
7. *Water Desalination in Developing Countries* (United Nations, New York), 1964 (ST/ECA/82), p. 28.
8. *Ibid.*, p. 56.
9. Hirshleifer, J. and others, *Water Supply—Economics, Technology and Policy* (University of Chicago Press), 1960, p. 34.
10. Ackerman, E. A. and Löf, G.O.G., *Technology in American Water Development* (Johns Hopkins Press, Baltimore), 1959, p. 50.

CHAPTER 2

TRADITIONAL IRRIGATION

Irrigation is the artificial application of water to overcome the deficiencies in rainfall for the growing of crops. Its practice today occurs under three main conditions:

1. In the arid and semi-arid regions of the world, where its use has been most extensive and where it has been practised for thousands of years. In areas such as Egypt, West Pakistan, coastal Peru and South-west Asia, cultivation would be virtually impossible without it. In these regions the water is derived partly from rivers which, like the Nile and Indus, rise in better-watered areas and flow across them, and partly from underground sources.

2. In areas which have a marked seasonal shortage of rain, like Monsoon Asia and lands with a Mediterranean climate. In the former region, irrigation makes possible the cultivation of crops during the rainless winter months, as the temperatures are high enough during this season to promote plant growth. In lands with a Mediterranean climate, the summer is the season of drought, and it is at this time of year that irrigation is widely used in such areas as the southern coastlands of France and Spain, the North Italian Lowland, the Central Valley of California and central Chile.

3. In generally humid areas, where the rainfall is normally sufficient to promote plant growth and where irrigation is used as a safeguard against drought and to promote higher yields. This form of irrigation is termed supplemental irrigation; that is to say, it supplements the local rainfall. It differs therefore from the two previous instances in that it is essentially a means of improving the existing kind of agriculture rather than creating an altogether new type of agriculture, as is frequently the case in arid areas. It is most widely used in the eastern half of the United States, in the Soviet Union and in western Europe.

It is not always possible to make a clear distinction between these three conditions, and some irrigated areas meet the criteria of both 2 and 3 above. In parts of Monsoon Asia, for example, in the Ganges Plain where modern projects provide water all the year round, 'controlled' irrigation not only provides the entire water supply for crops in the dry season but is also available to supplement the monsoon in the wet season. In many parts of South-east Asia, however, such projects do not exist, and cultivation is largely restricted to the summer months when the heavy monsoon rains provide the basis for uncontrolled irrigation.

Uncontrolled irrigation is the use of water from river floods, which are led through inundation canals into fields and which subsequently drain back of their own accord. In such situations, control devices are generally absent or inefficient. This form of irrigation has certain disadvantages. In the absence of large-scale water control devices, floodwaters may flood the fields before sowing is complete. The openings to the channels which lead the water into the fields may frequently become blocked with sediment and their effectiveness greatly impaired. At other times, the level of the river may not be high enough to allow the water to flow through the channels and into the fields. Consequently, if lifting devices are inadequate or absent, fields may suffer from lack of water even though it may lie just beyond them on the other side of a river levee. Too often, methods of transferring water from the rivers to the fields are crude, and primitive means of irrigation such as wooden buckets and hand scoops are commonly in use. Rainfed irrigation is also common in South-east Asia and is applied principally to paddy fields, which are surrounded by mud banks forming basins and retaining the natural rainfall to provide the wet conditions in which rice is grown. Such a system requires little, if any, artificial water control but suffers from the disadvantage that water cannot be stored for long periods, with the result that cultivation tends to be restricted to the rainy season and only single cropping is possible.

IRRIGATION IN EARLY TIMES

The precise origin of irrigated agriculture is not known, but there is no doubt that it has been in existence for many thousands of years in the arid and semi-arid regions of Asia, Africa and the Americas. There are frequent references in the Bible to irrigation, including the following passages from Genesis (2:10) and II Kings (3:16-17):

And a river went out of Eden to water the garden; and from thence it was parted, and became into four heads.

And he said, Thus saith the Lord, Make this valley full of ditches: For thus saith the Lord, Ye shall not see wind, neither shall ye see rain; yet that valley shall be filled with water, that ye may drink, both ye, and your cattle, and your beasts.

Certainly, irrigation antedates recorded history and it was practised in the Nile Valley between 3000 and 2500 B.C. Early rulers of Egypt were instrumental in developing the elaborate irrigation systems upon which their culture was based; technical developments which were first used at this time include the artesian well, the Nilometer for gauging streams, and the development of great canal systems for both irrigation and navigation. In addition, the earliest known mechanical aids for lifting water from one level to another were developed. These included such simple devices as the use of waterproofed baskets to lift water from the river into irrigation ditches as well as more complicated devices such as the *shaduf* and the *sakia*, all still in daily use in the Nile Valley.

By about 3000 B.C. the Mohenjo-daro civilisation of the Indus Valley had developed a great variety of tanks and irrigation canals. At much the same time the great Babylonian Empire flourished, rooted in a prosperous irrigated agriculture which drew its water, by an extensive system of storage and canals, from the Tigris and Euphrates. By about 500 B.C. Persia, under the rule of Darius, had also developed great irrigation works. There, water was brought to arid lands by tunnels dug for many miles into the surrounding mountains to tap underground sources, from which the water flowed by gravity. These tunnels (*kanats* as they are called in Persia) often extended hundreds of feet below the surface and are still constructed and used in much the same way as they were 2,500 years ago.[1] China also possessed great irrigation structures, whose antiquity rivalled that of Egyptian, Babylonian and Indian irrigation works. Irrigation in China probably began on a small scale in the loess hills around the great bend of the Hwang-Ho. As a more complex society evolved and a strong central administration developed, it became possible to extend irrigation to the plains and deltas to the east and to build the extensive control works and canals which the utilisation of the great rivers necessitated. A great irrigation development took place in the third century before Christ when the Imperial Canal, 700 miles long and one of the greatest engineering works in the world, was constructed.

In India irrigation developed considerably in the first centuries after Christ, both in the Ganges valley and in the south. In the deltas of the southern rivers, water control became a complex and large-scale undertaking made possible only by the existence of large and well-settled states. Barrages, tanks and canals developed in these regions and were copied by neighbouring countries as far away as Indonesia for the cultivation of rice.*

Irrigated agriculture also flourished in the Americas before Christ. The Incas of Peru developed a civilisation of great size whose features included large irrigation structures of considerable ingenuity. Similar evidence of advanced agricultural civilisations based upon extensive and skilful irrigation is also to be found in Chile and Mexico. Irrigation flourished in New Mexico and Arizona soon after the birth of Christ. It has been estimated that in the Salt River valley of Arizona, for example, more than 250,000 acres of land were irrigated by more than 1,000 miles of canals and ditches.[2]

Such irrigation developments were the products of complex civilisations which had progressed beyond the subsistence stage of agriculture. They required the construction of enormous public works, control of the water supply for irrigation and an inevitable development of bureaucracy. In Egypt an important official position was that of 'superintendent of the irrigated lands of the Pharaoh', and later the title 'chief of irrigation' was bestowed.[3] In short, a prosperous irrigated agriculture depended upon stable societies. Once these were undermined by war, conquest, disease or the silting up of reservoirs and canals, irrigated agriculture collapsed with them. On the other hand, the rejuvenation of irrigation has occurred in many places at many times.

From its recorded beginnings in Egypt and Asia, irrigation spread rapidly westwards and reached the Phoenicians, who were constructing irrigation canals as early as 1500 B.C. In the first

---

* For a more detailed description of irrigation in early times, v. Jacquetta Hawkes and Sir Leonard Woolley, *History of Mankind: Cultural and Scientific Development* (Allen & Unwin, London), 1963-65; especially II, Pt. 1, pp. 121-22; Pt. 2, pp. 382-83; Pt. 3, p. 728.

century before Christ, Julius Caesar introduced irrigation into the countries which he conquered, and by the first century A.D., irrigated agriculture was widely practised in the Roman Empire. During the Middle Ages, the Moors were among the leaders in spreading knowledge about irrigation, and they developed extensive irrigation systems in Spain during the twelfth century, with the result that some of the most arid regions of the country became the most productive. Subsequently, irrigation was practised extensively in Italy, France and other parts of southern Europe.

PRIMITIVE METHODS OF LIFTING AND STORING WATER

Until recent times, irrigation was based on relatively primitive devices for lifting and storing water, devices which have been in use for thousands of years in many parts of the world and which, to a diminishing extent, are still in use today, particularly in developing countries.

One of the most common of the primitive lifting devices is the Egyptian shaduf, or *shadoof*. It usually consists of two upright poles joined by a crossbeam at a point eight to ten feet above the ground. At right angles to the crossbeam is attached a long pole, at one end of which is hung a rope supporting a skin or bucket; and at the other end is a mass of clay or heavy weight to act as a counterbalance. The rope is pulled down manually and the bucket dipped into the stream or well. When the bucket is full of water, the rope is released, the counterbalance falls and the bucket rises. It is then pivoted round on the crossbeam and emptied into a canal or ditch from which the water runs into the field. A typical shaduf, known also as the *denkli* or *picottah* in India, can irrigate an area of about two acres.

A more elaborate lifting device is the Egyptian sakia or *sakiyeh*, known as the Persian wheel, or in India as the *harat*. It consists of a horizontal toothed wheel engaged to a smaller vertical wheel to which a series of buckets is attached. A beam is connected to the horizontal wheel and an ox or cow is yoked to the outer end of the beam. The animal, sometimes blindfolded to prevent giddiness, walks in a circular path, thereby revolving the horizontal wheel which in turn revolves the vertical wheel. The buckets, hung over a well, dip into it and scoop up the water, which they empty into a channel leading to the fields. Depending on the size of the wheel and the corresponding height of the lift, a typical sakia can irrigate an area of between five and twelve acres.

Both the shaduf and sakia are of considerable antiquity. Slightly more recent is Archimedes screw or *tambour*, a lifting device invented by Archimedes' of Syracuse about 200 B.C. It consists of a wooden cylinder between ten and fifteen feet long with a diameter of between one and two feet. Along the whole of its length the cylinder contains a corkscrew-shaped diaphragm, to the top of which is attached a crank handle. The lower end of the cylinder is placed in the water and the top end rests on the bank of the stream. The crank handle is turned manually and water is cranked up the cylinder, issuing from the top into a channel leading to the fields. Such a device has a lift of about three feet and accordingly irrigates only a relatively small area.

In parts of the Middle East and South-west Asia, the river current is used to lift water by means of water-wheels. The most famous examples, still in use, are in Syria where they are called *noria*. Probably the earliest machines in which water power was used to perform work, they consist of great wooden wheels, up to seventy feet in diameter, to which wooden buckets are fixed. Turned by the current of the Orontes River, the wheels raise the water and discharge it into aqueducts, frequently of Roman construction, which carry it away to irrigate the fields. In parts of North Vietnam, similar wheels are used, between twenty-five and thirty-five feet in diameter and built entirely of bamboo.

An equally ancient water-lifting device is the windmill, typical of the Greek islands. Wind power turns the sails of the mills to lift the water into small reservoirs, from which it is led into the irrigated fields.

Most of these primitive devices require human or animal power to operate them. Moreover, they can irrigate only relatively small areas and only then when the water in the river or well is sufficiently high to permit their use. They are obviously not necessary during the limited period when rivers like the Nile and Ganges flood their floodplains. At such times in Egypt and India, inundation canals are used to carry water to the fields. They have been used for hundreds of years and consist of ditches cut parallel to the rivers in the floodplains. The canals fill with water as the river rises and are therefore dependent upon the volume of water brought down by the river. If the river is low they are likely to remain dry and possibly fail precisely when they are needed most. Besides, their offtakes are liable to silt up readily.

In Egypt inundation canals were and are used to lead water into another relatively primitive form of irrigation, basin irrigation. Large areas of the floodplain of the Nile were enclosed with substantial earth banks, and the floodwaters of the river led by canal into the 'basin' thus formed until they reached a depth of between three and four feet. Many of these enclosures were very large, some enclosing areas of about 60,000 acres. Series of linked basins were sometimes formed which could be served by one through canal. After giving the area a thorough watering, the water was eventually drained out of the basin and the exposed area sown with crops, which needed no further water. Such a system has two great virtues: the floodwaters of the Nile bring with them fertilising silt which is deposited in the basin, and the waters running back into the river provide an effective form of drainage, thereby preventing excessive salinity. This method of irrigation, which is still in use, notably in Upper Egypt, is clearly dependent upon the fact that the River Nile annually spills over its floodplain; with a different river regime, the expense would be enormous. The great disadvantage of this method is that it allows only one crop to be grown a year, during the winter after the floods have subsided.

Reservoirs are equally ancient, and one of the earliest forms was the tank or *jheel*, the earthen embanked reservoir of India and Ceylon. Many Ceylonese tanks have supported irrigated agriculture for over a thousand years. While many fell into disuse as a result of conquest, war and plague, particularly malarial epidemics, others have been restored and repaired and a few have been continuously in use for more than a millennium.

A tank need not be thought of as indicating a very small reservoir; in north-east Ceylon, the Minneriya tank built in A.D. 900, whose surface dimensions measure six miles by two miles and with a reservoir capacity of 66,000 acre-feet*, serves an area of 11,200 acres, yielding two rice crops a year. The Parakrama tank, also in Ceylon and built in A.D. 1200, with a capacity of

---

* An acre-foot (43,560 gallons) is the amount of water required to cover one acre of land flooded to a depth of one foot. The rate of flow is measured in cubic feet per second. A flow of one cubic foot per second will furnish nearly two acre-feet in twenty-four hours.

57,000 acre-feet, serves an area of 21,000 acres.[4] Frequently, a whole stream may be reduced to a line of tanks, with the lower ones trapping and using water which has already been used in those above. Such tanks lose a great deal of water by evaporation and seepage, and unless cleaned regularly, they become filled with silt and are eventually rendered unusable.[5] In parts of Ceylon, the seepage water from tanks is utilised for coconut trees and gardens.

Tanks are used in some of the hillier parts of India and Ceylon to supply water for terrace irrigation. In areas of strong relief where level land is at a premium, terraces, often of considerable antiquity, have been laboriously carved into the hillsides. Irrigation works, sometimes of equal antiquity, have been constructed to supply them with water and may consist of tanks or tunnels through the hillsides. In the Szechwan Basin of China, where outcropping sediments often make natural benches to facilitate the construction of terraces, many farmers convert some of their terraces into storage ponds during the winter, thus ensuring an adequate water supply for spring irrigation. In this area fifty terrace levels, one above the other, are not uncommon.[6] Equally remarkable as a feat of engineering are the Ifugao terraces in northern Luzon in the Philippines, which cover an area of about 250 square miles. Terraces of this kind are irregular, following the configuration of the land, and are supplied by mountain streams with water that is led into irrigation channels.[7]

Wells of one sort or another have also been in use for many centuries as a form of year-round irrigation. Hand-dug wells have been constructed in almost every country in the world from time immemorial, and they still provide the principal source of water in many rural areas. It is estimated that over the centuries more than 30,000 kanats have been dug in Iran, of which 22,000 are still in operation. Kanats, which are found in many arid areas of suitable topography, are known as *karez* in Baluchistan, *korag* in Sinkiang, *foggara* in the Sahara and chains-of-wells in Cyprus. They consist of lines of wells or pits which run up hillsides or alluvial cones. The bases of the wells in each line are connected by tunnels to provide a continuous channel from the hillside ground-water source to the fields, where the channel comes to the surface (Fig. 2).

Water is still frequently raised from wells by primitive lifting devices; for shallow wells the shaduf is used and for deeper ones, the sakia. Individually, wells can irrigate only relatively small areas, the largest rarely exceeding twelve acres, but in aggregate they may be very important.

Primitive methods of storing and lifting water have obvious limitations. In the Nile Valley, for example, they served to irrigate only a narrow strip of land on either side of the river, and then only as long as the river itself carried a sufficient volume of water to fill the canals. Because of the lack of extensive storage facilities,

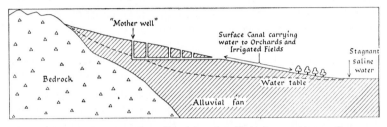

FIG. 2. A kanat. A line of horizontal wells is dug tapping underground water in the upper slopes of alluvial fans. A kanat may be tens of miles long and the mother well hundreds of feet deep.

primitive methods are unable to sustain a stable agriculture of any considerable extent. In years when the volume of water carried by the Nile River was low, relatively little could reach the land; such were 'the seven lean years' of the Bible. It has long been realised that these disasters could be overcome by storing water during flood times for use during the dry season, but an effective means of storing water on a large scale, with the accompanying development of modern perennial or year-round irrigation, has only been developed within the last hundred years.

PROPERTY RIGHTS IN WATER

In the arid lands, where irrigation was all-important, property in water long antedated property in land, so that property rights became associated with the uses of water for irrigation and drinking. The habits of men and the forms of their social organisations have often been influenced more by their close association with water than with the land by which they earned their bread.[8] That this characteristic continues is shown by the example of

Egypt both in the recent past and today. It has been suggested that the development of perennial irrigation during the last century has affected the very nature of the Egyptian village and the relations among its inhabitants. When the floodwaters of the Nile were the sole source of water, the villages had to be placed on mounds or hills to keep them above the water level, and the villagers had to work together to build dykes and basins and in general to engage in a corporate life based on their common needs. The coming of perennial irrigation meant that the villages did not have to be elevated and that the work of maintaining the irrigation system fell upon a central administration. As a consequence, the real purpose and motive of social co-operation, based upon agricultural necessity, vanished and Egypt was faced with the enormously difficult problem of a decaying and somewhat disrupted large village system.[9]

Throughout history, competition for the use of water has led to disputes of one sort or another and, not infrequently, complex legal tangles have resulted. In general, three different principles governing rights to the use of water are common in various parts of the world: the riparian, appropriation and equitable distribution doctrines. In some areas, like England and the eastern United States, where water is relatively plentiful, the riparian doctrine of water rights has developed, based upon common law. It gives the holders of land bordering on water, or riparian land, the right to a 'reasonable use' of water. Reasonable use is commonly defined to include domestic and agricultural uses, and may or may not include industrial use.

In some parts of the world, usually those more recently settled, like some of the western states of America, the appropriation doctrine of water rights law is generally applied. According to this, the rights to the use of water are vested in the person who first uses it. More recently this rather harsh doctrine has been replaced in some areas by that of equitable distribution, which makes it possible for non-riparian users to obtain the right to use a certain quantity of water by obtaining a permit or a court order and by meeting certain requirements. Separate provisions customarily apply to ground water.[10] In America its use is frequently determined by the rule of capture; that is, he with the biggest, deepest well may pump all the water he wishes even if he exhausts the aquifer and causes neighbouring wells to go dry.

Some of these doctrines are clearly the direct antithesis of sound conservation. However, practice varies enormously in different parts of the world and in areas that have long been farmed under irrigation it tends to be very complex. In Morocco, for example, the rights of preference for the use of water pass from human beings to animals, to crops and finally to industries. The farmers in the plains are allowed a certain time at the water source, be it a well, spring or pond, and the local community as a whole works out regulations concerning the use of water and fines governing its misuse. Over the centuries, elaborate series of agreements, usually verbal, have developed to deal with the construction and maintenance of irrigation works.[11] In Jordan, under Moslem law the major springs and rivers are in private control and water may be sold with or without land.[12] Competition for the use and control of water in arid countries such as Morocco and Jordan is age-old. A Babylonian code of water laws dating from 2050 B.C. assigned the following order to water rights: first, men and beasts; second, household use; third, irrigation; and fourth, navigation. It also decreed penalties for wasting water.[13]

There have been, and still are, many disputes over water, between Egypt and the Sudan over the Nile waters, between Iran and Afghanistan, between the United States and Mexico, and not infrequent rivalries between state governments in the American west. It seems inevitable that as the demand for water grows, so will controversy over its use. On the other hand, the equitable sharing of the resources of river basins by two or more countries is not uncommon. Where such collaboration has taken place, it has made possible the implementation of projects which neither country could have achieved by itself and which have richly rewarded both. Examples include the Soviet Union and Turkey with respect to rivers along their common frontier, the United States and Canada with regard to the St. Lawrence and Columbia rivers, the United States and Mexico along the Rio Grande, and the construction of the Aswan High Dam which is being made possible by agreement and co-operation between the Sudan and Egypt.

Bibliographical References

1. Cressey, G. B., *Crossroads : Land and Life in Southwest Asia* (Lippin-cott, New York), 1960, p. 149 *et seq.*; Spate, O. H. K., *India and Pakistan* (Methuen, London), 1960, p. 211.

2. Huffman, R. E., *Irrigation Development and Public Water Policy* (Ronald Press, New York), 1953, p. 13.

3. Westermann, W. L., 'The Development of the Irrigation of Egypt', *Classical Philology*, XIV, No. 2, April 1919, pp. 158-64.

4. Straus, M. W., *Report on South Asian Food, Water and Power Development* (U.S. Department of the Interior), 1952, p. 33.

5. Spate, *op. cit.*, p. 209. (*v.* also pp. 733-37 for detailed description of tank irrigation in south-east India.)

6. Cressey, G. B., *Land of the 500 Million* (McGraw-Hill, New York), 1955, pp. 180-81.

7. Grist, D. H., *Rice* (Longmans, London), 1953, p. 26.

8. *Water* (U.S. Department of Agriculture Yearbook, 1955), p. 2.

9. Berger, M., *The Arab World Today* (Doubleday Anchor, New York), 1964, p. 43.

10. *State Administration of Water Resources* (The Council of State Governments, Chicago), 1957, pp. 30-31.

11. Mihesell, M. W., *Northern Morocco, A Cultural Geography*, University of California Publications in Geography, XIV (University of California Press, Berkeley), 1961, p. 87.

12. Harris, G. L., *Jordan*, Survey of World Cultures Series (Hraf Press, New Haven), 1958, p. 154.

13. Huffman, *op. cit.*, p. 33.

CHAPTER 3
MODERN PERENNIAL SURFACE IRRIGATION

During the last century, technological advances have brought about a great expansion in irrigated agriculture. The first large-scale, modern irrigation systems, which usually consisted of a simple diversion dam linked to headworks and canals, developed in the second half of the nineteenth century in Egypt and India. In these countries the physical conditions were favourable. Gentle surface gradients permitted the construction of canals based on a relatively low and therefore relatively inexpensive form of headwork which had an extensive 'field of command' and could irrigate large areas. Moreover, large quantities of water were available from the Nile and the Indus and Ganges which, together with their fertile alluvial soils and virtually year-round growing season, enabled two or three crops to be grown a year. Northern India was especially favoured because of the gentle gradients of the Indo-Gangetic Plain and the fact that the diminished winter flow of rivers was reinforced in spring by the melting of the Himalayan snows, bridging the critical period before the advent of the monsoon rains.[1]

Gradually, as the more readily accessible land has been developed and the simpler storage utilised, projects of greater size and complexity have been required, culminating in the large, multi-purpose projects of today. In many developing countries of Africa and Asia, we find cheek by jowl some of the oldest and some of the newest irrigation structures, with primitive methods of lifting and storing water in close proximity to modern dams and canal networks.

The greater part of these modern projects is based on the year-round use of surface waters, frequently associated with large-scale, multi-purpose schemes, which may be conveniently divided into four sections: (*a*) storage and diversion, (*b*) distribution, (*c*) application and (*d*) drainage.

STORAGE AND DIVERSION

The regime of most great rivers is irregular. Frequently, they carry their greatest volumes of water following the torrential thaws of spring, which fill the river and which, without conservation, would rush heedlessly to the sea. At other times of the year, in late autumn and winter, they may be reduced to mere trickles of water. To control these rivers and to regularise their regimes by storing water in the dry seasons, dams and reservoirs are constructed.

Dams, known also as barrages and weirs, are barriers built across rivers or streams to control the flow of water. Today most dams have several functions, which may include the storage and diversion of water for irrigation, the raising of water for generating hydroelectricity, and the provision of flood control. Dams have been constructed for thousands of years, at first of earth and later of stone. There are records of a huge earthen dam across the Tigris and a large masonry dam across the Nile, both built in almost prehistoric times, while the remains of the ancient tanks of Ceylon and India bear witness to the fact that dam construction dates from a very early period. The crucial disadvantage of these dams was that eventually their lakes filled with silt and became useless. It was not until modern times that a dam was built with sufficient sluiceway near its base to allow all the floodwaters to pass through carrying their heavy load of silt so that the following clean waters could then be arrested. In this way, a dam and reservoir could be constructed across a silty river and yet remain reasonably free of sedimentation. The first example of such a dam is the Periyar Dam built in India in 1895. It was followed shortly after by the Aswan Dam built in 1902 across the Nile.

It is a simple physical fact, and one long realised, that if a river can be dammed upstream from the point at which its waters are to be used, then a difference in level can be created sufficient to allow the water to be led by gravity through canals and into the cultivated area. With diversion dams, like the Sennar across the Nile and the Sukkur across the Indus, the sluices or gates contained in them may be closed to create a higher level on the upstream side of the dam. In this way, a vast reservoir is created from which the water flows by gravity through the main canals.*

* When the level of the water in the reservoir falls below the entrance to the

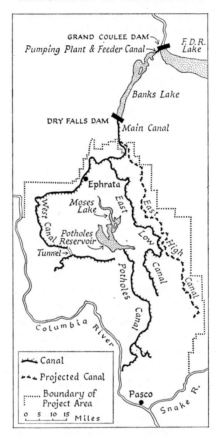

FIG. 3. The Columbia Basin project:
Main irrigation works.

Sometimes, the source of water may be lower than the area to be irrigated, especially if the river runs in a canyon, and the water itself often has to be transported considerable distances from the river to the fields. In such cases, complex systems of pumping stations and canals may be necessary to lift and move the water from the reservoir to the fields.

---

main canals, it may become necessary to lift the water into them. For this purpose, oil pumps are sometimes mounted on rafts upstream from the dam. Such pumping schemes are generally expensive to run and are therefore only practicable in areas like the Sudan Gezira, where crops command a high market price. (H. Tempany and D. H. Grist, *An Introduction to Tropical Agriculture*, Longmans, 1958, pp. 152-54.)

A typical example illustrating the complexity and scale of the storage and diversion of water in a modern irrigation scheme is the Columbia Basin project in the south central part of the state of Washington, in the north-west United States (Fig. 3). The project is typical of many modern schemes in that it is designed to serve multiple purposes: irrigation, power generation, flood control, improvement of navigation, stream-flow regulation and recreation.

Central Washington is one of the few locations in the semi-arid American west where the water supply exceeds the capacity of adjacent dry land to absorb most of it in irrigation works, but it has only recently been irrigated. The reason is that the great water supply is in the upper Columbia River, which flows into a canyon about 1,600 feet deep, from 60 to 150 miles from the irrigable land. To put water onto the land, it is therefore necessary to lift it 630 feet into the Grand Coulee, the diversion channel of the Columbia River's ice-age ancestor, and to carry it about 60 miles in canals, tunnels and inverted siphons to the edge of the irrigable area.

The key structure in the project is the Grand Coulee Dam, completed in 1941. It is 4,173 feet long and stands 370 feet above the surface of the river. It has a total height from bedrock of 550 feet including the lower section below the river surface, and weighs about 72 million tons. It is a 'gravity' dam; that is, it depends upon its weight alone to prevent water pressure on its upstream face from tipping it over or causing it to slide on its base. Behind Grand Coulee Dam, Franklin D. Roosevelt Lake extends 151 miles to the Canadian boundary and has a shoreline of 600 miles. The height of the dam and the maximum level of the reservoir were determined by the height of the Columbia River at the Canadian border, so that to prevent water backing into Canada, the water level in the lake is not allowed to rise more than 1,290 feet above sea level. The lake impounds about 9·4 million acre-feet of water, part of which is used to supplement the natural flow of the river in the winter when the flow is not sufficient to meet power demands. During spring and summer the river is fed by melting ice and snow. During the peak flow, usually between May and September, the eleven drum gates at the crest of the 1,605-foot-wide spillway are gradually opened and surplus water is allowed to pour over the dam.

At the western end of the dam is a pumping plant driven by

power generated from the dam's power station. The pumping plant lifts water from behind the dam some 280 feet through steel pipes into a feeder canal which flows into Banks Lake, an equalising reservoir twenty-seven miles long. Banks Lake is formed between two earth and rock dams across the Grand Coulee, a watercourse cut through the lava plateau by the Columbia River, when glacial diversion temporarily caused it to flow south during the Ice Age. From Banks Lake irrigation water flows across the project area by gravity, with some supplementary pumping, through a system of canals including the Main Canal, the West Canal and the East Low Canal. Near the centre of the project area is the Potholes Reservoir, south of Moses Lake, which conserves run-off water from irrigated lands in the north by means of a diversion dam, and directs it through the Potholes Canal for use in the southern part of the basin. These canals and reservoirs form the network of waterways that can now deliver water to almost half of the irrigable acres of the project area. By the end of 1961 the distribution system consisted of 288 miles of main canal, 1,623 miles of lateral canals and 735 miles of drains. Water has been made available each year to new acreages varying from 6,600 to 66,000 acres per annum. Thus, in 1964 facilities were on hand to irrigate approximately 470,000 acres of land comprising 5,448 farming units.

Before the full scheme can be developed, however, there is still much work to be done. The East Low Canal, expected to furnish water to the south-east tip of the project, will have to be extended, and the East High Canal, which will roughly parallel the East Low Canal and will serve water to the east of the area now irrigated by the East Low Canal, will have to be constructed. Also, miles of main and secondary waterways and related irrigation structures will have to be built throughout the project area. The pumping plant at the Grand Coulee Dam will require six more pumps to lift the greater water volume into the irrigation system in order to serve the full project. When completed, the total irrigable area will be more than a million acres and will serve water to about 10,000 farms.

DISTRIBUTION

Clearly, a large-scale perennial system of irrigation like the Columbia Basin project requires a complex network of dams, pumping stations and canals. In addition to the main dam, whose reservoir is the main storage unit, smaller diversion dams are needed to direct the water into an intricate canal system. The water is led from the dams into broad canals by gravity, and where these major canals, because of local physical conditions, are unable to receive their required water by gravity, pumping stations may

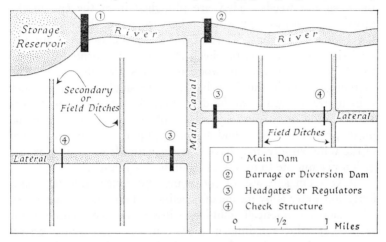

FIG. 4. A typical modern irrigation system (simplified). Water is stored behind the main dam (1) and released through sluices into the river, from which it is diverted into the main canal by a barrage or diversion dam (2). It is then released through headgates (3) into lateral canals from which it is diverted by check structures (4) into the secondary or field ditches.

be installed. These plants frequently receive their power from energy generated from power stations at the main storage dam.

From the main canals, water is diverted into a system which will distribute it throughout the farm (Fig. 4). The most common means by which this is done is with open ditches or laterals, and the flow of water into them is controlled by headgates or regulators. The ditches are generally permanent features and commonly follow property boundary lines, fences and edges of fields. They are frequently earth ditches, which may suffer from excessive losses owing to seepage and evaporation, especially in arid regions or in areas of porous, sandy or gravelly soils. In an attempt to eliminate such wastage, the use of plastic tubing in place of open ditches to carry water from the canal to the land has recently been introduced in the United States. Plastic tubing also has to its advantage portability and a fairly low initial cost, and it prevents the loss of land otherwise used for ditches.

Leading from the permanent open ditches are secondary or field ditches. These are usually more conspicuous because they are newly dug when required and consequently are not hidden by grass and weeds. They are ploughed in at the end of the growing season, as they would otherwise act as obstacles during harvesting. Water is delivered from these ditches to the areas to be irrigated by means of check structures or turnouts. These usually consist of metal or wooden fixtures, though they may be merely gaps cut in the ditch bank. Increasingly, however, water is being transferred from the ditch over the ditch bank into individual fields or furrows by means of siphons. These may be plastic, metal or rubber, and depending upon the size and volume of the water supply, may have flow capacities from as little as one gallon per minute to over 1,000 gallons per minute.

A very efficient way of conveying and distributing farm and irrigation water is by means of pipelines. This method has many advantages: it practically eliminates losses due to evaporation and seepage, it reduces maintenance work, makes water control easier, eliminates the problem of weeds which grow along the banks of the open ditches, and makes it possible for water to be carried by gravity or under pressure. Such pipelines may be permanent installations or portable. The former usually consist of buried concrete supply and distribution lines, while the latter consist of metal or flexible surface pipes. Because of the very high cost of installation, however, pipelines are still relatively uncommon, and they are generally found in areas where water is scarce and crops are valuable.

To ensure that irrigation water is used economically and efficiently, the irrigator must know the size of the stream he is using and the amount of water that he takes from it, so that he can divert the water from the ditch to the field and lower water safely from one elevation to another. In a modern irrigation system, the measurement and control of water are efficient and highly developed procedures. They include the use of such devices as weirs, division boxes, which divide a stream into two or more ditches and may be equipped with control gates, and checks, which are small, adjustable 'dams' placed in irrigation ditches to provide a means of controlling the depth of water serving turnouts. In order to avoid wastage and over-irrigation and to control the supply of water to individual fields, automatic water dividers and meters may be used and have, for example, recently been installed in parts of Bulgaria.[2]

These are some of the main engineering elements to be found in modern irrigation systems and represent a complex of factors which an efficient farmer has to consider. Having decided to what uses he wishes to put his land, he should then select the methods of irrigation best suited to them. However, at this stage, other considerations have to be taken into account. For example, the farm equipment at his disposal may have some bearing on the methods of irrigation under consideration: large-scale machinery will not be practicable on some of the small fields required for certain irrigation methods.

The amount of available labour must also be taken into account, since a system which may be installed cheaply may be very expensive to operate because of the amount of labour required. Some methods of irrigation require operators with a high degree of skill in adjusting the flow of water, while others can be operated by anyone who can open and close the water control structures. With some systems, a single irrigator can handle large streams of water, while others require an irrigator for each 200 to 300 gallons per minute of irrigation stream.

Last, but certainly not least, some schemes are considerably more expensive to set up than others, and in some countries, lack of capital is the decisive factor in determining the nature of the irrigation system.

APPLICATION

The methods by which irrigation is applied to the land should depend, under ideal conditions, on individual land features such as the slope of the land, the crops to be irrigated, the nature of the water supply and the ability of the soil to absorb and hold water. The wise application of irrigation therefore involves a considerable degree of expertise, based on the principle that enough water should be provided to satisfy the needs of the plants without causing waste and damage to plants or the land. The methods of irrigation in current use, which vary enormously in complexity all over the world, are most highly developed in technologically advanced nations like the United States. There one finds four general methods of applying water, all of which require virtually complete control of the water at all times: (*a*) by flooding, thus wetting all the land surface; (*b*) by furrows, thus wetting only part of the ground surface; (*c*) by sprinkling, in which the soil is wetted with a spray; (*d*) by subirrigation, in which the soil is wetted only a little if at all, but in which the subsoil is saturated. The first three methods come under the general heading of surface irrigation.

Flood irrigation* covers the surface of the field, or sections of it, with continuous sheets of water, which may be contained by low dykes or border ridges. The fields thus watered may be sub-divided into strips or basins. With basins, the basic principle is similar to that used for thousands of years in the Egyptian basins and elsewhere, with the vital difference that the farmer has complete control over the amount and timing of the irrigation. Water is frequently led from a supply canal by a lateral into a succession of secondary ditches (Fig. 5a). From the supply canal, water enters the top secondary or field ditch, in which a gap is made so that the water can flow across the field. As soon as the water reaches the bottom of the field, the gap is closed and another opened upstream in the secondary ditch. This process continues until the whole field has been flooded. A modified form of flood irrigation is contour ditch irrigation, in which the land is laid out in normal contouring and the contours are used as secondary ditches. The secondary ditches are usually closely spaced and contain small outlets at frequent intervals, so that the water will spread evenly over the land when the water surface is raised in the ditch. Siphon tubes can be used in place of open outlets to distribute the water over the field.

Another form of flood irrigation is border or strip irrigation, in which banks are made at intervals at right angles to the field ditches, thereby dividing the field into a number of strips generally varying from 10 to 20 yards in width and 100 to 400 yards in length. By this means the water is advanced down the narrow strip of land, entering the soil as it moves across the field. This method limits the area over which water can spread from the openings and is thus more suitable for use where the water supply is limited[3] (Fig. 5b).

---

* The term *flood irrigation* is also applied to the uncontrolled use of floodwaters. See p. 11.

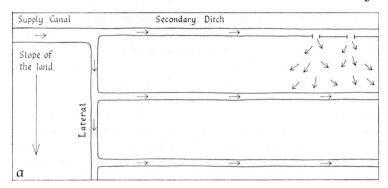

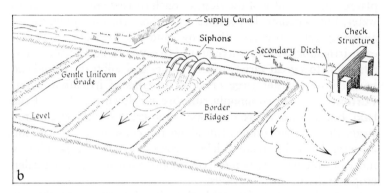

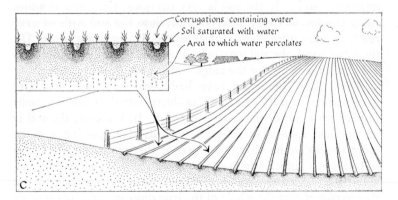

FIG. 5. The application of irrigation water. (*a*) Flood irrigation. (*b*) Border or strip irrigation. (*c*) Corrugation irrigation.

Flood irrigation generally requires large streams or canals, gentle topography (ground slopes should usually be no greater than three per cent) and careful levelling of the land. In theory, it should be possible to ensure that every part of the area to be irrigated absorbs the predetermined amount of water; but in practice, although all parts usually receive an adequate amount, some receive too much. For this reason, flood irrigation is more suited to close-growing crops like hay or permanent pastures.

Furrow irrigation is a method by which water is run in furrows, normally made by cultivating between crop rows. The earth is thrown up into ridges between the furrows and the seeds are planted in the centre of the ridges. Each furrow normally receives water, but occasionally potatoes and other crops are irrigated by applying water to every other row, and the rows are alternated each irrigation. Furrow irrigation is very common because it is adaptable to a great variety of land slopes and soil textures and can be used with either large or small streams of irrigation water. Furrows are most commonly run directly down the slope of the land, but in areas where the slope is too great and the stream too large, they are sometimes run along the contour to prevent soil erosion. In such a method labour costs are high, since each row must be watched. It is most commonly used for market-garden crops, orchards and vineyards.

Difficulties may arise with the use of furrow irrigation on unsuitable soils. If the soil is very pervious, the water running along the furrows may sink vertically into the soil without ever reaching the centre of the ridges where the seeds are sown. On the other hand, the soil may be so impervious that the water does not reach the centre of the ridge and the seeds do not germinate anyhow. The Americans have had some success in handling pervious, coarse soil by mixing clay slurry with the irrigation water to plug up some of the coarse material. If, however, the soil is impervious, Australian research suggests that growing a green crop, usually white clover, for two or three years improves the soil structure sufficiently to allow water to be taken up in a reasonable time.[4] A more general disadvantage of furrow irrigation is that to ensure that the whole of the irrigation area receives enough water, it is almost always necessary to overwater some parts.

A modification of furrow irrigation is corrugation irrigation (Fig. 5c). Water is applied to the ground in rills, corrugations or small shallow furrows, from which it soaks laterally through the soil, wetting the area between the corrugations. This method is generally used in areas where the land surface is moderately steep and irregular and on fine textured soils. It ensures uniform wetting and limits erosion on steep lands. It is commonly used for close-growing crops such as hay and small grains.

Sprinkler or spray irrigation applies water to the surface of the soil in the form of a spray, and is virtually a form of artificial rain. There are two main types of sprinkler: the sprinkler head and the perforated pipe. The first is much more common, and while it may be permanent it is more likely to be partially or fully portable. A common type of sprinkler head is the revolving one, which distributes water radially; the fixed head type, with a more limited 'throw', is more suitable for closely spaced orchards and vegetable plots. This form of irrigation has advantages over other surface irrigation. It can be adapted for use on almost all types of soil, especially sandy soils which absorb water rapidly. It enables erosion to be controlled on steep land and can often be used on soils that are too shallow, too steep or too rolling to be irrigated by surface methods. Small streams of water can be used efficiently with this method, and it is adaptable to all the major crops with the exception of those, like rice, that require standing water. A uniform application of water is made possible, and the amount and timing of the irrigation can be easily controlled. Land is not needed for irrigation structures, and so larger areas are available for cropping. Finally, it lessens the problems of weed control and excessive tillage, which may result from the construction of ditches needed for surface irrigation.

There are, however, a number of disadvantages inherent in the use of sprinkler systems. The water distribution is easily affected by the wind, which may disturb the pattern of wetting so that some parts get too much water and some too little. The power requirements necessary to maintain the water pressure are usually greater than for other methods of irrigation, and the water used must be clean and free from debris. To ensure the most economical use of the equipment, a constant supply of water is needed. Most important of all, the initial costs of installing such systems are very high, and they may require frequent expenditure during operation. For these reasons, sprinkler systems are largely restricted to the developed areas of the world, principally the United

States, the Soviet Union and western Europe, where sprinkler irrigation has increased considerably in the last decade. It is especially popular as a form of supplemental irrigation in areas with adequate rainfall, as it requires the least alteration of normal techniques of cultivation and normally no alterations in the land contour.

Subirrigation or subsoil irrigation applies water beneath the ground rather than on the surface. By means of lateral ditches or mole or tile drains, a water table is maintained at some predetermined depth below the soil surface, in the case of vegetables and small grains, usually between eighteen and twenty-four inches. The lateral ditches, which are always filled with water, are commonly spaced between fifty and seventy-five feet apart, and the lateral movement of water from them maintains a uniform water table. Alternatively, water may be delivered below the soil surface through porous drainpipes, where it seeps into the soil. From the water table the water seeps upwards to the plant roots through capillary action. This method of irrigation requires complete control of the elevation of the water table to ensure that the plant root zone in the soil is kept free from excess water but continually supplied with capillary moisture during the cropping season. Lands suitable for this method of irrigation are rather limited and occur on very few farms, since it requires a special combination of natural conditions. It needs a layer of permeable soil immediately below the surface to allow the free movement of water, and a level surface which should be approximately parallel to the water table. Moreover, during extremely dry summers the major open ditches which supply the water may become saline and cause irrigation to be suspended. Subirrigation is suited to most crops, allows cultivation and other surface operations to be carried on without concern for the irrigation period, and takes up only a limited amount of land for the relatively few ditches it requires.

In any one farm of sufficient size with a variety of crops, soils and landscape features, several of these methods of irrigation may be in use. Indeed, it is not uncommon for several methods to be used on a single field, depending upon the crop being grown and its stage of growth.

DRAINAGE: SALINATION AND WATERLOGGING

Getting the water onto the land is only part of the problem that faces the farmer; of almost equal importance is the disposal of water after use. Too much water in the soil can be worse than not enough, while inadequate planning and improper irrigation frequently result in salination and waterlogging. Salination occurs because the roots of the plants absorb the irrigation water but exclude most of the salt it contains. The salt then remains in the soil zone upon which the plant depends for growth and eventually renders the soil sterile. As most irrigation water contains between one half and three or more tons of salt per acre-foot, and as desert irrigation, for example, commonly requires between four and ten acre-feet of water annually, salination can occur very rapidly in such areas. It could be prevented if sufficient water were applied to the land both to satisfy plant requirements and to leach the salt through the soil into properly constructed drainage channels to carry the water away. Salination may be increased by leakage from the larger canals, which causes the water table to rise closer to the surface. In other areas, the water table is not of itself high enough to harm crops by drowning them, but as the plants exhaust deficient irrigation, saline water is drawn up by capillary action from the water table to the root zone and the surface. In the absence of frequent and adequate irrigation, this movement of saline water to the surface and its subsequent evaporation result in continual deposits of large quantities of salt on the surface of the land.

The consequence of lack of effective drainage and resulting salinity and waterlogging in the Punjab are graphically described by James Morris:

> If you look down at the Punjab from an aircraft, you will see here and there below you, splotching the green fields like mould on the wall of an old house, patches of grey decay, rising patternless and ominous across the landscape. This is salination, a rotting of the land caused by a rise in the level of the underground water table, which forces the salts of the earth to the surface and gradually turns field back to desert. It does not steal inexorably forward, like an encroaching sand dune, but erupts unpredictably in disconnected patches, now desolating a village in Gujerat, now withering away all possible means of livelihood from the farm lands of Shahpur. It reminds me of some nightmare fable of science fiction, so

unearthly does its progress seem to be, and for several decades now it has been nibbling away at the welfare of the Punjab. Today, the Punjabis lose at least 150 acres of land every afternoon of the year: even in the last years of the Raja, the British used to say that two or three cricket pitches were going under every day.[5]

This desolation has been brought about by year-round irrigation, which has caused the water table to rise. Before modern diversion dams and large canals brought water throughout the year, the water table in this area was between seventy and one hundred feet below the surface. To prevent such catastrophic consequences, which are all too common in other areas, such as China, the Soviet Union, Egypt, the Euphrates delta and parts of the western United States, there must be complete and efficient control of irrigation water. It is difficult to overestimate the menace of salination and waterlogging; indeed, reclaiming lands ruined through faulty or misused irrigation is almost as important as bringing new lands under irrigation for the first time.

If reclamation is to be successful, the basic problem is to lower the water table so that it is kept below the root zone. This may be achieved in a number of ways: a grid of deep ditches may be laid along the boundaries of the fields, or lines of tiles laid in the fields to collect the water and convey it to a collector ditch. The latter method is used extensively in the Central Asian steppes, where the Russians utilise large drain-laying machines. Russian scientists have also recently been experimenting with the use of dilute sulphuric acid to neutralise saline soils and thereby speed up the leaching process by several years. The acid reacts with the saline soils to form basic sulphates in a mild solution of hydrochloric acid. The sulphates, which are soluble, are then carried off with the leach water. According to Russian scientists, such a process is rapid, requiring only one vegetative period for completion, and it is claimed to be simple and not too expensive. It does, however, require an effective drainage system.[6] Some reclamation of saline lands is also being undertaken in the Imperial Valley of California, where old abandoned farms are being bought up by entrepreneurs, networks of ditches dug, porous tiles put in, and the fields flooded for a period of approximately one year, during which time it is quite often possible to obtain a crop of rice. However, such reclamation requires a great deal of capital and considerable technical expertise.

Many areas, particularly in the arid parts of Asia, cannot be conveniently or economically recovered by normal drainage processes. One method of restoration in these circumstances requires the installation of tube wells for pumping the areas to be drained and using the pumped water for further irrigation elsewhere. This method is of growing importance in parts of the Indo-Gangetic Plain (v. p. 42), but it can be very costly, sometimes proving more expensive than bringing in new irrigated areas. The use of tube wells for this purpose is likely to increase when cheap hydroelectric power becomes available on a larger scale.

In any case, the size of the problem is immense; for example, it is estimated that during the next ten years Egypt will have two million acres which should be drained, that in Pakistan more than 100,000 acres are still being ruined every year through salinity and waterlogging, and that India may have as many as ten million acres similarly affected.[7] In a recent American report on the large-scale reclamation of saline and waterlogged lands in West Pakistan, it has been estimated that an effective reclamation programme, linked with measures to increase agricultural productivity, will take twenty-five years and involve a total cost of about 2,000 million dollars.[8]

However, it is necessary not only to reclaim areas that have already been spoiled, but also to prevent further ruin. This can only be done by a more efficient use of water, and one way of ensuring this in the future will doubtless be by using automatic control systems. Russian scientists have recently developed an experimental system at the Kirghizia Automation Institute in Central Asia. There an irrigation canal is partitioned into separate sections, and in each section a stable water level is maintained automatically. It is held that this system will eliminate disastrous local shortages of water by maintaining stable levels of water in the irrigation canals serving a large area. Such a system is very expensive, but it is claimed, doubtless under favourable conditions, that the capital costs can be regained in less than two years. Ultimately, it is hoped that large canal systems will be controlled by computers. Data on the condition of the irrigated areas, including the humidity of the air and soil, the density of the soil and the nature of the crop, would be fed into a computer, which would then estimate the water requirements for given areas and select optimum water regimes for each section of each canal and for the system as a whole. The first results of recent experiments along these lines suggest that they bring about considerable savings both in the consumption of water and in the cost of irrigation.[9]

To summarise, an efficient, modern irrigation system should properly perform the following functions: (*a*) store water so that it is available in sufficient quantities whenever required, (*b*) deliver water to all parts of the cultivated area, in amounts needed to meet crop demands during peak use periods, (*c*) provide complete control of water, (*d*) measure the amount of water at entry into the farm irrigation system, (*e*) divide water into required amounts for use in different fields, (*f*) dispose of waste water after use, (*g*) provide for the reuse of water on the farm, (*h*) allow for the free movement of farm machinery, and (*i*) distribute water evenly into the soil of each field. Properly utilised, such a system allows for the most efficient use of water and makes irrigation possible without soil erosion, saline or alkaline accumulation, or waterlogging.

Such a system clearly demands both capital investment to cover the high cost of installation and a considerable degree of technical expertise to use it to its best advantage. While both requirements may be available in the more technologically advanced countries, it is hardly surprising if they are markedly absent in developing countries, whose farmers are poor and lack the knowledge to make best use of modern irrigation techniques.

Bibliographical References

1. Lord Hailey, *An African Survey* (Oxford University Press), 1957, p. 72.
2. *Science and Technology for Development, III* (United Nations, New York), 1963, (E/CONF.39/1), p. 44.
3. Haw, R. C., *The Conservation of Natural Resources* (Faber & Faber, London), 1959, pp. 190-92.
4. Penman, H. L., 'Irrigation in Britain', *Journal of the Royal Society of Arts*, March 1963, p. 285.
5. Morris, J., *The World Bank: A Prospect* (Faber & Faber, London), 1963, p. 173.
6. Greenwood, N. H., 'Developments in the Irrigation Resources of the Sevan-Razdan Cascade of Armenia', *Annals of Association of American Geographers*, LV, 1965, pp. 300-2.
7. *Science and Technology for Development, III, op cit.,* pp. 42-43.

8. *Ibid.*, *I*, p. 6.
9. *Soviet Weekly*, July 10, 1965, p. 1.

Additional Sources

After a Hundred Years (U.S. Department of Agriculture Yearbook, 1962),
   pp. 203-4.
Thorne, W. (Ed.), *Land and Water Use* (American Association for the
   Advancement of Science, Washington, D.C.), 1963.
U.S. Department of Agriculture, Agricultural Information Bulletins:
   No. 166, Sprinkler Irrigation in the Pacific Northwest, November 1956.
   No. 190, Salt Problems in Irrigated Soils, August 1958.
   No. 197, The Quality of Irrigation Water, December 1958.
   No. 199, Irrigation on Western Farms, July 1959.
   No. 217, Salt Tolerance of Field Crops, March 1960.
U.S. Department of Agriculture, Miscellaneous Publications:
   No. 923, Soil and Water Conservation in the Pacific Northwest, 1957.
   No. 926, Irrigation Water on the Farm, July 1963.

CHAPTER 4

MODERN IRRIGATION BASED ON GROUND WATER

Ground water is distributed very unevenly beneath the surface of the land. Variations in subsurface materials frequently result in quite marked local differences both in the water-yielding capabilities of aquifers and in the depths at which adequate supplies of water can be reached. Although early irrigation was very largely based upon surface waters, the sporadic production and use of ground water has continued for thousands of years where conditions have been favourable and subsurface water has been easily obtainable. Such irrigation may be on a small scale if it depends on ancient lifting devices; with modern mechanical devices it may embrace considerable areas, and since it is generally available all year round, it supports perennial irrigation. In California, Texas and Arizona, for example, several million acres are under perennial irrigation from ground-water sources.

Ground water is often discharged in the form of artesian wells and springs. Artesian wells are often found in basin-shaped structures where the strata, consisting of alternating pervious and impervious beds, are inclined. Precipitation occurs at a distant, higher point where the pervious rock is exposed to the intake of water. The water then percolates deep underground beneath the floor of the basin to form an aquifer and is held there under considerable pressure by the weight of the overlying water. If wells are then drilled down through the overlying rocks into the aquifer, the pressure may be sufficient to force the water up to the surface. More frequently, it is necessary to lift the water by pumps. The quality of the water thus obtained varies considerably. In some places it may be sufficiently pure to promote the growth of crops, while elsewhere, as in parts of Australia, it may be so heavily mineralised that it can only be used for watering stock. Artesian springs are formed by a similar accumulation of water, which may occur naturally if faults in the strata allow the water to seep upwards through the impervious layer and so reach the surface. Many Saharan oases exist where artesian water locally reaches the surface in this manner, or where the water table is sufficiently close to the surface so that funnel-shaped hollows,

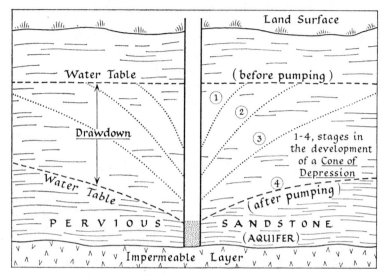

FIG. 6. A well (simplified) showing the effects of continuous pumping.

varying in width from a few feet to one hundred yards, may be dug to reach it.

MODERN MECHANICAL DEVICES FOR LIFTING GROUND WATER

The development of mechanical means for lifting large amounts of water has had to wait for the coming of the internal combustion engine and the utilisation of electricity. Together, these scientific advances mean that lifting is no longer dependent on human and animal labour. Pumping plants now in use range from very small, one horse-power, oil-driven engines lifting water for individual farms, to huge pumping installations using hydro-electricity like that at Grand Coulee Dam. Small, oil-driven pumps are becoming increasingly common in many parts of the world. In recent years, thousands have been installed in the Nile Delta, an area which in the past relied upon more primitive means of lifting water but where oil is fortunately cheap and easily obtained.

Electrically operated tube wells are of growing importance in some parts of the world. They are found in large numbers in parts of the Indo-Gangetic Plain, where a number of small, artificial falls, which adjust the slopes of the canals to those of the country they traverse, have been used for small hydroelectric stations; these provide power to pump water. Tube wells are sunk by machinery and are so called because the well shaft, possibly only a few feet in diameter, is lined with steel tubing which is perforated where it meets water-bearing material. The water comes into the shaft through the perforations and is lifted to the surface by an electrically driven pump. A typical well raises far more water than the Persian wheel, which it has superseded in many areas, and commands an area of about 1,000 acres. As it may provide more water than a single farmer can use, it is often run on a co-operative basis.

Tube wells are considerably more expensive than primitive forms of irrigation; it is estimated, for example, that in India a standard tube well costs about £1,700 and that the per-acre cost of tube well irrigation is about twice that of canal irrigation. Moreover, these wells can only be installed where electric power to operate the pumps is available. Nonetheless, some 5,000 tube wells have been sunk in India in the past decade.[1] Much less wasteful in human and animal time and labour, they are doing a great deal to revolutionise rural life in parts of the Indo-Gangetic Plain. They make possible the exploitation of considerable amounts of deep underground water, which in turn promote a more productive agriculture. They are also extremely important in parts of West Pakistan as a means of reclaiming land which decades of over-irrigation have made waterlogged and saline, and are also very valuable in areas which cannot be economically reached by canal irrigation.

ADVANTAGES AND DISADVANTAGES OF USING GROUND WATER

The advantages of using ground water are numerous. It is often available at or near the point of use and consequently does not require a water distribution network. For this reason, although it is generally more expensive than direct river diversion, this method is considerably cheaper than the surface storage of water and usually easier to develop. Ground water may be available in areas where existing supplies of surface water are already being put to uses other than irrigation, and it can be withdrawn as and when it is needed. There is less fluctuation in supply than may be the case with stream flow; ground water tends to be more uniform in temperature and freer from soluble mineral load than surface water, and it is generally free of turbidity and bacterial pollution. It is therefore particularly suited, in regions which can generally rely upon surface waters, for irrigating relatively small areas isolated from streams and for providing stand-by or supplemental facilities. In arid areas, where no perennial rivers flow, the development of ground-water resources is crucial and may be the only practical solution to the problems of water supply.

The use of ground water is not without its problems, however. Sometimes it is available only at an excessive depth or in inadequate quantities. Occasionally it may be of poor quality, because although usually unpolluted and relatively free of sediment, it is often highly mineralised and may therefore be unusable. In some circumstances it may prove more expensive than surface water, because its use requires the expenditure of energy for pumping, while surface waters can be used to produce energy. Most important is the fact that there is only a finite amount of ground water available in any one area, so that if extraction exceeds infiltration, the 'capital reserve' of water accumulated over many years will sooner or later become exhausted.

When pumping exceeds the rate at which water can enter the aquifer, the water level in the wells falls and a general levelling in the surrounding water table results. This levelling takes place most quickly nearest the well and forms a cone of depression, a conical-shaped lowering of the water table, the height of which is called drawdown (Fig. 6). This change in turn causes the formation of a steeper gradient to the water table close to the well, which then causes the flow of ground water into the well to increase. However, this increase only lasts for a short period. If a number of wells operate fairly close together, their cones of depression may intersect to produce a general levelling and lowering of the water table. In some areas, water is being pumped out so fast that underground reservoirs which may have taken centuries to accumulate are being rapidly depleted with no possibility, as yet, of an alternative, continuous perennial supply. This is frequently the result of a vicious circle: in parts of southern California, the availability of ground water has resulted in increased agricultural production, which has led to a rise in population with a consequently increasing demand for ground water. In many arid areas the rate of annual accretion of underground water is quite small, so that if depletion is to be avoided, the water should be available only for small-scale use.

An even more serious consequence of the depletion of ground-water supplies is that as the good water is pumped out, salty or otherwise unusable water may flow in and cause underground reservoirs to be ruined before they are emptied. Moreover, as ground water is often closely related to stream water, the pumping of water from wells alongside rivers may result in a depletion of stream flow. In some areas the pumping of ground water may causc land subsidence; this has happened in Japan, especially near riverside or seaside locations, and has led to the introduction of artificial recharge wells.[2]

In areas where too much ground water has been removed, remedial measures may be necessary. These may take the form of preventing the inefficient use of water, a reduction of pumping from all wells, the prohibition of further development, the re-clamation of used water, the replenishment of ground water by surplus stream water, and the importation of water from other areas. It may be, for example, that the answer to the growing shortage of water in southern California and Arizona lies in the large-scale diversion of water from the humid areas of the Pacific North-west and Canada, and a scheme along these lines is currently being considered.

If ground-water supplies are to be used to the best advantage, a number of factors must be taken into account. These include the degree of replenishment of ground water and the rate at which it travels, the rate at which the water table fluctuates with rainfall and declines with future use, and the possibility of the intrusion of saline water or the subsidence of land brought about by pumping. Unfortunately, far too little is known about these complex matters, so that farmers are often faced with the difficult choice of whether to use water or conserve it for the future. Ground water on the whole is less used and understood than surface water; yet in many areas it offers perhaps the most encouraging source of additional supply in the near future and the greatest promise for practical and economical growth. It is likely to become of particular importance to the developing countries, for many of them contain arid regions where rainfall is rare and irregular, coming in short, violent run-off washes, often full of dissolved salts, and where intensive evaporation reduces its effectiveness.

In such countries, particularly those with no great rivers, the development of ground-water resources may be the only answer to the problem of water supply. For example, Tunisia relies on ground water for ninety-five per cent of its supplies, Morocco for more than seventy-five per cent, and Israel for about seventy per cent, while in Saudi Arabia it is practically the only source of water.[3] It is of considerable importance in other arid areas such as the western United States, Western Australia, North Africa, Iraq, Afghanistan, Pakistan, India and Central Asia, and in many of these countries large schemes for extending the use of ground water are in progress.

Potentially of great importance is the existence of a vast fresh-water reservoir underlying a large part of the Sahara Desert. The Inter-Calary Continental Albienne Nappe, as it is called, is the most prolific aquifer yet found and stretches more than 500 miles south from the Atlas Mountains in Algeria. It may also extend under Tunisia and the deserts of Fezzan in Libya. The layer of water is estimated to be up to 3,000 feet thick. Another large underground reservoir stretches north from the Ennedi Hills in Chad towards Egypt, reaching the Qattara Depression near El Alamein. Both these reservoirs are replenished by heavy precipitation in the mountainous regions to the north-west and south of the Sahara Desert, and the water they contain may eventually help to provide the basis for some irrigated agriculture in the desert.[4] Ground water is also being increasingly used by humid countries such as Denmark, Belgium, West Germany and the Netherlands, and is likely to grow in importance in these areas as a source of supplemental irrigation. In the world as a whole, however, the use and production of ground water still remains sporadic and relatively undeveloped.

Bibliographical References

1. 'India's Agriculture', *Focus*, XIV, No. 1, September 1963, The American Geographical Society, p. 4.

2. *Proceedings of the Fourth Regional Technical Conference on Water Resources Development in Asia and the Far East*, Flood Control Series No. 19 (United Nations, New York), 1962, (ST/ECAFE/SER.F/19), p. 103.
3. *Large-Scale Ground Water Development* (United Nations, New York), 1960, (ST/ECA/65), p. 5.
4. *Possibilities of Increasing World Food Production* (Food and Agriculture Organisation, Rome), 1963, p. 69.

Additional Sources

Highsmith, Jr., R. M. (Ed.), *Atlas of the Pacific Northwest* (Oregon State University Press, Corvallis, Oregon), 3rd ed., 1962, p. 42.
Monkhouse, F. J., *Principles of Physical Geography* (University of London Press), 4th ed., 1960.
A Place to Live (U.S. Department of Agriculture Yearbook, 1963), p. 84 *et. seq.*
Smith, G., *Conservation of Natural Resources* (Wiley, New York), 2nd ed., 1958, pp. 90-115.
Strahler, A., *Physical Geography* (Wiley, New York), 2nd ed., 1960.
Thomas, H. E., *Conservation of Ground Waters* (McGraw-Hill, New York), 1951.
Ward, R. C., *Hydrology* (McGraw-Hill, London), 1967.
Water (U.S. Department of Agriculture Yearbook, 1955), pp, 63-76.

CHAPTER 5
STORAGE AND CONSERVATION

Irrigation farming is, in general, very wasteful in its use of water. Wastage is due partly to the farmer's lack of knowledge of the water requirements of his crops. It may also be due to the quality of the water being adversely affected so that larger quantities are needed to obtain the necessary plant growth. Above all, immense losses occur during the large-scale storage and distribution of water in reservoirs and in canals and ditches, and for this reason the conservation of water is becoming increasingly important.

Until recently it was believed that the amount of water required by crops to promote maximum growth varied considerably. In other words, each crop had its own 'water requirements'.[1] Recent research has led to a drastic revision of these ideas, and it is now being suggested that the irrigation of a given area,* at a given time of the year, requires the same amount of water almost irrespective of the crop being grown. The logical consequence of this theory is that from an economic point of view, irrigators should grow the crop which yields the highest economic return per unit of area and per unit of time.[2]

The principal factors influencing the consumption of water by a given crop are field evaporation, seepage and the efficiency with which the land is prepared and water applied. Of all crops, rice is the most dependent on irrigation because the rice plant has to be under water during the planting season. In Japan the water requirements of the crop vary from 2·3 to 4·3 acre-feet for the entire season, with the standard depth of water in the field being from one to two inches. In the Murrumbidgee irrigation area in Australia, on the other hand, rice cultivation requires about six acre-feet per season, the difference being due to dissimilar geo-

---

* There are, of course, considerable differences in the water requirements of crops grown in different areas. These arise from a number of factors: some crops have a longer growing season than others, some are grown at a season of the year when solar radiation is greatest, and some are usually grown on light soils, which may be liable to a higher loss of water by seepage than less permeable soils.

47

logical and hydrological conditions, climatic variations, the density of the crop and the layout of the fields.[3] In the Imperial Valley of California, it is estimated that because of excessive evaporation, between six and seven acre-feet of irrigation water are needed each season.

As irrigation water is generally expensive, it should be used as efficiently as possible. This calls for a more accurate knowledge than we presently have of the water requirements of crops for optimum growth. Too often, farmers tend to use as much water as is made available to them even though it may result in over-watering. In many cases, an effective means of controlling the supply of water would encourage farmers to use it more efficiently and sparingly.

THE QUALITY OF IRRIGATION WATER

The efficiency of irrigation farming depends not only upon the accurate determination of the water requirements of crops but also upon the quality of the water. The main factor in determining the suitability or otherwise of irrigation water for promoting plant growth is the amount of dissolved mineral matter it contains. Water containing fertile silt and mineral nutrients may have considerable fertilising value. For this reason, river water is generally preferable to water from other sources. But excessive amounts of silt (or very fine silt) frequently have an unfavourable effect on a plant's growth. Irrigation water, particularly if it is obtained from underground sources, may be highly charged with sodium chloride or other salts, which may have a harmful effect on crops. While no fixed limit can be set for the amount of dissolved mineral matter which makes water unfit for use in irrigation, it has been estimated that water with more than 100 parts of dissolved mineral matter per 100,000 can in no circumstances be safely used.[4]

It is likely, too, that the temperature of irrigation water has a marked effect on crop yields. Early irrigated agriculture took place along rivers, where limited volumes of water were drawn from warm surface or shoreline zones or from shallow wells. As agriculture has moved farther from the sources of water and become more widespread, more water has been required and modern dams have been built, frequently containing cold water held in reservoirs not far from snowfields. This water is discharged rapidly along canals and into fields and may not warm up much in the process.

The use of cool water probably brings about a reduction in soil temperatures, which may in turn reduce crop yields by disturbing the optimum root temperature. As yet, however, little is known about the relations of crop growth to water and soil temperatures.[5]

Pollution and degradation are two further factors affecting the quality and supply of irrigation water. Pollution, notably from the disposal of urban sewage and industrial waste, can cause serious water losses. Some of the chemicals used in modern agriculture may also render water unusable, and there is a danger, particularly in some arid areas, of radioactive material polluting ground-water supplies, either through underground explosions or the burial of radioactive waste. Since water-bearing strata and artesian basins are connected over a considerable part of the globe, radioactive elements may, in time, reappear in places far from those in which underground explosions have occurred or radioactive wastes have been buried. To some extent it is possible to reclaim polluted water by the use of chlorination and activated carbon, and control of the dumping of industrial waste could help to prevent pollution occurring in the first place. On the whole, however, little has been done either to prevent water pollution or to reclaim polluted water.

Degradation of irrigation water is the natural diminution in quality caused by the increasing concentration of impurities as water is lost through evaporation and transpiration. Although rainfall is substantially pure, it soon collects impurities as a result of its contact with the earth's surface. These impurities, which include both mineral and organic matter, are held in solution and suspension, and the amount varies according to the local nature of the surface rocks. Waters in arid areas are generally more highly charged with dissolved minerals than those in humid areas, and the more soluble rocks also tend to result in more impurities. In many arid areas the loss of irrigation water through evaporation and transpiration is about two-thirds of the water applied. The remaining water contains both the original salts held in solution and those leached from the soil, in one-third of the volume of the original water. As a result of this threefold concentration, such irrigation water often becomes waste water, unfit for any further use. The concentration of salts in the Gila River in Arizona in 1952 increased from an average of 555 parts per million at Kelvin to nearly 5,000 parts per million below Gillespie Dam. The latter concentration was so high that no further use could be made of the water.[6] This degradation of irrigation waters could perhaps be reduced by the use of plants such as Nitella, which grow on the water surface and concentrate fairly large amounts of such minerals as sodium, potassium, calcium and magnesium. The cultivation of these plants could reduce the mineral content of irrigation water sufficiently for many uses, while the plants themselves could be harvested and used for animal feed.[7]

THE CONSERVATION OF WATER

Irrigation water in storage and in transit from the reservoir to the field is subject to loss in three ways: by leakage, by evaporation and by transpiration. These can cause so much waste that in Mexico, for example, only fifty to sixty-five per cent of the total amount of irrigation water leaving a given source ever reaches the fields if it is conveyed in unlined canals.[8] In the Fergana Canal in Soviet Central Asia, the loss from seepage is anything from seventeen to forty-five per cent, and comparable losses occur in parts of the western United States.[9]

The loss of precious irrigation water by leakage from earth ditches and unlined canals is particularly heavy in arid regions or in areas of porous, sandy or gravelly soils, where it constitutes a critical problem. This loss can be reduced by installing some kind of watertight lining in ditches and canals, and in some areas, like the western United States, the use of concrete ditch-lining has long been the standard practice. Mexico now lines all new irrigation canals as they are built, and the national plan calls for the gradual lining of all existing unlined ones.[10] This remedy may bring additional benefits by helping to reduce the cost of storing water and the amount of run-off, stopping the growth of weeds, eliminating erosion and reducing unauthorised diversion to a minimum. By minimising leakages, it may help to prevent the formation of marshland in the vicinity of the channels.

The major drawback to the extensive use of concrete lining is the relatively high cost of materials and installation, which despite modern, cheaper methods is still often too high to be practicable. A wide variety of cheaper materials, to replace the concrete which is widely used at present, is being developed and tested in order to overcome this problem. These materials include asphaltic membranes, rubber linings, soil cements, plastics and waxes. But while these materials effectively seal ditches and prevent seepage, they are more easily damaged than concrete. There is the possibility of adding chemicals which move into the soil with the water and render it less liable to seepage: in Australia, sodium tripolyphosphate has been used and found reasonably effective if the soils have a clay content of five per cent or more.[11] However, such chemicals, which must in no way pollute the water, have yet to be developed as a practical proposition on a large scale. In India, where lining construction and design are largely determined by the local availability of materials, labour and equipment, bricks and tiles have been used where neither the raw materials nor the necessary machinery for making concrete are readily available. Bitumen in various forms is also used, both in the construction of new canals and as a means of renovating and sealing old canals. Pakistan has successfully used a lining consisting of a bitumen membrane interposed between two layers of brick tiles, and in Egypt a number of sand asphalt canal linings have been laid with very satisfactory results.[12]

Another common cause of seepage is corrosion, which is particularly liable to occur in metals. Where water is carried in metal pipes, it may eventually cause the metal to corrode and become leaky. As a result, much attention has recently been given to finding substitute materials for making pipes and well-linings. These include pre-stressed concrete, synthetic materials using asbestos, and plastics of various kinds.

If a body of water is exposed to air and sunlight, evaporation from the surface will take place and result in losses of water, which may be extremely heavy in arid areas. It is estimated, for example, that in the western United States the gross annual evaporation from exposed water surfaces in reservoirs, lakes, canals and ditches is nearly 29,000 million cubic metres.[13] One way of reducing such losses is to lessen the surface area of water exposed to evaporation. This can be done by constructing small, deep reservoirs rather than large, shallow ones or by reducing the surface area of existing reservoirs, as is being done experimentally in the Soviet Union. A very important source of irrigation water in Soviet Armenia is Lake Sevan, the largest lake in the Caucasus, which suffers from evaporation losses thought to be in the region of 1,000 million cubic metres a year. Russian scientists are working on a project to decrease the surface area of the lake by thirteen per cent, which involves lowering the surface level by twenty metres. This will reduce the ratio of surface area to volume in the large remnant lake and will, it is hoped, lead to a minimum saving of 130 million cubic metres of water annually. [14]

Another method of preventing the evaporation of storage water is by covering it. On a small scale this might be possible by placing a solid cover on a small surface cistern, but on a large scale it becomes impossible. Instead, much has been done in recent years to investigate the possibilities of a protective film which might be spread over large surfaces. Such a film must be able to retard the movement of water vapour from the surface, but at the same time must not prevent the free movement of oxygen, carbon dioxide and other gases through the surface. It must be non-toxic to life, resistant to wind action, dust or physical disturbance by boats, and able to restore itself after a disturbance. Two alcohols which form a monomolecular film, hexadecanol and octodecanol, are commonly used, notably in Australia, the Soviet Union and the United States.

In Australia, hexadecanol is used to counteract evaporation in small dams by means of small rafts which release this insoluble chemical and cause it to float on the surface of the water as a white waxy substance.[15] In this way, evaporation losses have been reduced by a quarter or more. Unfortunately, this particular method is unsuited for storage reservoirs greater than two acres, where the wind ruffles the water and disrupts the film. Hexadecanol has also been used in Australia as a fine powder, which is blown through a tube at the stern of a moving boat and spreads over the water as a thin film. In the United States the same results are obtained by aerial spraying. This method is quick, economical and efficient, and under favourable conditions has cut evaporation losses by as much as half. The film has to be repaired daily, however, though this can be done quite easily. As yet, no really effective 'cover' has been developed that will be of use over large surfaces for reasonable periods of time.

On the whole, it is probably better to conserve water by concentrating on improving the storage and distribution facilities themselves through improved design and siting. The safest way of preventing evaporation is by the use of pipelines or underground storage. Unfortunately, the cost of artificial underground storage is likely to be very high, except in some areas where natural underground reservoirs, such as aquifers, are not carrying their full potential. There water can be stored in a number of ways: by digging pits, wells and shafts to carry rainwater directly underground; by spreading extra water on the surface of permeable rocks to increase natural infiltration; by building water intakes near rivers and lakes to increase the natural exchange of water from the surface to underground; and where the aquifer may be full but water is lying on the ground, by heavy pumping, which increases the rate of natural infiltration. Water-spreading is the most economical of these methods and is widely used in a number of countries including the United States, France, West Germany, Australia and the Soviet Union.

Transpiration losses occur when water is used by phreatophytes, plants with high water requirements but no economic value. These are commonly found growing along river banks and irrigation canals and in lakes, and it is estimated that in the western United States such plants annually waste nearly two million acre-feet of valuable water. In some areas, as in the Sudan, where the White Nile makes its slow passage through the wide-spreading marshes of the Sudd, they may even consume up to forty per cent of the volume of water.

One of the most harmful of phreatophytes is the beautiful water hyacinth (*Eichornia crassipes*), whose massive infestation and speed of development threaten agricultural productivity in many parts of Africa and South-east Asia. The water hyacinth has only become a menace on a large scale in the past decade. A native of South America, it was taken by garden lovers to South Africa, from where it travelled northwards, first to the Congo with its ideal habitat of swamps and warm, slow-moving water, and then, between 1956 and 1958, to the Sudanese reaches of the Nile. The plant grew so rapidly that by 1964, dense, opaque mats of leaves were reported to be fringing the Nile to a depth of three to ten metres for a distance of a thousand miles. Because of their excessive transpiration, estimated at three and a half times the normal evaporation rate for clear water, the plants cause shortages of water in lands where there is a perpetual need of it. By establishing themselves in irrigation ditches, they narrow them, slow down the flow of water and clog water pumps. Unfortunately, the cost of controlling the hyacinth is very high. In the Sudan, control units consisting of aircraft and other vessels equipped with high pressure pumps to eject a hormone spray cost nearly £600,000 a year.

The threat of the water hyacinth to irrigated agriculture in both the Sudan and Egypt is acute, since at any time the infestation of the White Nile may escape past its present northern limit, the Jebel Aulia Dam above Khartoum. If it does, it could spread very rapidly to the Aswan High Dam, a thousand miles farther down the Nile. The Sudan itself could be more seriously affected than at present if the weed should succeed in spreading to the Blue Nile, which is still free of it. If this happens, it might well threaten the Gezira cotton-growing area, which takes its water direct from the Blue Nile. Both the Sudan and Egypt are well aware of the danger, and Egypt is already contributing a third of the control costs.

If the water hyacinth and similar plants could be eliminated, or their transpiration rate reduced, then considerable savings in water could be effected. Several possible methods of dealing with the water hyacinth are being tried by the Food and Agriculture Organisation of the United Nations. A possible biological control centres on the manatee, a large water mammal sometimes called a seacow, which feeds on the hyacinths. Unfortunately, the manatee's rate of consumption is too slow to cope with the rapid spread of the weed, and in any case, given an alternative choice of diet, it prefers to take it. Experiments have been undertaken with a type of water snail which eats the hyacinth, but unfortunately it is a carrier of the dreaded disease bilharziasis, which is already all too common in Egypt and the Sudan.* Unless a more effective and innocuous form of biological counter-attack can be found, the only practicable mass control is spraying, coupled with public education about the weed's dangers. The present hormone-spraying programme in the Sudan uses a preparation known as '2, 4-D'. Its main drawback, apart from the cost, is that it is harmful to cotton.

* Bilharziasis is second in importance to malaria among the world's parasitic diseases and, unlike malaria, is advancing. It is 'man-made' in the sense that it expands more rapidly in the vicinity of irrigation projects throughout the semi-arid tropical regions of the world. In the Gezira, for example, the number of cases of bilharziasis has increased over a period of fifteen years from one to twenty per cent of the adult population. In parts of Egypt the rate has increased from five to seventy-five per cent in the same period. Since an estimated 150 million people are affected by this disease, it is of vital importance that more is known about it and its relation to irrigation. (*World Health*, World Health Organisation, July-August 1964, p. 27.)

As a result, spraying can only be done in the three summer months of May, June and July, after the cotton has been picked and before the seeds are sown. An educational programme is necessary because plants may unwittingly be carried along by river boats, by fishermen and even by charcoal burners, who stuff holes in their sacks with them. In spite of all these problems, given the will and the financial resources, it should be possible to maintain a reasonable control over the plant.

It is probable that many cultivated crops transpire more water into the atmosphere than they require for their physiological functions of growth and maturity. It is theoretically possible to use chemicals to influence plant respiration so as to reduce transpiration and yet leave growth unaffected. Australian experiments to spray plants with waxy chemicals, which partially close the leaf stomata, have resulted in a reduction of the water loss by transpiration in the order of fifty per cent. However, plant growth has also been reduced by about twenty-five per cent, and only half the surface of the leaves can be treated in this way; the rest must be left open or the plant will 'decompose'. As yet, too little is known about plant physiology to make the production and application of such chemicals a practical proposition. Nor is much known about how the eradication of aquatic vegetation affects such things as stream flow, flood capacities and channel degradation. It may be possible to develop rapid-growing, quick-maturing varieties of crops which, because they have a shorter growing season, consume less water than the present varieties. Another possibility is to develop substitute crops or varieties that, in some areas, can be grown during cooler and more humid months.

The supply of irrigation water may also be decreased by sedimentation in storage reservoirs and irrigation canals. Lake Mead, for example, received one and a half million acre-feet of silt in the first fifteen years after the completion of Hoover Dam; at that rate of sedimentation the lake would be rendered useless in another sixty years. However, the construction of Glen Canyon and other storage features on the Colorado River above Hoover Dam should reduce the flow of sediment into Lake Mead to an insignificant amount. When storage dams are planned and designed in the western United States, an estimate is made of the magnitude of the silt problem, and new projects are developed only if storage capacity is unlikely to be seriously affected by sediment accumulation during the first two hundred years in the life of the reser-voir.[16] The attitude of some construction engineers seems to be that this is a problem that can be deferred, on the grounds that either an increasing demand for water will eventually make costly mechanical methods of removing or bypassing the sediment an economic proposition, or other, cheaper means of desedimentation will be developed.

In recent years, a number of reservoirs have been built with 'silt-traps', deep areas into which it is hoped the silt will settle. But in some reservoirs, sedimentation has occurred more rapidly than was expected; this is particularly true of arid areas where there is little or no vegetation cover to prevent soil erosion. More-over, recent experiences have not proved silt-traps to be as effective as was expected, since the sediment, instead of sinking to the deepest parts of the reservoir, seems to be deposited at all levels.

Material may also be deposited where the river debouches into the reservoir, eventually forming a delta through which it may be necessary to dredge new channels to maintain the flow of water. A more effective method of maintaining the flow is to construct small dams upstream from the main reservoir, which catch the silt and prevent it from filling the lower reservoir. However, these methods are usually very expensive, particularly in areas where dykes have to be built to prevent the backed-up water from damag-ing property, and they are inevitably impermanent.

The deposition of silt at the base of the dam itself poses another difficult engineering problem. At the Aswan dam, the first flood-waters of the Nile, which are heavily laden with silt, are allowed to pass through, and only when the river begins to fall and the silt content is considerably reduced are the sluices gradually lowered. This is not effective under different river regimes, however, and other methods have to be sought. Research is being carried out into the possibility of constructing 'self-cleansing' reservoirs by building dams with holes in the base which can be opened to form scour sluices; these let out both water and the silt deposited near the base of the dam. This technique is called flotation transport and has been incorporated with some success in the Iril Emda Dam built by French engineers on the Oued Agrioun River in Algeria. This method, however, only removes the lighter material deposited alongside the dam itself, and to handle the deltaic deposits a small dam has been constructed across the river just above the point at which it enters the reservoir. This impounds waters which are released through large sluice gates to scour the mouth of the river, carrying the deltaic material along to the point where it can be taken out through the scour sluices in the main dam.[17] The main disadvantage of this method, particularly if the reservoir also serves a hydroelectric station, is the loss of water and power involved whenever it is necessary to open the scour sluices.

Silting can also be partially reduced by a variety of engineering devices, including the construction of dams shaped to promote the maximum flow of water and so prevent the accumulation of silt, and the use of machines which extract silt from reservoirs and canals and dump it into specially prepared basins.[18] But the only really effective, long-term method of preventing sedimentation is by reducing the amount of silt that enters the river. This can only be done by regarding the watershed as a total entity and by evaluating the changes in sediment characteristics resulting from future activities in drainage basins. Long-range and large-scale planning is necessary and requires such measures as the reclamation of areas affected by soil erosion. In some areas, like the Nile Basin, such measures are clearly not practical or economic; in any case, the silt carried along by the Nile is of great value in ensuring the continued fertility of the soil. Where economic considerations are all-important, it may be cheaper to provide silt storage in reservoirs than to prevent erosion in the watershed areas.

A problem allied to the sedimentation of reservoirs is the gradual silting up of irrigation canals. This has proved so great a problem in the All-American Canal, which carries water from the Colorado River to the Imperial Valley, that a desilting works has had to be installed at the Imperial Dam at a cost of one and a half million dollars. As the annual cost of dredging the canals before the desilting works came into operation was in the region of one million dollars, it has proved to be an economic proposition. Water is passed at speed from the canal into three desilting basins, where most of the silt is deposited. The material is then fed into a central collecting trench, from which it flows through a series of pipes back into the Colorado River below the Imperial Dam. These works desilt and divert 15,155 cubic feet of water per second into the All-American Canal for use by Californian farms, and

2,000 cubic feet per second into the Gila Gravity Main Canal for use in the market gardens of Arizona.[19] The problem of silt deposition is also acute in the irrigation canals in the drier areas of the Soviet Union, where much research into the construction of effective silt-control structures is being carried on. In the Central Asian republics, when the silt in some of the irrigation canals reaches a depth of about eighty centimetres, a special sludge pump is used to throw the silt out into wide basins constructed along the sides of the canals. Other methods use baffle boards, which divert the fine sand and heavy silt moving along the bottom of the river channels through special sluice gates, while the upper strata, which are lower in silt content, are diverted into the irrigation canals.[20]

In an attempt to bring about large-scale reductions in water losses and to promote the more efficient use of water, a number of countries have introduced conservation plans. In Israel an over-all plan for water conservation operates for all land under irrigation. In addition to some of the methods outlined above, carefully designed waterway systems, multi-purpose ponds and judicious watering are all common.[21] A water-conserving practice in northern Kazakhstan, and in other areas of the Soviet Union, is snow-ridging with tractor-drawn machines which pack the snow and push it into contour ridges in order to hold as much as possible on the field. It is estimated that by this method as much as four hundred tons of additional water per acre can be conserved as soil moisture.[22] Much irrigation water is also derived from snow-melt in the mountains. The degree of melting and the time and rate of release of the meltwater are influenced in some areas by the degree of forest cover. On bare slopes, the snow melts more quickly, and a greater loss of water through evaporation and run-off is likely to occur. If the forests on the slopes could be managed so as to increase the water yield from the snow cover, more water would be available for use downstream. There is more and more evidence to suggest that this is a feasible proposition.[23]

In some areas, there is undoubtedly considerable scope for the extension of irrigated agriculture based upon the storage of water on individual farms. Farm storage has been practised for thousands of years, but few studies have been made of the comparative aspects of storing water on the individual holdings in a catchment area, as distinct from allowing it all to run into one large dam. The two systems may not, in fact, compete with one another, as there are many sites which are unsuitable for large dams but which may lend themselves to the construction of small farm dams. This is particularly true of hill country or gently undulating land containing small valleys with flat floors; these provide suitable sites for small dams with a high ratio of storage to excavation. Recent experiments along these lines in the region between Sydney and the Blue Mountains in Australia, where the term 'water harvesting' is applied to the schemes, have produced encouraging results. Given suitable topography and soils, it has been shown that small dams can provide water for irrigation at a cost comparable with water stored in large public dams. If this method can be developed economically, it may make possible the irrigation of many areas that can never be served by large-scale projects.[24]

Another way of saving water, albeit on a small scale, is by dew conservation. Israeli conservationists in the Negev Desert are experimenting with piles of small pebbles placed at regular intervals in straight lines with no mud or sand between them. The pebbles heat up in the day and cool down at night much more quickly than hard-packed soil, so that by morning the air next to the pebbles has cooled sufficiently to yield a little moisture. This dew trickles through the open spaces in the piles of pebbles and thoroughly wets the ground beneath. This method of obtaining water is based on that used by peoples living in this region before the birth of Christ and which then provided the basis of a flourishing garden agriculture. By this means, it is possible to obtain about one twenty-fifth of an inch of moisture on a clear summer night, representing approximately fifteen inches a year in desert regions. As yet, no large-scale device has been perfected which will do the job as well as the piles of pebbles. If some inexpensive and effective installation could be devised, it would be of inestimable value.[25]

It is quite clear that as the demand for irrigation water increases, water conservation will become more and more important. Modern civilisation imposes a heavy and growing demand on our limited water resources, and the steady rise in water consumption is causing a considerable concern about our supplies, particularly in the industrially advanced countries. Since irrigation is the largest consumer of water in most countries, efficient methods of irrigation promise the largest savings. There seems to be a growing recognition that we can no longer take our water supplies for granted and that education in water-saving is generally necessary.

Bibliographical References

1. Addison, H., *Land, Water and Food* (Chapman & Hall, London), 1955, pp. 24-25.
2. Clark, C., *The Economics of Irrigation* (Pergamon Press, Oxford), 1967, p. 7. For a critical review of Clark's thesis, see *Geography*, LIII, 1968, pp. 208-209.
3. Grist, D. H., *Rice* (Longmans, London), 1953, pp. 21-22.
4. Tempany, H. and Grist, D. H., *An Introduction to Tropical Agriculture* (Longmans, London), 1958, p. 149.
5. Water Resources Centre, *Suggestions for Research in Water Resources*, Contribution No. 18 (University of California, Berkeley), July 1958, pp. 33-34.
6. Woodward, D. R., *Availability of Water in the United States with Special Reference to Industrial Needs by 1980* (Industrial College of the Armed Forces, Washington, D.C.), 1956-57, p. 30.
7. *Suggestions for Research in Water Resources, op. cit.*, p. 9.
8. *Science and Technology for Development, II* (United Nations, New York), 1963, (E/CONF.39/1), p. 75.
9. Dominy, F. E., 'The Water Rush in Russia', *Reclamation Era*, L, No. 1, February 1964, p. 2; *Soil and Water Use in the Soviet Union* (U.S. Department of Agriculture Report), June 1959, p. 37.
10. *Science and Technology for Development, II, op. cit.*, pp. 75-76.
11. Cochrane, G. R., 'Reducing Water Losses in South Australia', *Geography*, XLV, 1960, pp. 297-99.
12. *Science and Technology for Development, II, op. cit.*, p. 76.
13. *Ibid.*, pp. 76-77.
14. Greenwood, N. H., 'Developments in the Irrigation Resources of the Sevan-Razdan Cascade of Soviet Armenia', *Annals of Association of American Geographers*, LV, 1965, p. 298.
15. Cochrane, *op cit.*, p. 298.
16. 'Facing Sediment Problems', *Reclamation Era*, XLIX, No. 2, May 1963, pp. 49-51.
17. Duquennois, H., 'New Methods of Sediment Control in Reservoirs', *Water Power*, May 1956, pp. 174-180.
18. *Science and Technology for Development, II, op. cit.*, p. 75.
19. Hogner, D. C., *Water Over the Dam* (Lippincott, New York), 1960, pp. 157-81.
20. *Soil and Water Use in the Soviet Union, op. cit.*, pp. 37-42.
21. *Farmer's World* (U.S. Department of Agriculture Yearbook, 1964), p. 71.

22. *Ibid.*, pp. 72-73.
23. *Suggestions for Research in Water Resources, op. cit.*, p. 2.
24. Geddes, H. J., 'Harvesting Water for Irrigation', *Span* (Shell International Chemical Company), VII, No. 2, 1964, pp. 89-91.
25. Milne, Borus and Margery, *Water and Life* (Atheneum Press, New York), 1964, pp. 113-17.

CHAPTER 6

THE HUMAN LANDSCAPE
OF IRRIGATION

We have so far been largely concerned with the technical aspects of irrigation. But it must be stressed that irrigation is as much an expression of human organisation and its adaptation to the physical environment as it is a technical achievement. In terms of land use, field patterns and settlement patterns, the landscapes which result from irrigation vary both in extent and degree. In Monsoon Asia and to a lesser extent in the Mediterranean lands, which are regions of seasonal rainfall, the human geography of hundreds of millions of acres has been considerably determined by irrigation. But the degree to which irrigation has transformed the landscape is greatest in the arid and semi-arid regions of the world, where in places the contrast between the desert and the sown is one of the most striking of geographical phenomena. In nearly all these major regions, there is a marked difference between the landscape of traditional, small-scale peasant irrigation and that of modern, large-scale projects. In the more humid areas of the world, the contribution of supplemental irrigation is slight, and it has affected the landscape and agrarian pattern relatively little. In order to illustrate the various contributions of irrigation to human geography, it is necessary to examine in detail some of the landscapes which result from its practice in different parts of the world.

THE ARID AND SEMI-ARID REGIONS OF THE WORLD

In these regions, the introduction of irrigation has brought about an almost total transformation of the landscape, though the scale of this transformation may vary from a few acres in a Saharan oasis to a million acres in the Imperial-Coachella valleys of southern California. The life-giving properties of irrigation in arid lands are nowhere more apparent than in a desert oasis, a clump of green in an otherwise brown and barren landscape. In the Sahara Desert and the Arabian peninsula, oases typically occur in lines or groups and are most numerous at the edges of highlands. They

vary in size from tens to thousands of acres, and the great majority
of them are dependent upon underground water. They are often
situated in hollows out of which rise the green tops of palm trees.

Under particularly favourable circumstances, the artesian
water may rise to the surface naturally, but far more often it has

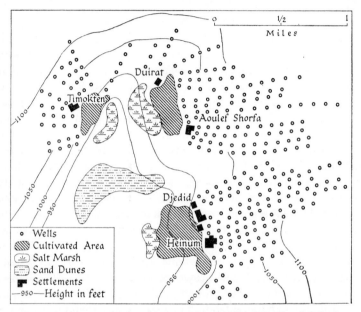

FIG. 7. The Aoulef Oasis, Tidikelt, Algeria. The Aoulef Oasis
lies in the heart of the Algerian Sahara at the southern edge of
the Plateau of Tademait, and is served by foggara which run in
long, parallel lines from the higher ground to the cultivated land
on the lower slopes and on the floor of the valley. Settlements
lie scattered in groups on slightly higher ground above the cultivated land. (*Based on 'Atlas of the Arab World and the Middle
East', Macmillan, 1960, p. 13*)

to be lifted from shallow wells, usually by primitive devices like
the shaduf and sakia. In some oases, seepage water is collected in
kanats or foggara (Fig. 7), and the water is led by small irrigation
channels to groves of date palms and small, intensively cultivated
plots where corn, vegetables, melons and tobacco are grown.
Wheat, millet and beans are also common and in the Sahara are
usually planted in the autumn to be harvested before the summer
heat. As in other areas of traditional peasant farming, cultivation

involves much human labour, and as a result, individual productivity is low. Agricultural techniques are primitive, and im-
plements rudimentary or non-existent. Along the higher edges
of the oasis fringing the cultivated land are the settlements, consisting of mud brick houses with flat roofs. Many Saharan oases,
like those in Libya and Algeria, have declining populations because modern motor roads are being built, increasing the drift of
the younger people away to the towns. As a result, the houses fall
into disrepair and the desert encroaches upon the cultivated land.

Few areas illustrate more strikingly the transformation that
irrigation can effect on the landscape than the Nile Valley in Egypt.
Almost nowhere else in the world is the transition from fertile,
watered land to barren desert so abrupt; over great distances the
cultivated land gives way to the desert within a few feet of the
outermost irrigation canal. Cultivation is restricted to a narrow
strip on either side of the Nile, which is situated in a trough with
an average width of about twelve miles, bounded by limestone
scarps. Only in the delta is the irrigated land extensive. The
cultivated land is seamed by a network of canals and ditches, which
divide up the land into an irregular pattern of small, rectangular
fields of varying shades of green, yellow and brown, depending
upon the crops being grown. This bright patchwork quilt contrasts sharply with the dull, brown monotony of the desert. Villages
are located on the higher ground on the edge of the irrigated area
or within the cultivated land. They are usually found near standing water, as each village has its own pond or well, and consist of
mud brick houses with flat roofs, often surrounded by a clump
of date palms.

Egypt is an example of traditional peasant irrigation farming,
but of a rather special kind. It combines the traditional features of
small holdings, primitive techniques of cultivation, and low yields
with the provision of perennial irrigation, which permits cultivation the year round over most of the area. In 1952, before the
larger holdings were broken up and redistributed, more than a
quarter of the cultivated land of Egypt was owned by a few
thousand landowners with holdings of at least 125 acres each, while
a third was owned by two and a half million peasant farmers in
plots of less than 8 acres each, of whom two million possessed less
than an acre. Most of the large holdings were worked by small
farmers or smallholders, who followed the instructions of the

landowners concerning irrigation methods and choice of crops. Since 1952 a programme of agrarian reform has redistributed several million acres confiscated from the large landowners; unfortunately, this has scarcely improved the situation, as Egypt's rapidly growing population and the consequent pressure on the land have prevented the consolidation of holdings which would make more efficient farming possible.[1]

At present, the peasantry lack modern equipment and rely largely on primitive wooden ploughs with metal-tipped shares drawn by oxen. The shaduf and sakia are still widely used, and only ten years ago they were more common than oil pumps. As far as the provision and distribution of water are concerned, Egypt is served by efficient, modern structures and techniques, but her land is still cultivated in age-old ways and its agricultural productivity remains relatively low.

The other major irrigated area of the Nile Valley is the Gezira Plain of the Sudan. In its landscape, land use, and social and economic organisation, it provides a considerable contrast with Egypt. Before the coming of large-scale irrigation, intensive agriculture in the Gezira was almost entirely restricted to narrow strips along the rivers, from which water could be fairly easily lifted. Most of the region was covered with stunted thorn bushes and grasses, which supported poor herds of cattle. Rainfall was uncertain, varying considerably from year to year, and evaporation was high. Today, though it covers less than one per cent of Sudan's land area, the Gezira contains seven per cent of the population and produces eighteen per cent of the gross domestic product. A remarkably level, monotonous clay plain, it is well suited to irrigation, with its heavy, black clay soil which prevents the water from seeping away too quickly. Moreover, as the plain slopes away to the north-west, it facilitates the flow of irrigation water from the Sennar Dam along the main irrigation canal, which is situated on the eastern side of the irrigated area (v. p. 189).

About one million acres are under irrigation, of which half is cultivated one year and half the next. The development of such a large-scale project involved the investment of considerable capital, and this was achieved by persuading foreign companies to provide the money and expertise, in return for which they were allowed to recover their original investment and make a satisfactory profit before handing the scheme over to the Sudan government.

The Sennar Dam, the key structure of the scheme, was completed in 1925, and as more and more land was later brought under cultivation, it was divided into plots of forty acres, each plot consisting of four fields, which were handed over to tenant farmers. The plots are reissued to the farmers each year only if they are farming them properly, and they are not permitted to buy extra plots in case a few wealthy men secure control of most of the land.

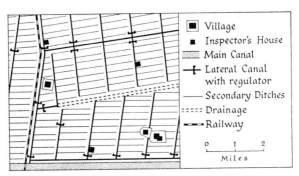

FIG. 8.   Irrigation in the Gezira, Sudan. The rectilinear landscape of the Gezira is typical of a modern, large-scale irrigation scheme in an area of gentle relief. Settlement is concentrated in nucleated villages which are spaced at regular intervals of three or four kilometres and sited at convenient distances from the main canal. This always contains water even when not in use for irrigation. (*After Barbour*)

An eight-year rotation is commonly used, consisting of cotton, fallow, millet, fallow, cotton, fallow, fodder beans and fallow. Cotton is therefore grown one year in four, and the government insists on the cultivation of millet and fodder beans for livestock to avoid the harmful effects on the soil of cotton monoculture.

Cotton is planted in August and supplied with water from channels which run from the lateral canals across the fields (Fig. 8). A typical forty-acre plot may be divided into as many as two hundred little plots, which are surrounded with earth banks to prevent the water from running away. By Egyptian standards, the scheme is lavish in land; this is made possible because the Sudan is fortunate in being thinly populated. Nowadays, however, forty acres is too much for one farmer to cope with, and in recent years new holdings on the Gezira are twenty acres each, while on the Manaqil extension to the south they are only fifteen acres.

The farmers live in regularly spaced villages which closely resemble one another and typically contain a school, a clubhouse, a dispensary, a few general shops and a well, while the houses consist of the ubiquitous mud-dried brick. The landscape of the Gezira is a monotonous one of straight lines and squares, a flat, featureless plain intersected by canals, drains and roads. The monotony is relieved only by occasional clumps of trees planted under government direction, and the dispiriting atmosphere which this sameness produces has contributed to the drift of younger people away to the towns. Moreover, the coming of irrigation has brought about the spread of the disease bilharziasis. Nonetheless, the scheme is undoubtedly successful, and today over 700,000 people live on the Gezira and almost another 200,000 enter it annually to pick the crops. In the words of McLoughlin, 'To visualise, construct, maintain and expand such a highly organised operation in an under-developed African nation among semi-nomadic, non-industrial, mainly illiterate peoples is without question one of the outstanding twentieth century economic accomplishments'.[2]

In terms of natural environment, the Imperial Valley of southern California is in many ways similar to that of the Nile Delta. It too lies in a desert, is served by a great river which rises in a distant, well-watered region, and suffers from extreme aridity and high summer temperatures which make agriculture impossible without irrigation. There the similarity ends. As far as land use, agricultural practices, and social and economic organisation are concerned, it is vastly different. By Old World standards, its farms are few but large, numbering about 5,000 and averaging 100 acres in size. Cultivation is highly commercialised, and large-scale farming operations employ a great amount of machinery which prepares the fields, plants them, cultivates them and harvests many of the crops which grow in them. But despite the high degree of mechanisation, a great deal of labour is required. Such labour is seasonal, itinerant and cosmopolitan, consisting of Mexicans, Chinese, Japanese, Filipinos and Negroes.

The area was first settled by white men and irrigation systems were first developed at the turn of the century, but not until 1940 when the All-American Canal was completed was water diverted from the Colorado River to make possible a great extension of the irrigated area. As this engineering achievement involved the expenditure of vast sums of money, it was made possible only through the agency of the federal government. The high cost of the water so produced has led to a cultivation of crops which for the most part have a high market value per acre. A growing season which is one of the longest in the United States, between 303 and 323 days, makes possible the cultivation of a great variety of crops. Particularly important is early market-garden produce, especially lettuce, carrots, cabbage, cantaloups, tomatoes and peas. Many of these are grown in winter, when cultivation is impossible over most of the country. Citrus fruit, flax, barley, sugar and cotton are also grown, and high crop yields are obtained; for example, between 2,000 and 4,000 pounds of barley per acre are common. Alfalfa is an important part of the crop rotation, occupying about forty per cent of the cultivated area, as it helps to build up the soil. Between five and seven cuttings a year are obtained and fed to livestock for fattening. In terms of the great variety of crops and the high yields, the Imperial Valley is one of the most successful irrigated areas in the world.

As in similar areas of large-scale modern irrigation in the United States, the landscape is a geometric pattern made up of large, square fields, canals, ditches and roads. Occasional clumps of trees, planted along roads and around farmhouses, help to relieve the monotony. Farmhouses are large and widely spaced, and most of the population in the area lives in small nucleated towns like El Centro, Calexico and Holtville, where ancillary industries, such as fruit-canning and the servicing of agricultural machinery, are concentrated. By comparison with irrigated areas in the Old World, the Imperial Valley is thinly populated. Because of the great distances to markets, particularly those on the east coast, and the perishable nature of many of the crops, produce has to be refrigerated and despatched quickly by road and rail. For these reasons, co-operative marketing associations, now among the best developed and most influential in the world, have grown up. The agricultural economy in this region increasingly requires a very high investment in machinery, land and the provision of water. Consequently, a growing proportion of the land is owned by wealthy farmers, capitalist firms, banks and co-operative societies; these are able to provide the technical means of developing an area which, unlike comparable regions in Africa and Asia, does not have a large, settled population.

AREAS OF SEASONAL RAINFALL: MONSOON ASIA

Perhaps the most distinctive contribution of irrigation to the landscape of this area is the elaborate, gleaming pattern of the ricelands of South-east Asia. Extending along the littoral plains from southern India and Indonesia to central China, they form an irregular patchwork of every possible shade of green stretching across the alluvial plains and in some places rising up the hillsides in tier upon tier of terraces. These flooded fields, known as *sawahs* in Indonesia and Malaysia, are usually quite small, typically about fifty square yards in extent, though in the Red River delta of North Vietnam they may be as large as half an acre. They have all been meticulously and laboriously levelled to produce a perfectly horizontal surface so that the depth of water is the same everywhere. It is to produce these level surfaces that terraces are constructed in broken country like parts of the Philippines, Java and China. They are divided by earth banks, which are usually between fifteen and twenty inches high and which are able to retain water for eight or ten days. In the lowlands, the fields are bordered by banks which may be between six and twelve inches high and which frequently serve as paths as well as boundaries.

The water in these rice paddies is not stagnant. By a most elaborate system, dating from ancient times in some areas, water from springs and streams is led onto each field, from terrace to terrace and through interconnecting sluices in the plains. Simple dams regulate the flow of water, and where necessary it is carried along bamboo pipes to the sawahs. A typical, controlled irrigation system in Java consists of a masonry dam with sluice gates which allow floodwaters to escape, and a main canal which runs around the upper boundary of the irrigated area. From the main canal, the water is distributed to the fields by gravity. Over much of the area, modern control works do not exist, and man is often the principal beast of burden, raising irrigation water in the dry season with scoops, baskets and treadmills.

The rice is first sown in seed beds consisting of rich, carefully tended soil. In parts of India these seed beds show up as small, black squares contrasting sharply with the grey soils of the paddy fields. The young rice plants are then transplanted to the paddies, in which the whole family labours. The heavy ploughing, with buffaloes yoked to little, wooden ploughs or primitive harrows, is done by the men, but all are concerned in the planting, the continual weeding and the harvesting, in which the rice is cut stalk by stalk with a little, sharp knife, called an *ani-ani* in Indonesia. Fish are sometimes bred in the flooded fields and caught as the weeding proceeds, before the water is drained off for the ripening period, only a few days before the harvest. Where there is sufficient rainfall or irrigation water, as in parts of Java and North Vietnam, two rice crops can be harvested by careful preservation and use of the water supply. Elsewhere a different crop is planted in the dry months after the rice has been harvested, and this may be maize, sweet potatoes, soya beans or vegetables.

Such a laborious and intensive system of irrigation and cultivation demands close organisation among the farmers. The maintenance and repair work of the irrigation systems, the cleaning of ditches and the supervision of the distribution of water all require close co-operation. Irrigated rice-farming is man-powered and 'horticultural', and demands a great deal of ingenuity and effort if high yields are to be obtained. At the same time, it permits a high density of population, and in the ricelands of South-east Asia are some of the highest agricultural densities in the world, reaching 2,000 people per square mile in parts of the Yangtse delta. The peasants live very largely in villages and small towns, the villages forming strings of green islands which stand out in the otherwise featureless plains of paddy fields (Fig. 9).

In areas of hilly terrain, as in parts of southern India and Ceylon, a distinctive tank landscape has developed. Rice is cultivated with water supplied from 'tanks' (*v. p.* 16), and while the landscape of such an area is not particularly striking on the ground, from the air and on the map it presents a remarkable and unique appearance (Fig. 10). It is a landscape intensively reshaped by man, in which depressions have been very skilfully embanked to produce a levelling-out effect and 'a skyline of planes imperceptibly merging with one another'.[3] Strings of large tanks run along valleys, aligned along contours. Often they are paired on either side of larger rivers. Most tanks are semicircular, crescentic or fish-tail shaped. Except for a few months of the year during the late summer and autumn, when they are full of water from the heavy rains, the tanks are practically dry and the landscape is predominantly brown and dusty. There is generally little woodland, and trees are found only along the roads and in the gardens of the village houses. On the hills, cattle graze on the steeper slopes, and millet is grown under dry farming on the gentler slopes. The irrigated fields, in which rice is the principal crop, lie in the valley below the tank. They are served with water from

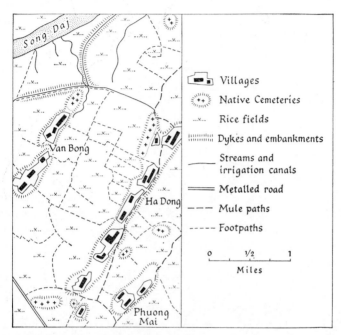

⊞ ■ ▪	Villages
ⵢⵢⵢ +++	Native Cemeteries
...ᵛ...	Rice fields
⁞⁞⁞⁞⁞⁞	Dykes and embankments
——	Streams and irrigation canals
══	Metalled road
— — —	Mule paths
- - - -	Footpaths

0   ½   1
Miles

FIG. 9. Ricelands of the Red River delta, North Vietnam. This area lies a few miles south-west of Hanoi. The land is given over almost entirely to the cultivation of rice and is seamed by a network of paths, streams and canals. The rivers and main canals are used for irrigation, navigation and domestic purposes. Apart from the settlements, the only other areas not devoted to cultivation are the native cemeteries. (*After George*)

channels which stem from the tank and subdivide into ditches along the sides of the fields. When the water level in the tank subsides, water is raised by primitive lifting devices.

Villages are fairly compact and are situated beside or at the foot of the tank. In parts of southern India they often consist of two hamlets, an upper-caste one with reasonably good houses made of mud walls and tiled roofs, each with its fruit trees and vegetable patch, and a lower-caste one usually consisting of poorer

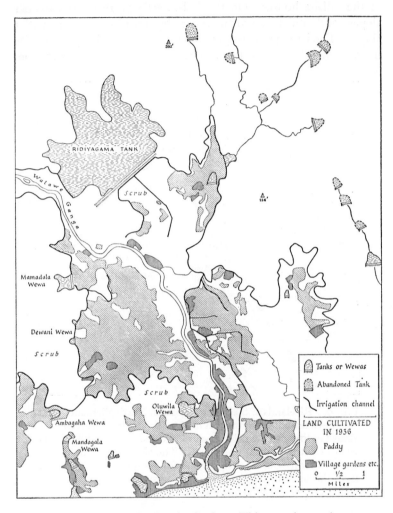

FIG. 10. Tank irrigation in Ceylon. This area in south-east
Ceylon receives an annual rainfall of fifty inches or less. There
are two main types of tank irrigation: smaller tanks, like those in
the north-east corner of the area, many of which have been long
abandoned, based on river valleys and laid out in lines so as to
reinforce one another; and larger tanks which are not on river
valleys, such as the Ridiyagama Tank, fed by a channel from
the Walawe Ganga.

houses with thatched roofs. On the whole, tank irrigation does not support a prosperous agriculture. A great deal of water is lost in evaporation, as the tanks have a considerable surface area in proportion to their storage capacity. Moreover, sooner or later, the tanks become silted up and useless, and there is little room for the construction of new ones. Occasionally, bunds fall into disrepair, and the reservoirs become swamps and promote the spread of malaria. In parts of Ceylon, this dismal process has produced a decaying tank landscape and agricultural economy.

A very different kind of irrigated landscape from both the rice fields of South-east Asia and the tank country of southern India and Ceylon has developed on the *doabs*, the large interfluvial tracts of the Upper Ganges and Indus valleys. Typical of a region where irrigation is not essential is the Upper Ganges region of Uttar Pradesh in India. With fertile soil and sufficient rainfall, adequate crops can be grown under natural conditions. However, irrigation has increased considerably in this area in recent years, partly to make double cropping possible and partly because of the security it provides. It is one of the most intensively cultivated regions in India, producing food crops, especially wheat, oilseeds, cotton and sugar cane. In this area of seasonal contrasts, *rabi* crops of wheat and vegetables are grown in the cool winter season under irrigation, and *kharif* crops of millet, rice, cotton and maize in the hot summer season, with rainfall supplemented by irrigation where necessary. Irrigation water is provided both by canals which stem from the main rivers and by wells (Fig. 11). In most places the water table is too low to tap by shallow wells, and more permanent, masonry-lined wells are necessary to support cultivation. Modern tube wells are also increasingly being installed.

The landscape is one of small holdings, the great majority being less than five acres, which are subdivided into small, hedge-less and fenceless fields. Numerous livestock are kept, but because of the pressure on land, there is very little grazing, and cattle are left to fend for themselves along the roadside verges and in patches of wasteland. After the crops have been harvested, the cattle are grazed on the stubble. The population is very dense for a rural landscape, averaging 1,000 people per square mile in places, and is found mainly in nucleated, evenly spaced villages of sun-dried brick houses, market gardens and mango groves. The holdings are too small and fragmented for efficient farming, and methods

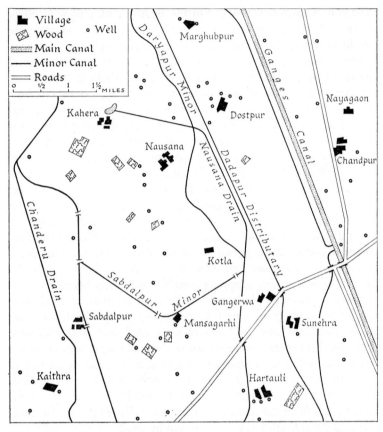

Fig. 11.   Canal and well irrigation, Uttar Pradesh, India. This area is about twenty-five miles south-east of Delhi between the Jumna and Ganges rivers. It was first intensively settled in 1891 when the Ganges Canal, its main source of water, was completed.

of cultivation are generally primitive, based on the inadequate tools and storage and market facilities of the farmers. In a few areas, consolidation has taken place and has brought about some saving of land, since fewer earthen bunds and access points are required. In general, however, the area is typical of peasant irrigation farming, densely populated and intensively cultivated but with low agricultural productivity.

Farther west is the Chenab Doab in West Pakistan, a semi-arid region which in many ways resembles the Sudan Gezira. Until the end of the last century, cultivation was restricted to relatively narrow strips along the main rivers, where the water table was sufficiently near the surface to be tapped by shallow wells. In the somewhat higher ground of the doabs, the water table was too deep to be effectively utilised, and as the rainfall was light and irregular, they were largely given over to scrubland and nomadic

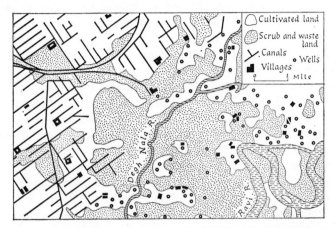

FIG. 12.   Irrigation on the Chenab Doab, West Pakistan. This map shows part of the Chenab Doab, about seventy miles south-west of Lahore, as it was fifty years ago, and clearly illustrates irrigation colonisation in progress. There is a marked contrast between the planned settlement pattern of the Lower Chenab Canal Colony in the west, based on modern canal irrigation, and the older cultivated area to the east, based on water obtained largely from shallow wells. (*After Spate*)

pastoralists, or poor dryland farming supporting a scanty population.

The transformation of the doab landscape was wrought by British irrigation engineers, who completely changed its hydrographic character from the eighteen-eighties onwards. Canals were built, tapping the main rivers and spreading water across the doabs. Perennial irrigation was brought to large areas, and canal colonies were established like the one near Lyallpur between the Chenab and Ravi rivers (Fig. 12). This colony is now more than fifty years old and was developed after the construction of the Chenab Canal. The land was divided into squares of about twenty-five acres each, the amount which one main ditch could water.

Pioneer farmers moved into the area and many were allocated twenty-five-acre squares, large holdings by traditional Indian standards. Since then, however, many of the original holdings have been divided up among families, and others have been sold, entirely or in part, so that today there is a great variation in size.

The landscape of the new canal colonies as seen from the air differs considerably from the old, traditional landscape which it replaced. Instead of the irregular pattern of villages, scattered cultivation based upon shallow wells, and large areas of uncultivated land, there is a regular, regimented landscape, divided up into a checkerboard of squares and rectangles. Roads and irrigation channels form straight lines, and villages are rectangular and evenly spaced along the roads, their mud houses built with flat roofs and small windows and each with its small market garden. Wheat and cotton are the main crops of the area but some sugar cane and rice are also grown. The relatively few patches of poorer, uncultivated land are either devoted to scrub, on which the humped zebu cattle graze, or planted with trees which provide fuel and timber.

The coming of modern canal irrigation to the doabs has brought about an enormous increase in population. Before the area was transformed by the irrigation engineer, population densities in the Chenab Doab averaged twenty people per square mile; today they exceed six hundred per square mile. But large-scale irrigation has not proved to be an unmixed blessing. It has made possible an excessive application of water to the land, which, without adequate drainage facilities, has brought about widespread waterlogging and salinity.

AREAS OF SEASONAL RAINFALL: MEDITERRANEAN EUROPE

Like Monsoon Asia, Mediterranean Europe is an area of seasonal rainfall, but receives its precipitation in winter and experiences drought in summer. It too presents a contrast between landscapes which have been farmed under irrigation for centuries and those which have been developed quite recently as the result of large-scale schemes. Typical of a landscape which has been transformed by irrigation over many centuries is the plain of the River Po in Italy. To an exceptionally high degree, it owes its character to human intervention, principally through irrigation, drainage and soil amelioration. As the soils of this region were naturally infertile, a radical transformation of their physical structure and chemical composition was necessary before they could be cultivated. In some parts of the lowland, the process of soil improvement has been going on since classical times, and centuries of use have produced a covering of artificial soil which renders indistinguishable the geological differences between one agricultural area and the next. The extension of irrigation on a large scale dates from the Middle Ages, when it was carried out by the abbeys. During the Renaissance the city states built such canals as the Naviglio Grande between Milan and Turin, the Canale della Muzza and the Naviglio della Martesana, which leads off from the Adda. After 1860, irrigation works were developed by the Italian government, including the eighty-five-kilometre-long Cavour Canal completed in 1886, and the extension of the irrigated areas was greatly accelerated in the nineteen-thirties.

Today, the North Italian Lowland is an intensively cultivated area with a high density of rural population, exceeding 300 people per square mile. Its advanced and specialised agriculture shows marked regional differentiations. In some areas the traditional crops of wheat, maize and rice are grown, while elsewhere special-ised fodder and industrial crops such as hemp and sugar beet are produced. An area that specialises in the cultivation of fodder is the Lodigiano, around Cremona. From there to Milan and be-yond, the landscape is rectilinear in pattern, with fields, mainly between five and fifteen acres in size, bordered by irrigation and drainage ditches. Earth roads, bordered by lines of pollarded poplars, alders and willows, add further straight lines to the landscape. The holdings in this area are usually quite large, aver-aging 250 acres, because the need for careful planning and technical control favours large units, and the fertility of the irri-gated land makes owners reluctant to subdivide holdings. The most important crop is rotation pasture, which occupies more than ninety per cent of the cultivated land, with the rest being devoted to rice, wheat and maize.

The traditional farming unit is the *cascina* or dairy farm, con-sisting of capacious buildings grouped around a central square, including the *padrone's* house, living quarters for the workers, cartsheds, stables, cowsheds and other buildings. Abundant fodder resources from the irrigated pastures mean that the area can support high densities of dairy cattle, mainly Friesians and

Bruni Alpini from the high valleys. The cows are almost entirely stall-fed, principally on the luxuriant grass of the rotation meadow, so that there are few obvious signs in the landscape of extensive stock farming. The chief product is cheese, especially the semi-fat *grana parmigiana*, a thin, hard cheese which is used as a condiment. In addition, *steacchino*, a short-ripening cheese, *caciocavallo*, *provolone*, *bel paese* and *gorgonzola* are produced. There is much mechanisation of the processes of dairy farming, and most landowners employ large numbers of permanent labour. Maize is also important in the economy of the area, and rice is introduced for one year after the pasture so that, in the process of submergence, the soil will be cleaned. A typical rotation includes one year of maize, three years of meadow and one year of rice.

The settlement pattern consists partly of isolated cascine and partly of small, nucleated villages. The latter often consist of a number of cascine intermingled with ordinary houses. In recent years, there has been a drift of younger people away from the cascine as Milan and its rapid industrial growth exert a pull. In all, however, this is a prosperous landscape, densely populated for a rural area, and one in which irrigation has helped to bring about a considerable change over the centuries.[4]

Another area in which irrigation farming has been carried on for centuries but with great differences in landscape, land use and social organisation is the coastal lowland of south-east Spain. Typical of the irrigated farmlands of this area is the Murcian *huerta*. An area of intensive cultivation, it supports one of the densest rural populations in Europe, in places almost 2,000 people per square mile. An 'oasis', based on the Rio Segura and its tributaries flowing down from the Sierra de Segura, it consists of the lowland town of Murcia and a number of smaller settlements like Mula, Lorca, Cieze and Caravaca. A typical settlement includes numerous houses, each with its small, intensively cultivated market garden, often little more than an acre in size and each supporting a family. The population in the irrigated lowlands extends over a wide area, in marked contrast to the nucleated villages of the dry hills, which are clustered round a well or hilltop.

In the Murcian huerta, cultivation is based on the application of a great deal of human labour, which makes possible high yields and an intensive land use. Intercropping is common, and maize is often sown while potatoes are still in the ground. In terms of the most effective use of labour, however, agricultural productivity is low. The chief crops are vegetables, maize and fruit, and two or three crops a year are obtained. Lemons are particularly important there, and oranges, pimento, peaches, apricots, almonds, vines and dates are all grown in considerable quantities. In addition, numerous dairy cattle are kept.

The huertas of south-east Spain, which extend in a broken line from the Pyrenees to the Straits of Gibraltar, form one of the finest and most productive irrigated areas in the world. With their densely populated 'garden suburbs' of small, intensively cultivated plots and numerous trees, they provide a marked contrast to the bare limestone hills which surround them. Irrigation water is obtained partly by means of old lifting devices like the noria and partly from canals. Increasingly, however, modern barrages, canal networks and mechanical pumps are providing ample supplies of water. Murcia, for example, is served by major barrages on the Rio Segura and its tributaries the Quipar, Mundo and Guadalentin. Unfortunately, this ample supply of water sometimes results in too much being applied to the land, and rapid salination occurs in places.

In some of the inland areas of Spain, recent irrigation and colonisation schemes have produced landscapes which are quite different from that of the coastal huertas. This development is due in part to the relative newness of these projects, many of which have been developed in the last twenty years. One of the most recent is the Badajoz Plain of the Guadiana valley, where before 1950 less than half the area was cultivated and less than one per cent irrigated. Since cereal dry farming and extensive grazing were the main agricultural activities, large areas were unproductive. Methods of cultivation were primitive, yields were low, many peasants were landless, and there was much unemployment. Holdings were large and estates (*latifundies*) were often farmed inefficiently by absentee landlords. The compulsory purchase of the land by the Spanish government and the introduction of irrigation by means of an enormous capital investment are working a transformation on the landscape. This transformation is a complex process involving more than the mere distribution of water. Deep ploughing is necessary to uproot trees and shrubs, and land has to be levelled to avoid erosion and smooth out irregularities which irrigation water could not reach.

Once irrigation water was available, the latifundies were sub-
divided into small holdings of between ten and twelve acres to
facilitate irrigation and were allocated to colonists. New nucleated
villages were built to house the farmers and their families, from
which they go out to work the fields. In the Badajoz Plain, forty-
nine villages will be built in all, each containing up to four hundred

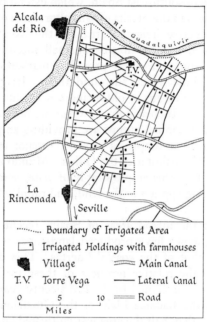

FIG. 13. The Las Torres irrigation settlement, Guadalquivir
Valley, Spain. This settlement is a government-sponsored project begun in 1936. Unlike the more recent areas of irrigation
colonisation with their nucleated settlements, here each farmhouse stands on its own property, since the local villages were
already in existence when the project was developed. However,
the rectilinear field pattern and the size of holdings, about ten
acres each, are typical of most irrigation settlements.

houses, with a radius of activity of two to three kilometres. The
new villages contain social and cultural amenities and provide
models of social organisation hitherto unknown in Spain. The
nucleated village is the commonest settlement form in new
Spanish irrigation schemes, though, exceptionally, individual
houses may be built on the holdings, as in the Las Torres settle-

ment near Seville (Fig. 13). By contrast, the colonisation and irrigation schemes in southern Italy have, for the most part, adopted the policy of individual holdings, each with its own farmhouse, thereby creating a different settlement pattern. In other respects, however, notably the size of the holdings, the rectangular pattern of fields, roads and canals, and the newness of the landscape, the various schemes are similar. As most of the colonists are new to the techniques of irrigation farming, which are very different from those of dryland farming, most projects offer a considerable training and advisory service. With its help, the people grow a wide range of crops; in the Badajoz area these include grain, vegetables, fruit and industrial crops.

The coming of irrigation to the middle Guadiana plains has transformed the landscape from the irregular sporadic pattern of poor, dryland farming into an ordered, prosperous landscape of regularity, marked by the straight lines of field boundaries, canals and roads. The productivity of the land has increased many times, and what was once a thinly populated area has absorbed thousands of peasant farmers. This successful colonisation has been made possible by the introduction of irrigation, because whereas under dryland farming an area of 250 acres required only eight peasants to work it, under irrigation farming a similar area requires fifty-three cultivators.[5]

IRRIGATION IN THE HUMID AREAS OF THE WORLD

In the eastern half of the United States and in western Europe, irrigation is very largely supplemental in character, because under normal conditions, there is sufficient rainfall to support plant growth. This form of irrigation has made relatively little impact on the landscape. The installations are usually portable and are to be seen in the fields only for limited periods in the summer when supplementary water is required. Moreover, although their use is growing, they are found on only a very small proportion of the cultivated land. As far as land use is concerned, while the introduction of supplemental irrigation has greatly increased crop yields, it has had little influence on the types of crops which are grown. In England, where grassland is probably the farm crop most responsive to irrigation, it may have helped to increase slightly the area of land under rotation grass, and it is also being increasingly used for greenhouse crops. In general, however, its influence on the landscape and on land-use patterns is minimal and quite insignificant when compared to irrigation in the arid regions of the world.

Bibliographical References

1. George, P., *La Campagne* (Presses Universitaires de France, Paris), 1956, pp. 161-64.
2. McLoughlin, P. F. M., 'The Sudan's Gezira Scheme: An Economic Profile', *Social and Economic Studies* (University of the West Indies), XII, No. 2, June 1963, pp. 179-99.
3. Spate, O. H. K., *India and Pakistan* (Methuen, London), 1960, p. 731.
4. Robertson, C. J., 'Italian Rice in Its Regional Setting', *Geography*, XX, 1935, pp. 12-27; Robertson, C. J., 'The Agricultural Regions of the North Italian Plain', *Geographical Review*, XXVIII, 1938, pp. 573-96.
5. Naylon, J., 'The Badajoz Plan', *Erdkunde*, XX, 1966, pp. 44-60.

Additional Sources

Dumont, R., *Types of Rural Economy* (Methuen, London), 1964.
Fisher, C. A., *South-east Asia* (Methuen, London), 1964.
Houston, J. M., *The Western Mediterranean World* (Longmans, London), 1964.
Perpillou, A. V., *Human Geography* (Longmans, London), 1965.
Robequain, C., *Malaya, Indonesia, Borneo and the Philippines* (Longmans, London), 1958.

CHAPTER 7
ECONOMIC ASPECTS OF IRRIGATION

The successful expansion of irrigation farming has been one of the most striking features of the growth of world agriculture during the last century. Today more than 370 million acres, about thirteen per cent of the world's arable land, are producing irrigated crops, compared to a few million acres at the turn of the century. Moreover, development is continuing at an ever increasing rate all over the world.

This expansion is frequently based upon large-scale projects involving enormous capital expenditure, sometimes taking the form of multi-purpose schemes which aim to develop the resources of a whole river basin. The capital investment involved in such schemes is immense; for example, the cost of the Columbia Basin project will be almost £350 million and that of the Aswan High Dam more than £400 million. In the United States such sums can only be provided by the federal government, and they are completely outside the limited financial scope of developing countries. As a result, large-scale projects presently being implemented in such countries as India, Pakistan and Egypt can only be developed by foreign capital and are contingent upon loans, principally from the United Nations agencies, the United States and the Soviet Union.

Elsewhere, where money is lacking or physical conditions are unsuitable and large-scale water resources absent, small-scale projects have been undertaken, often very successfully. In the Italian Apennines the construction of some 3,000 small artificial lakes for local irrigation has resulted in a great increase in production. In many countries, such relatively modest schemes are more likely to be within their financial capabilities, and they frequently offer greater prospects of success than more ambitious projects.

There is no doubt that the introduction of properly conducted irrigation farming into areas formerly barren or devoted only to dry farming can be extremely beneficial and can help to solve both human and economic problems. In Spain, for example, the labour requirements for irrigated farming are, on the average, about four times those for dry farming; in this way irrigated farming helps to absorb some of the landless and unemployed rural population.

In the rice-growing areas of South-east Asia, irrigation farming has provided considerable quantities of food in a given acreage and has permitted the individual farmer to support his family on a very small area. As a result, regions of what Wittfogel terms 'intensive hydraulic farming'[1] have come to support very dense populations. Although farming is intensive and agricultural techniques are often very subtle, the absence of labour-saving tools and modern lifting devices in these regions has meant a maximum of human labour and unending drudgery for the individual peasant. In the Red River delta of North Vietnam, where rice is grown largely by uncontrolled irrigation, one harvest of paddy requires up to 200 days of work for about two and a half acres of riceland, and a field with two annual harvests requires as much as 400 man-days of work a year.[2] In such areas it would be quite possible to reduce the quantity of agricultural work and eliminate much of the drudgery of peasant farming by the introduction of more modern techniques of irrigation farming. This could reduce the rural labour force, but it would immediately create the problem of finding employment for surplus agricultural labour in a country with a rapidly growing population and few industries, and it might well induce considerable rural depopulation.

In general, irrigation farming gives much greater crop yields than dryland farming, and in many countries permits double cropping. In Spain the irrigated area sown annually exceeds the total area of irrigated land, on the average by almost 130 per cent, while in Egypt the advent of perennial irrigation has made possible the cultivation of two or three crops a year, enabling agricultural productivity more or less to keep pace with the rapidly growing population.

Another advantage of irrigation is that it frequently enables a much greater variety of crops to be grown than is possible under natural conditions. In the Upper Ganges valley of India, perennial irrigation makes possible the cultivation of both winter crops like wheat and vegetables and summer crops like rice, cotton and maize. However, the automatic application of water to the land does not necessarily lead to a great increase in growth. In Australia the results of the use of irrigation on pasture were at first very disappointing, largely because the grasses then being grown did not respond well to the changes in habitat brought about by irrigation. It thus became necessary to introduce a new set of pasture plants with different growth characteristics.[3]

Irrigation does not only affect crops and crop yields, but it also determines, to a considerable extent, the social organisation of the farming units. In an area of indigenous peasant irrigation-farming such as Java, the distribution of water is often regulated by so-called 'irrigation societies', which consist of all those owning ricelands irrigated from single watercourses. A typical society will consist of the farmers from ten to fifteen hamlets and will have in its care a single dam and canal to supply many very fragmented holdings. Its main functions are the management of water resources, the co-ordination of planting, the maintenance of irrigation works, the distribution of water among the individual fields and the responsibility of deciding when planting shall take place. A complex organisation, it levies fines and assessments, constructs hundreds of small water-dividers to direct the flow of water, arranges crop rotation schemes, and keeps records.[4]

In a large-scale modern project like that of the Gezira, the distribution of water is regulated by the state, which establishes a social and economic organisation for this purpose. A partnership exists between the government, which provides the land and the water; the Gezira Board, which acts as agent for the government and supervises the supply of water through the minor canals, the details of farming and the marketing of the cotton; and the tenant farmers. The Board was set up to replace the private Gezira syndicate which financed the original scheme. Its regulations are enforced by inspectors who ensure an adequate standard of farming. In return for its services, the Board takes ten per cent of the net return, while the farmer receives forty-four per cent plus another four per cent in the form of social services, and the government takes the remaining forty-two per cent.

Such close regulation of irrigated farming would not be acceptable in a capitalist economy like that of the United States, where federally sponsored projects have established a different form of organisation. In the Columbia Basin project, about seventy per cent of the land is privately owned, having been sold by the federal government to individuals in holdings of about eighty-five acres. As the project was planned as a family-type development, designed to provide farms which would yield a living for one family, the sale of land is subject to anti-speculation laws, and no farmer is allowed to own more than one holding. The federal government, through its Bureau of Reclamation, sells irrigation water to the farmers at assigned charges. It is hoped that in this way and by the sale of hydroelectricity generated at Grand Coulee Dam, it will eventually be possible to liquidate the capital costs of the project. It is clear, therefore, that the nature of such social and economic organisations is determined by the character and scope of the irrigation systems and the economic and social framework of the countries in which they are located.

In almost all the countries which have embarked upon large-scale programmes to extend irrigation, the state has played an increasingly dominant role, largely owing to the inadequacy of private enterprise. This inadequacy is partly the result of the technical difficulties involved and the expense and complexity of large-scale developments, and partly because, to private investors, such programmes represent long-term returns. To the state, on the other hand, they frequently represent 'profitable' investments: they may bring about the improvement and conservation of national resources, increased agricultural production, an expanded national economy, higher government income from taxes and, at the same time, help to promote social peace and security. In the Renmark and Mildura areas of the Murray valley in Australia, irrigation has led to marked civic progress in the form of better roads, improved water supplies, and educational and other public facilities which would undoubtedly have been impossible if the surrounding land had remained as dry-farming country. In some countries like Italy, France and Spain, irrigation projects help to redress the balance between prosperous industrialised regions and under-developed rural ones. From an economic point of view, investment in agriculture will inevitably be expensive; generally speaking, the same returns can be acquired from industry at a considerably lower cost. However, if money is to be invested in land reform and development, returns may be best obtained from irrigation, because of the social benefits it brings, as it is particularly suitable for family farming.[5] This suitability stems from the fact that, under efficient irrigation farming, a considerably smaller holding than in the previous system of dry farming will provide sufficient economic return to support a family.

Clearly, the capital and operating costs of providing irrigation and the returns that can be expected under different conditions vary widely. The variable factors which influence costs include the type of water supply, the size of the project, whether government-sponsored or provided by private enterprise, the type of equipment in use, the climate of the region, the type of crop grown and the skill of the farmer. There are such enormous variations in almost all these respects between technologically advanced countries like the United States and Great Britain and developing countries like India and Egypt that comparison becomes virtually impossible. In a highly developed, capitalist economy like that of California, irrigation farming is big business and very expensive. There, farmers are frequently entrepreneurs of large corporate organisations; along the western half of the San Joaquin valley, farms average 10,000 acres in size and represent investments in land alone of the order of £150,000 to £300,000. One well sufficient to irrigate a square mile often amounts to an investment of almost £20,000.[6] In England the capital costs of installing supplemental irrigation are also likely to be considerable (though not as great as those in California). It has been estimated that, six or seven years ago, the capital cost of irrigating up to twenty acres of land from water in a near-by stream was approximately £12 10s. an acre and that to irrigate twenty to one hundred acres from a more distant water supply cost £20 an acre.[7] Since such capital resources are quite beyond the means of farmers in poorer countries, the large-scale extension of irrigation can only take place as the result of government action.

While in some instances the success of irrigation projects has been remarkable, in others, results have too often been mediocre and below expectations, despite enormous capital expenditure. In some countries this may be due to the incorrect siting of projects. P. N. Hore points out that recent major schemes in West Bengal do not water the areas of greatest need.[8] This is largely due to the fact that these schemes supply areas of 'apparent irrigation needs' rather than those with 'real priority of irrigation needs'. The former areas, determined by rainfall deficiencies alone, may be very deceptive and not worth irrigating, possibly because the soils are lateritic or otherwise poor, or because the areas are difficult of access or hard to drain. On the other hand, areas with greater natural rainfall may offer much better prospects for increasing agricultural productivity by the extension of irrigation. Before a major scheme is undertaken, it is essential to determine real irrigation priorities, and Dr. Hore outlines a rigorous application of geographical method to this problem. Not infrequently, the poor returns from irrigation projects may result from this lack of detailed planning and an inability to see irrigation farming as involving much more than the construction of expensive dams and canals. Too often, the storage reservoirs are liable to silting up because no adequate steps have been taken to control soil erosion in the catchment areas of the rivers which supply them. On occasion, water which has been stored and conveyed at great expense is eventually used to irrigate land which may be quite unsuitable for intensive cultivation. The lack of an adequate drainage system may lead to excessive losses and wastage of water with a consequent undue rise of the water table, often with brackish water, over large areas. There are many examples of the misuse of deep-lying aquifers, with the consequent rapid exhaustion of ground-water resources.

It is clear that, ideally, long and careful planning is necessary to ensure the success of a large-scale irrigation project. Unfortunately, in many of the developing countries in particular, time is the one thing that cannot be spared if already bad economic conditions are not rapidly to worsen. This is a familiar dilemma in such areas and, as in so many other respects, it may be better to take a calculated risk and put the development into effect immediately, instead of waiting to minimise the attendant risks at the expense of an already depressed economy and a low morale. Even under such conditions, however, some preparatory planning is essential. This might take the form of surveying the potential water available, experimenting to find out which crops are best suited to the areas concerned, training farmers in the use of irrigation water, conducting a soil survey and examining the feasibility of developing a transport network for getting the produce to market. These measures can be implemented while the main dam is under construction. Only upon the basis of these surveys should the main canals and distributors be designed and located, because one of the major reasons for the low utilisation of irrigation water in new projects is the incorrect siting of the main canals.[9] Large and impressive dams are all very well and may serve admirably as national status symbols, but they are too often accompanied by inefficient distribution systems, which convey water to farmers who continue to irrigate in accordance with age-old practices and traditions little influenced by modern science and technology. It is essential therefore not only to build large dams, but also to ensure both the efficient application of water to individual farms and an efficient drainage system to prevent salinity and water-logging. In short, the mere provision of water for irrigation on a large scale is not by itself sufficient; it is essential to ensure that it is efficiently used.

Nor must we assume that, given equal opportunity, financial incentives and the necessary resources, all farming communities will respond similarly in their productive efforts. That this is not so is shown clearly by the varying degrees of enthusiasm with which Indian farmers have made use of the water provided by modern irrigation schemes. A good example of the reluctance to make use of the water provided by a modern project is to be found among some of the farmers of Mysore in southern India. There, the Tungabhadra scheme, a major irrigation and hydroelectric project, first made water available on a large scale in July 1953. It was designed primarily for 'light' irrigation of dry crops such as millet, groundnuts and cotton, which were already being exten-sively cultivated in this region. Although in many parts of the country irrigation water is taken up as soon as it reaches the fields and farmers are eager for more, in Mysore the water was not wanted, even though for the first few years it was offered free. The prevalent attitude was one of cheerful optimism, an attitude that is not uncommon in other areas of marginal rainfall.

The reasons for such optimism are not entirely without foundation: next year is always likely to bring a reasonable amount of rain, and the farmer can always console himself with the thought that he can take the canal waters if the rains fail. In an effort to combat such attitudes, the government set up its own model irri-gation farms to show that with the use of canal water, yields could be considerably increased. Unfortunately, however, the farmer is not primarily interested in increasing his productivity; rather, he looks upon irrigation simply as an insurance against drought. In any case, the mere application of irrigation water will not give the maximum increase in crop yields; this can only be achieved by using more scientific methods of cultivation. As things stand at present in this area, the millet grows almost by itself. The farmer simply broadcasts the seed after superficial ploughing and then returns only to harvest it. Unlike more modern methods of cultivation, no great investment of capital, labour or technique is required, and since there is no shortage of land in this particular area, the yield is sufficient to feed the farmer and his family and often to tide him over during an intervening drought as well.[10]

In other parts of India there are superstitious barriers to the use of irrigation water. In Orissa, where the Hirakud scheme, one of the largest hydroelectric, flood control and irrigation projects in the country, has recently been completed, there is a prevailing belief that one cannot grow rice or any other crop on the same land twice in the same year, even though the water provided by the scheme now makes this practicable. There is a further local belief that once water has been used for the generation of power, it loses some vital 'electricity' that is essential to promote plant growth. As a result, many peasants in this area do not readily agree to use the water even when it is demonstrated that by doing so they can rapidly double their yields and their income.[11] In an effort to overcome this prejudice, the state government is not only giving irrigation water free for the time being, but is also constructing the field channels as well, a task that is normally the responsibility of the farmer.

In short, while irrigation can revolutionise a peasant's life, it can only do so to the extent that he is willing to co-operate. Shackled by lack of land, shortage of capital, absence of markets and communications, stunted by debts, illiteracy and malnutrition, and imbued with a profound respect for established social and religious customs, the Indian farmer has had little opportunity or inclination to change. As a result, at the end of India's second five-year plan period in 1961, some three and a half million acres of irrigable land remained unirrigated, while of the area under irrigation only twelve per cent was under double cropping. To persuade peasant farmers to adopt new methods, to build a bridge between traditionalism and modern technology, is bound to be a long and difficult business. The case of India illustrates the fact that too often in developing countries the farmers are inadequately prepared for the advent of much larger supplies of water than they had hitherto dreamed possible. This being so, they may be suddenly faced with such day-to-day problems as the correct timing of irrigations, the desired depth of wetting per irrigation and the amount of water required to wet a given depth of soil, as well as the problem of how to apply the required amount of water per irrigation, how to co-ordinate irrigation practices with other agricultural treatments and how to overcome adverse soil, water and climatic conditions during the irrigation season.

Such problems can only be solved by means of education and by continuous co-operation between civil engineers and agriculturalists. Examples of the success of such co-operation are to be found in the work of the Soil Conservation Service of the United States Department of Agriculture and the fifteen Irrigation Field Service Stations sponsored by the Israeli government. The need for education of this kind is also being realised by some of the developing countries. Zambia, for example, has for some years run a pilot scheme on the Kafue Flats for introducing African dryland farmers to the modern, intensive irrigated farming system. A great deal of inertia had to be overcome both on the part of the farmers, who had much to learn that was quite foreign to their experience, and on the part of many younger Africans, for whom farming conjured up an image of a bare existence with much hardship and few rewards. The Kafue scheme has apparently been successful on both counts: the farmers have responded well to the challenge, and the whole scheme has created a different agricultural image, in which modern irrigation farming seems to give a better life for a man and his family.[12] The scheme still operates on a relatively small scale but certainly has considerable possibilities.

In some areas a problem perhaps more intractable is the present land-ownership pattern, which may make irrigation very difficult or impossible. In parts of Turkey, for example, the land is divided into such small fractions that no modern irrigation can be economically feasible if those fractions are to be cultivated individually. In India the fragmented holdings of most villages are a problem which has become more and more acute with time, as each son, in succeeding generations, has received an equal share of each type of land owned by the family. The scattered location of the plots discourages efficient cultivation and makes irrigation difficult, while the bunds bordering the plots occupy much precious land. Consolidation is being effected on a voluntary basis by the exchange of plots, but progress has been uneven and slow. What seem to be needed are 'irrigation co-operatives' like those that have been successfully evolved in Taiwan.

In the developed parts of the world, the use of supplemental irrigation has increased considerably in recent years. This is due to a number of reasons: the growing realisation that its use increases yields and profits; the occurrence of periods of drought; the development of improved irrigation equipment, especially portable, lightweight pipes and sprinklers; relatively high farm incomes, which make it possible for farmers to invest in expensive irrigation systems; and the dissemination of better information on the moisture requirements of crops and pastures. In England the use of supplemental irrigation has grown partly because the official weather service and the agricultural advisory service have aided the farmer by providing him with the information which helps him decide when to irrigate and how much water to apply. However, the successful use of supplemental irrigation is naturally dependent on good farm management, and it is largely conditioned by the ability and willingness of the farmer to adopt it and by the availability of adequate supplies of good water. While it may prove very profitable in dry years, it may give little benefit in normal years, so that rather than install expensive equipment, many farmers prefer to take a chance on the adequacy of the rainfall. The greatest demand for supplemental irrigation occurs during periods of drought, and it is precisely during these times that the supply of water from streams, ponds and wells is lowest. Then high-value crops are usually the first to receive it.

In some regions there may be a choice between using water in an area of relatively high rainfall or damming and diverting it to an area of lower rainfall to supplement the natural precipitation. In most cases, supplemental irrigation in an area of lower rainfall results in greater economy in the use of water, enables a maximum area to be irrigated with a given amount of water, and allows full use of what rainfall does occur. In Queensland, for example, the development of supplemental irrigation in areas which receive between twenty-five and forty-five inches of rain a year has led to between thirty and forty per cent higher yields of sugar cane than in non-irrigated areas where the rainfall exceeds eighty inches a year.[13] In many cases, capital investment in irrigation might be better spent on extending its use in the humid areas of developed agriculture rather than concentrating on regions where agriculture has made little progress. An American agricultural economist has written, 'Too little attention is being given to irrigation in districts that already have a high rate of output. Too much attention is being given to the glamorous projects that will make the deserts bloom. We might better concentrate our limited capital to extending irrigation into the existing farmlands rather than developing new areas.'[14] He had the United States in mind when he wrote these words; they are obviously not applicable to those countries which are very largely arid and where no cultivation is possible without irrigation. But, in general, supplemental irrigation is becoming an integral part of agriculture in the humid areas of the United States and western Europe, particularly those areas liable to occasional droughts, and its use is almost certain to increase.

It is precisely in these regions, however, that the public attitude towards water is to regard it as a God-given commodity to which each man has an inalienable right. A by-product of this attitude is the wasteful use of water, too frequently encouraged by an economic system which invites the public use of as much water as possible. As the future development of our water resources becomes more expensive, it is likely that we shall have to set up a pricing structure to discourage the wasting of water.

During the last fifty years, our whole concept of where and how water should be stored, moved and utilised has changed dramatically. This change is the direct result of great technological developments which have made it possible to store and move surface waters on an ever increasing scale, to lift and transport underground water, to improve our techniques of applying water to the land and of treating polluted and waste water, and to plan on an over-all scale the many uses of water. But if we have made enormous strides in the regulation and treatment of water, many of the ways in which we use the water are wasteful and inefficient. As the world population rapidly increases, so the pressure upon our water resources will grow. Water will be in greater and greater demand for a variety of uses, of which irrigation will be but one of many. Higher living standards bring about an increased demand for water for household purposes. Many of the developing countries see industrialisation as the panacea for their economic ills, but industry is an avid consumer of water and of land that might otherwise be devoted to irrigated agriculture. On the other hand, a growing agricultural productivity is essential to any effective industrial expansion.

To the question, Is water put to its best use in irrigation? the answer in many countries must clearly be Yes; elsewhere there is reason to believe that the industrial use of water is far more valuable, so that in many areas of shortage, irrigation may well have to give way to other claims.[15] In the words of G. F. White, a noted American authority on the subject of water conservation, 'Always before in arid areas the threat of water shortage has been accompanied by the knowledge of unused potential supplies awaiting exploitation. Now, as limits loom ahead, only the most heroic schemes for long-distance transport or for new technology can stand in the way of compulsory choices among alternative uses for a given supply.'[16] It is becoming apparent that the unquestioned abundance of water which has hitherto existed in many areas will change with growing demand, so that there will be increasing competition for water both between the different categories of users, and in some areas between adjoining countries. Unfortunately, there is widespread lack of knowledge about the natural, economic and social aspects of water resources, and relatively little is being done to dispel this ignorance. There is a pressing need for a greater understanding both of the physical nature and limitation of water and of the relative importance and value of the several uses to which it can be put. It has been observed that 'water is everybody's problem and nobody's business'. If we are to remedy this state of affairs, then it becomes necessary to educate people as to the true character of our water problems. Otherwise, in democratic societies at least, an informed and enlightened public policy becomes well-nigh impossible.

From time to time the very permanency of irrigated agriculture has been called into question. Previous civilisations based on irrigated agriculture have perished or shifted, partly as a result of the encroachment of salinity and waterlogging and the silting up of reservoirs and canals. Today, many productive areas in many parts of the world have been destroyed by similar causes. If the pattern is not to be repeated, much more attention will have to be given to such problems. On balance, however, it would seem that irrigated agriculture is here to stay, and barring a global catastrophe, it is virtually certain to increase in the years ahead.

Bibliographical References

1. Wittfogel, K. A., 'The Hydraulic Civilization', in William L. Thomas, Jr., Ed., *Man's Role in Changing the Face of the Earth* (University of Chicago Press), 1956, p. 342.
2. Gourou, P., 'The Quality of Land Use of Tropical Cultivators', in Thomas, *op. cit.*, p. 342.
3. Wadham, S. M. and Wood, G. L., *Land Utilization in Australia* (Melbourne University Press), 1964, p. 303.
4. Geertz, C., *Peddlers and Princes* (University of Chicago Press), 1963, p. 90.
5. Naylon, J., 'The Badajoz Plan', *Erdkunde*, XX, 1966, p. 59.
6. Hartman, D. N., *California and Man* (Brown, New York), 1964, p. 235.
7. Culpin, C., *Farm Mechanization Management* (Crosby Lockwood, London), 1959, p. 112.
8. Hore, P. N., 'Rainfall, Rice Yields and Irrigation Needs in West Bengal', *Geography*, XLIX, 1964, pp. 114-21.
9. *Science and Technology for Development, III* (United Nations, New York), 1963 (E/CONF.39/1), p. 39.
10. Nair, K., *Blossoms in the Dust* (Praeger, New York), 1962, pp. 47-49; Lewis, J. P., *Quiet Crisis in India* (Doubleday Anchor, New York), 1964, p. 166.
11. Nair, *op. cit.*, p. 141 and 141n.
12. 'Supplement on Zambia', *The Times*, London, October 24, 1964, p. vii.
13. *Science and Technology for Development, III*, *op. cit.*, pp. 43-44.
14. *Farmer's World* (U.S. Department of Agriculture Yearbook, 1964), p. 75.
15. White, G. F., *The Changing Role of Water in Arid Lands* (University of Arizona Press, Tucson), November 1960, p. 9.
16. *Ibid.*, p. 6.

THE REGIONAL GEOGRAPHY
OF IRRIGATION

INTRODUCTION

No precise and accurate figures of the total extent of the world's irrigated lands are available. A number of estimates have been made but these should be treated with caution. Claims by individual countries are sometimes inflated to include areas under supplemental irrigation, which are often irregularly used, and others which are only potentially irrigable. However, a fairly conservative estimate of the extent of the world's irrigated area in the early nineteen-sixties, based upon sources available to the United Nations, suggested a figure of 370 million acres, or thirteen per cent of the world's arable land, as shown in Table 1. Table 2 shows the amounts of irrigated land in individual countries and is also largely based on reliable United Nations sources.

It should be realised that over large areas of the world the old and the new work side by side, and while modern projects are more dramatic and more hopeful for the future, great areas, particularly in Asia, depend on time-honoured methods. In a book of this kind, attention must rightly be focussed upon the new schemes, but this should not obscure the continuing importance of the old.

TABLE I

Areas	Irrigated Land (Millions of Acres)	Percentage of Total Area
Asia (excluding the Soviet Union)	239·8	64·8
United States	37·0	10·0
Soviet Union	30·7	8·3
Europe	21·8	5·9
Africa	14·1	3·8
North & Central America (excluding the United States)	12·6	3·4
South America	11·8	3·2
Australasia	2·2	0·6
Total	370·0	100·0

The Irrigated Areas of the World by Major Regions

(Based on United Nations estimates cited in *Farmer's World*, U.S. Department of Agriculture Yearbook, 1964, p. 76.)

In general, a regional treatment has been followed, because irrigation, old and new, must be seen against the differing physical, human, historical and economic backgrounds of the world's major regions.

TABLE 2

Country	Irrigated Land (Millions of Acres)	Year
China	183*	1960
India	88	1967
United States	37	1964
Pakistan	27·4	1963
Soviet Union	23·5	1966
Indonesia	15·9*	1962
Mexico	10·6	1964
Iraq	9·1	1963
Japan	7·7	1966
Italy	6·9	1960
Egypt	6·9	1965
France	6·2	1960
Spain	5·6	1965
Iran	4·9*	1960
Turkey	4·9	1957
Australia	3·4	1966
Chile	3·4	1963
Korea	3·2	1965
Thailand	3·2	1965
Peru	3·0	1963
Sudan	2·5	1959
Philippines	2·4	1965
Bulgaria	2·3	1966

The Irrigated Areas of the World by Countries

(Based largely on United Nations estimates cited in *F.A.O. Production Yearbook*, Vol. 21, 1967, Rome, 1968, pp. 9-10.)

* Approximate figures based on national estimates.

It will be seen that Asia has by far the largest area under irrigation, with 240 million acres or almost two-thirds of the world's total. This is almost certainly a more accurate estimate than one based on claims made by the Asian countries themselves, which would put the figure at approximately 340 million acres. Asian countries also head the list of those with the largest irrigated areas, and the alluvial river basins of China, India and Pakistan all support a great extent of irrigated agriculture. The only other countries with comparable areas are the United States and the Soviet Union. Irrigation has expanded considerably in all these countries and in the world as a whole during the last fifteen years (in 1949 the world had a total of approximately 200 million acres under irrigation), and further extensions are under development or planned. Europe too has witnessed an expansion in irrigated agriculture in recent years, as has Africa, but on a smaller scale. In the United States, Canada and Mexico, there are considerable growing areas under irrigation. But development in South America has been slow and sporadic, and Australasia has only a very limited area under irrigation, the greater part of which is to be found in the south-eastern part of Australia.

There is no doubt that it is possible, within the present limits of technology, to add greatly to the present irrigated area. The possibilities are perhaps most extensive in Africa, the Near East and Central Asia, but there is also further scope in South-east Asia, India, Pakistan, Ceylon and China. The practicability of extending irrigated agriculture depends largely upon the availability of water and capital for irrigation works; the limiting factor is not a lack of engineering technique but rather of capital. Meanwhile, although the implementation of irrigation projects now being developed or under consideration will not increase the world's cultivable area by a very large percentage, it will make a marked contribution to food production, since crop yields from irrigated lands are proportionally greater than those from non-irrigated lands.

CHAPTER 8

MONSOON ASIA
JAPAN AND KOREA

In 1966 Japan had about seven and three-quarters of a million irrigated acres, representing more than half her cultivated land and devoted almost entirely to the cultivation of rice. Unlike most other countries in Monsoon Asia, Japan has little uncontrolled irrigation. Water from mountain streams is diverted by numerous diversion dams into a network of canals and ditches and thence into individual fields. Often hand- and foot-pumps, as well as diesel and electric pumps which are increasingly replacing them, are used to lift water from the larger canals into fields and distributary ditches. Scattered throughout the country are tracts of irrigated lowlands served by extensive irrigation systems, whose regulation is frequently governed by so-called irrigation unions, co-operative ventures created by groups of hamlets. There is also a great deal of terracing on the higher lands, and water is ingeniously led from upland lakes and rivers to the higher terraces, from which it filters to terraces below. Multiple cropping is very common, especially in the warmer southern half of the country, and transplantation is much in use, partly because it saves irrigation water. In the relatively efficient way in which it uses irrigation water, with correspondingly high yields, Japan provides a considerable contrast with most of the countries of South-east Asia.

As most of Japan's cultivable land is already being used, no great extension of irrigated agriculture is possible. However, a number of modest new projects are under construction. These include the Tedori River scheme, providing irrigation for 25,000 acres, the Nabeta project to reclaim land from river estuaries and to provide water for 1,580 acres, the Nobi project (57,000 irrigable acres), the Toyokawe project (54,000 acres) and the Iwate Sanroku project (30,000 acres).

In Korea irrigation is important and is practised on a large scale, principally for the growing of rice. An estimate for 1961 suggests that the country then had approximately three million acres under irrigation,[1] but this figure is probably exaggerated, and in any case, most of the irrigation is uncontrolled. The best rice-growing areas are in the southern part of the country, where the methods of cultivation and irrigation are primitive.

CHINA

Irrigation has been practised in China for more than four thousand years and has developed into a traditional type of farming that is intensive in character, involving the use of much fertiliser, the minute preparation of the soil and the application of considerable amounts of human labour. Although modern methods and large-scale irrigation projects are being developed, traditional techniques of irrigation farming are still very generally in use and include such primitive lifting devices as treadmills and, particularly in the north, shallow, donkey-operated wells.

Most reliable reports suggest that China has more irrigated land than any other country in the world, though much of it may be only periodically subject to irrigation. In 1949 China had approximately 40 million acres under irrigation, representing sixteen per cent of her cultivated land. By 1959 the Chinese claimed that the total area of irrigated land had grown to 168 million acres, which, if accurate, represents an increase of culti-vated irrigated land from sixteen to sixty per cent in ten years.[2] An unofficial report cited in the Production Yearbook of the Food and Agriculture Organisation of the United Nations gives a figure of 183 million acres for 1960.[3] While such figures are probably exaggerated, there is little doubt that the area under irrigation in China has greatly increased in the last twenty years. This increase has taken two major forms: innumerable small-scale local develop-ments at the village level and the construction of a few large-scale, multi-purpose projects.

At the local level, villages have co-operated in the construction, extension and repair of ponds, ditches, culverts and canals. It has been estimated that between 1950 and 1954, for example, irrigation work was completed on 8,400,000 ponds and ditches and 900,000 wells.[4] Frequently, the local extension and improve-ment of irrigation schemes have included the construction of tiny hydroelectric power stations with capacities of up to forty or fifty kilowatts, used for pumping and for local flour mills.[5]

On a much more ambitious scale are plans to control the major Chinese rivers by constructing multi-purpose projects which envisage building series of dams to control floods, generate hydro-electricity, facilitate navigation and make water available for irrigation. The most ambitious of such schemes is probably the San Men project on the Hwang-Ho (Fig. 14), where the key structure, the San Men Dam, 2,600 feet long and 500 feet high, has been

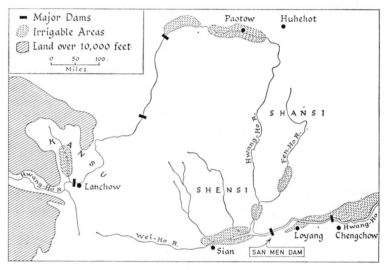

FIG. 14.   The San Men project, China.

built across the San Men Gorge. In addition to the main dam, forty-five smaller ones and twenty-six reservoirs will be built upstream and on tributaries as part of an immense scheme to control the Hwang-Ho, prevent floods and reduce soil erosion. When completed, the scheme will provide irrigation for millions of acres never before watered and will develop great quantities of hydroelectricity. Construction work has been going on for some years, and although the development seems to have been hindered by the withdrawal of Russian technical assistance, considerable progress has been made. The second largest dam on the Hwang-Ho, at Lanchow in Kansu, was due to begin operation in 1963, and the whole of the project for conquering the Hwang-Ho was scheduled for completion by 1967.[6] There are equally vast plans for the construction of multi-purpose barrages along the Yangtse, notably in the gorges between Ichang and Chungking. In northern China the multi-purpose Miyun Dam project has recently been completed. Situated by the Great Wall, near the Kupei Pass, it is primarily a water-conservation scheme, providing irrigation for about a million acres of cultivated land, much of it under rice.[7]

Another large-scale project which has evoked great interest is the Huai River Plan. The Huai River is in northern China, about half-way between the Yangtse and Hwang-Ho valleys, and runs through a fertile valley which has been subject to regular and disastrous flooding. Work began on the taming of the river in 1950, and the authorities claimed that it was completed by 1962 and that it has made possible the irrigation of more than eight million acres. The emphasis was placed on flood control, though not at first with complete success, as some flooding occurred in 1956 and 1957.[8] The development of such large-scale irrigation projects is, of course, determined to a considerable extent by the capital expenditure involved and by the prospect of adequate returns in the form of increased agricultural productivity. Occasionally, such schemes may be adopted even if they are not likely to prove immediately productive, in order to provide employment whereby a rapidly growing working population may be partly absorbed.

Despite such developments, it is most unlikely that China could have increased her area of irrigated land more than four times, from 40 to 168 million acres, between 1949 and 1959. A more reliable figure for this period is probably that given by the International Commission on Irrigation and Drainage of 77,300,000 irrigated acres in mainland China in 1955.[9] In the past decade, however, there has undoubtedly been notable expansion of irrigated agriculture.

Four main types of irrigation are commonly used in China. By far the most important is the network of canals scattered over most of central and southern China, especially in the Yangtse delta and the Cheng-tu Plain, which are the most productive regions of the country. In the monsoon region south of the Yangtse are many tanks in the form of ponds and reservoirs, in which fish and lotus are important by-products. In northern China, wells are the most important form of irrigation and are of two types, shallow wells from three to ten metres deep found mainly in the plains, and deeper ones in the foothills between fifty and one hundred metres deep. In the Tarim Basin of Sinkiang and in the arid Kansu Corridor, kanats, known locally as korag, are an important source of irrigation water.

The greatest extent of irrigated land is in the central and southern parts of the country, south of approximately 33°N. There, a complex and extremely varied network of canals, ditches and ponds provides water primarily for the ricelands of the Yangtse and Si valleys. In these areas more than half the total acreage is under irrigation, and in addition to rice, winter wheat and vegetables are grown. Primitive, age-old methods of lifting water, such as man-powered treadmills and the use of buffalo to turn geared wheels, are found alongside intricate and large-scale distribution systems. In the plain of Cheng-tu in west Szechwan, a model system of irrigation, developed as long ago as the third century A.D., operates today on principles which have scarcely changed in almost two thousand years. Streams flowing down from the western mountains are dammed where they debouch onto the lowland and are led into multiple channels fanning out across the plain. By these means, intensive cultivation is carried on, supporting one of the densest agricultural populations in China.

In northern China, irrigation is less important, though extensive canal systems are found in a few areas of the Hwang-Ho Basin, such as central Sian, where an elaborate network of canals and ditches has been in use for more than two thousand years. In this area, water from wells is used extensively to supplement natural precipitation for growing vegetables, cotton, opium and tobacco. In Sinkiang, which is mainly uninhabited desert, a number of oases along the base of the Tien Shan Mountains and the Tarim River, such as Kashgar, Yarkand, Urumchi and Turfan, grow wheat, cotton and fruit under irrigation, with much of the water being supplied by kanats. The Chinese have announced their intention of developing a number of modern irrigation projects in this remote province, and some remarkable achievements have already been made. One of these is the transformation of part of the Dzungarian Basin, which lies to the north of the Tien Shan Mountains and is fed with water from snow-melt in the Manass and near-by rivers. During the period from 1950 to 1965, the Chinese claimed to have constructed forty-five reservoirs and canals totalling 12,500 miles in length, with over 30,000 locks, sluices, culverts and aqueducts. As a result, the Manass Basin has been converted from desert into a fertile basin covered with a system of tree-lined canals fed from reservoirs. Over 800,000 acres are presently reputed to be under irrigation, devoted largely to the cultivation of grain and cotton. In addition, a new city called Shihotzu has been built in the Manass Basin, as well as a number of factories to process local products including cotton, paper, timber and sugar. The reservoirs are also being used for breeding fish on a large scale.

China's efforts to increase her irrigated acreage have been hindered by the fact that in most parts of China where additional water would be helpful, there are few feasible sources of supply. Moreover, the irrigation system suffers in places from the usual problems of waterlogging and salinity, and attention to methods of solving these would seem to offer the best prospects of increasing yields.

In Tibet an elementary but effective and apparently unique form of irrigation is practised. This is the Tibetan pond-irrigation system whereby roughly circular ponds, about 900 feet in diameter, are built up from ground level by dykes. The bottoms are paved with stone slabs, and the ponds are officially considered full when the water is six feet deep and within one and a half feet of the top of the dykes. The water is led out through sluice gates into many small, winding channels and so into the fields. Such systems were certainly in use before the Chinese invasion of Tibet.[10]

SOUTH-EAST ASIA

The incidence of heavy monsoon rains in summer permits uncontrolled and rainfed irrigation over much of this area, but these rains only allow single cropping. Clearly, a considerable extension of perennial irrigation is required if crops are to be grown at times other than during the summer rains. This is becoming essential if the rapidly growing population of the area is to be fed. Unfortunately, the countries of South-east Asia are hampered by lack of capital and technical expertise and by endemic political instability.

Another characteristic of this area is the great variation between one country and another in regard to irrigable areas. In Cambodia only three per cent of the cultivated land is irrigated by modern, controlled methods; in Burma it is six per cent; in the Philippines, about twelve per cent; in Thailand, sixteen per cent; and in Taiwan, sixty-six per cent. Accurate estimates of the areas under irrigation in South-east Asia are not readily available, and recent statistics published by the United Nations, although giving some idea of the extent of irrigated areas, should be treated with caution, being based on what are probably optimistic figures supplied by the countries concerned; this is particularly true of the additional areas which they hoped to bring under irrigation in the last few years (Table 3).

TABLE 3

Country	Irrigated Land ('ooos of Acres)	Year	Planned Increase to ('ooos of Acres- Year of Completion)	
Burma	1,860	1965	—	
Cambodia	168	1966	—	
Ceylon	983	1966	1,030	(1968)
Indonesia	14,789	1960	15,926	(1962)
Korea	3,178	1965	3,262	(1966)
Laos	1,853	1961	—	
Malaysia :				
Federation of Malaya	635	1964	702	(1965)
Sabah (North Borneo)	30	1966	—	
Philippines	2,372	1966	—	
Taiwan	1,210	1966	—	
Thailand	3,200	1962	5,229	(1966)
Vietnam	1,510	1961	4,135	(1966)

The Irrigated Areas of South-East Asia

(Based on figures cited in *F.A.O. Production Yearbooks*, 1966 and 1967, and *Economic Survey of Asia and the Far East*, 1963, p. 125.)

Over the greater part of the area, rice is the most important crop, cultivated intensively both in the densely populated alluvial lowlands like the Mekong and Menam valleys, and in upland terraces laboriously carved out of the hillsides. In Taiwan (Formosa), irrigation is particularly important and has led to a considerable increase in rice production, both in extent and in crop yields, which in turn has led to a rapid growth of population. The significance of relatively efficient irrigation farming is well shown by comparing Taiwan with Hainan, another island off the Chinese mainland. Not radically different in physical environment, fifty years ago they each had similar populations of about two and a half million. Today, Taiwan has a population exceeding ten million, while that of Hainan has remained constant. The difference has largely been brought about by efficient irrigated farming based upon the extension of irrigation to more than one million acres in Taiwan. More land can now be devoted to rice cultivation, and the harvesting period is longer. Together with a great deal of double cropping, these improvements have provided the basis for a greatly increased population.

Two main irrigation systems are currently in operation: (a) the *Taoyuan*, employed in the Taoyuan tableland in north-west Taiwan, consisting of ponds, streams, creeks, canals and ditches, and (b) the *Chianan*, in use along the west coast and based upon aqueducts and artificial reservoirs which feed canals. The latter system is gradually deteriorating because of water erosion and silting. Reservoirs are leaking, canals are in poor shape, and the mechanical equipment at the water gates has broken down. The restoration of the system will be difficult and expensive.[11]

In the Philippines, more than two million acres were under irrigation in 1966, of which little more than ten per cent were under government-administered schemes. For the rest, irrigation schemes are small, local and of limited effectiveness. Most of the irrigated land is situated in the lowlands, especially in central Luzon, but about 70,000 acres of terraced hillsides are irrigated in northern Luzon for growing rice. The most important crop is sugar cane; rice generally depends on natural precipitation, but where controlled irrigation is available, double cropping is possible. In the last ten years a few large irrigation dams have been built on the major rivers, such as the Magat Dam, which was opened in 1957 on a tributary of the Cagayan River and which irrigates more than 50,000 acres. Besides these, a number of projects for the extension of the irrigated area are planned, one of the most important being that in the Pampanga River valley of central Luzon.

On the mainland of South-east Asia, irrigation is important in the four Indochinese states of North and South Vietnam, Laos and Cambodia (Fig. 15). In North Vietnam the most important agricultural area is the Tonkin delta of the Red River, a densely populated, intensively cultivated region largely given over to paddy. In many ways the area closely resembles southern China in that the fields are irrigated by an intricate system of canals, distributaries and lifting devices. Traditionally, irrigation is only partially controlled, but under the French administration a number of dams and canal networks were constructed, making it possible to regulate the water levels in some of the rice-growing basins. As a result, about one-third of the total paddy area of

FIG. 15. Major irrigated areas in Indochina. Shown on the map are the sites of the proposed dams of the Mekong River project. (*Based on D. G. E. Hall, 'Atlas of South-East Asia', Macmillan, 1964, p. 48*)

Tonkin is served by modern irrigation works, where double cropping is possible.

The Mekong delta is South Vietnam's most important agricultural area, but it is less densely populated and less intensively cultivated than the Red River delta of North Vietnam. In normal years it is a region of surplus rice production, cultivated by flooding the fields in virtually uncontrolled irrigation. Similar methods of cultivating wet rice are used in Laos, particularly in the narrow alluvial floodplains along the Mekong valley. In the centre of the country and bordering the Mekong River is the plain of Vientiane, which has an area of about 750,000 acres but of which only a small part is presently cultivated. The limiting factor is the lack of water in the dry season, and the only possible crop is wet rice, which is grown during the rainy, summer season. Even then, however, there can be rainless periods lasting several weeks. If a regular and plentiful supply of water could be assured from the Mekong and its tributaries the Nam Ngum and Nam Lik, the productivity of the area could be enormously increased, as could that of similar areas lower down the Mekong. It is hoped that the Vientiane Plain will eventually be provided with irrigation by the Pa Mong unit of the Mekong River project.

Cambodia is fortunate in having an abundance of good land, and this fact, combined with a dominant belief on the part of the Cambodian farmer that nature will continue to be bountiful, results in little interest being shown in methods of improving agricultural production. Unlike many neighbouring countries, there is no great population pressure on land resources, and only ten per cent of Cambodia's forty-four million acres is continuously cultivated. Low population density and low intensity agricultural methods are reflected in the fact that only limited areas are used to grow a second rice crop under irrigation during the dry season and that up to twenty-five per cent of the riceland lies unused each year. Like the other countries of Indochina, Cambodia relies on the uncontrolled irrigation of its paddy fields, and the most important cultivated areas are at the confluence of the Mekong, Tonlé Sap and Brassac rivers, where between two and two and a half million acres of paddy are inundated each year during the flood season. The only area in the country with improved irrigation works is the province of Battambang, the 'rice bowl' of western Cambodia.

Agricultural production in each of the four countries of Indochina could be increased considerably by the more efficient use of large-scale, controlled perennial irrigation. If such a development is to take place in this region it will require a sufficient, dependable and well managed foreign-aid programme and, above all, the assurance of domestic and regional tranquillity. That the potential for such development exists has been recognised by the countries of Indochina themselves. Early in 1958 South Vietnam, Laos, Cambodia and Thailand proposed that a survey of the Mekong River Basin be undertaken to provide a realistic basis for any subsequent development of the area, with particular reference to the possibilities of extending perennial irrigation, generating hydroelectricity and improving navigation. The survey, undertaken by the United Nations Economic Commission on Asia and the Far East (ECAFE), has shown that the Mekong and its tributaries have abundant supplies of water which are not as yet being fully developed. Moreover, these rivers, now broken by falls and rapids, have enormous potential for water storage and power and could provide the basis of a water transport network much superior to that provided by nature.

The Mekong River project is a twenty-year plan to develop the middle and lower reaches of the Mekong, and initial proposals include the construction of five main dual- or multi-purpose dams at Pa Mong, twenty miles above Vientiane, the capital of Laos, at Khemarat on the Laos-Thailand border, at Khone Falls on the Laos-Cambodia border, at Sambor in Cambodia and at Tonlé Sap, also in Cambodia (Fig. 15). The Pa Mong project would provide controlled irrigation for the Korat and Vientiane plains, the Sambor project would render irrigable a considerable area below Kratie in eastern Cambodia, and the Tonlé Sap scheme would regulate water supplies over a large area of western Cambodia. But if the Mekong River project is ever to come to fruition, it will require an enormous amount of foreign aid and technical assistance, and even more important, peace and regional co-operation in Indochina. Nor is it by any means certain that the immense cost required could not be put to better use in other less spectacular ways in the countries concerned.[12]

In th meantime,e ECAFE is proposing to set up a number of pilot farms to show local farmers what can be achieved by irrigation, in preparation for the implementation of large-scale irrigation farming in the lower Mekong Basin. One pilot farm has already been established in the Vientiane Plain of Laos about twelve kilometres south of Vientiane. Initial results, such as increased crops of rice, have been encouraging, and the introduction of wheat, maize and beans on an experimental basis has helped to diversify the farming.

In Thailand, as in Indochina, rice is the major crop, grown mostly with water from the Menam River and its tributaries. In 1962–3, about 3,200,000 acres were irrigated, of which more than four-fifths were in the Central Plain and fewer than 300,000 acres in the north-east, where the inferior quality of the soils limits the potential for irrigation.[13] Everywhere, the familiar pattern of inundation from rivers and the pumping and lifting of water when the river is low predominates. Ancient devices for lifting water are very common and include closely woven baskets, scoops, 'dragon bone' pumps known as *rahats*, which are treadmills operated by propeller-type windmills or by human feet, and occasional water-wheels. In many localities, especially in northern Thailand, enormous bamboo water-wheels may be found, usually about thirty feet in diameter and equipped with numerous short, bamboo scoops. Set up along the river banks, slowly rotating and laboriously groaning, they are a familiar feature of this part of the country.[14] More recently, oil pumps have been installed in many areas.

In the last forty years the rice yield per acre in the country as a whole has decreased by about sixty per cent, despite an increase in the area under cultivation. This is a direct result of the growth of population and a consequent demand for rice, which has led to more and more land being put under cultivation, land that, because of inadequate irrigation, is basically unsuitable and yields poor crops. In an attempt to improve this situation, the government in 1952 initiated the Greater Menam project, with a loan of eighteen million dollars from the World Bank. The project involves the construction of a number of major barrages across the rivers in the Menam Plain, where rice production has been made possible in the past by the annual flooding of the Chao Phraya (Menam) River network. The plain is seamed by a network of canals which carry the water by gravity to the fields, but until recently the lack of artificial controls meant that it was impossible to regulate the duration and depth of flooding. The Chainat Dam, first of some fifteen projects designed to modernise the irrigation system of the central plains, was finished in 1956 (Fig. 16). When completed, the scheme will improve the supply of water to 1,350,000 acres of irrigable land in the Menam delta, provide supplemental water to about 860,000 acres now under irrigation but without an adequate supply, and make available an additional 80,000 acres of land not previously irrigated. Another project under construction is the Yan Hee Dam, 260 miles north-west of Bangkok on the Ping River, a branch of the Chao Phraya. A multi-purpose scheme to provide hydroelectricity and flood control

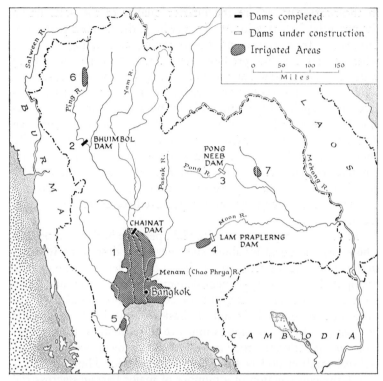

FIG. 16. Major irrigation projects in Thailand: (1) Greater
Menam project, based on the Chainat Dam completed in 1956,
(2) Yan Hee project, based on the Bhuimbol (formerly Yan Hee)
Dam completed in 1964, (3) Nam Pong project, based on the
Pong Neeb Dam, (4) Lam Praplerng project, based on the Lam
Praplerng Dam, (5) Kaeng Kracharn project, (6) Mae Taeng
project and (7) Pao River project.

facilities as well as irrigation water, it will eventually cost more
than sixty million pounds. In addition to the generation of power,
which first began in 1963, it will permit double cropping in areas
presently under uncontrolled irrigation and extend irrigation to
more than 500,000 acres of new riceland.

In north-east Thailand, a programme of tank irrigation is being
developed whereby run-off water is caught during the rainy season
in large ponds and stored to be used in the dry season. About one
hundred such projects have now been completed.

Nearly all the irrigated land in Indonesia is on the island of

Java, where irrigation has been carried on since time immemorial. Irrigation is essential in this densely populated island, as it experiences frequent dry periods, which occur even during the rainy season in some areas. Most of the irrigated land is in the northern lowlands and consists partly of modern irrigation works composed of masonry dams and canal networks constructed by the Dutch, and partly of older, more primitive systems, frequently based on the simple diversion of running streams or rainfall (Fig. 17).

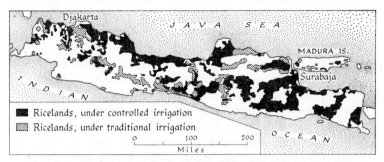

FIG. 17. Major irrigation areas in Java. Nearly all of Java's controlled irrigation is concentrated in two main areas: in the alluvial lowlands along the northern coast between Djakarta and Surabaja, and in the volcano-strewn east-central part of the island. (*After Fisher*)

Villages have acted together to build dams of stones without mortar, of tree trunks or bamboo, which although generally effective are unable to stand up to occasional floods. On the slopes of the uplands, terraces are common, fed by small canals, open dykes, or coconut or bamboo pipes from rivers.[15] Rice is the major irrigated crop and normally two harvests are obtained, but sugar cane and tobacco are also important. Irrigation is important in Bali, where it is used for the cultivation of rice both on the lowlands and on the terraced uplands. The terracing there is particularly elaborate, and an ingenious system of aqueducts, in some cases carried by tunnels through the hillsides, has been constructed to distribute water from reservoirs to the fields. In Sumatra, irrigation is practised on a limited scale with water-wheels to lift water from the rivers onto the fields. At present, Indonesia claims to have about sixteen million irrigated acres under cultivation.

Irrigation in Malaysia is devoted almost wholly to the cultivation of wet rice, and on the Malayan mainland it is highly localised in alluvial areas, particularly in the north-west and north-east, close to the Thai border, where it is grown principally by Malays. Malaya has about half a million acres under paddy, of which approximately twenty per cent is under controlled irrigation. As a result, double cropping is not very common, yields are relatively low, and rice has to be imported to feed the population. However, Malaya plans to increase its irrigated acreage by implementing the Trans-Perak River scheme, west of Kampar. Work has begun and when completed will render about 180,000 acres of jungle irrigable for the cultivation of rice. Market gardens, often under entirely controlled irrigation and a speciality of the Chinese, are common around the major towns. In Sabah (North Borneo), wet rice is grown on a small scale under irrigation by Malays. The irrigated area is at present about 70,000 acres but this could be considerably extended, and a number of larger schemes are under construction. These include projects at Papar and Tuaran which are based primarily on pumping, and the new Keningau development scheme of which the first stage, a four-and-a-half-mile main channel, has recently been completed. In addition, a number of small-scale, government-sponsored schemes have been carried out, including one at Tomani in the upper reaches of the Sungei Meligan.

The major irrigated area of Burma is in the semi-arid 'dry zone' around Mandalay, which receives less than forty inches of rainfall a year. Irrigation water is secured either from small reservoirs constructed in the hills or from canals which tap streams descending from the near-by mountains. Burma had approximately 1,860,000 acres under irrigation in 1965, devoted almost entirely to the cultivation of rice. The larger canal systems are maintained by the government and include some which are very old and others which were constructed in modern times by the British. Relatively little use is made of the Irrawaddy and Chindwin rivers, which could provide large supplies of irrigation water should the capital become available for the construction of dams and canal networks.

A major irrigation project currently under construction is that based on the Kyetmauktang Dam, near Mount Popa in the Myingyan district of Upper Burma about eighty miles south-west of Mandalay. The project began in 1961 and is the joint work of Burmese and Soviet engineers, using local labour and materials.

The dam is already complete and its reservoir is slowly filling with water; it will eventually supply more than 50,000 acres. Two main canals are under construction: the left canal, which is six miles long and which was due for completion in October 1965, when 10,000 acres of paddy were to be irrigable; and the twenty-six-mile-long right canal, which will provide water for 20,000 acres of paddy and 20,000 acres of cotton, kenaf, fruit, maize and vegetables. The completion of the project will also make double cropping possible.

INDIA AND CEYLON

At present, about twenty per cent of India's cultivated land is under irrigation. As in China, irrigated farming has been carried on since ancient times, but only in the last hundred years have modern, large-scale irrigation works been built, chiefly for commercial and colonial speculation, especially in grain and cotton. It is necessary therefore to distinguish between those regions in which traditional agriculture is carried on and those which have been equipped with modern means of irrigation. Over extensive areas, traditional methods of irrigation are still in use. In parts of the Indo-Gangetic Plain, there are many shallow wells from which water is lifted by Persian wheels. There too inundation canals relying on the floodwaters of the rivers are still found, and in southern India tanks are used extensively. Even in those areas supplied with modern, perennial irrigation works, the techniques of cultivation are often relatively primitive, based on small, uneconomic holdings and using inadequate tools. Any improvement in the conditions of the peasantry in the near future will depend to a large extent on the success of a number of grand schemes for rural development and irrigation. These schemes differ from those introduced at the end of the last century in that they will be integrated into a general programme to develop the agricultural economy instead of being oriented towards creating new types of crops and cultivating them to provide produce for export.[16]

Since gaining independence, India has launched a series of five-year plans for the economic development of the country, in which priority has been given to the extension of irrigated agriculture. By this means it is hoped that new land will be brought under cultivation, that the area in which two or more crops a year can be grown will be enlarged, and that yields per acre will be raised. When the first five-year plan was launched in 1951, India had a total irrigated area of 51·5 million acres. By the end of the second plan (1960-61), the area had been increased to seventy million acres,* and by the end of the third plan (1965-66), India had hoped to irrigate an area of ninety million acres. This target was not reached, however, as the irrigated area had only risen from 74 million acres in 1964[17] to 88 million acres in 1967. Undoubtedly, a considerable increase in irrigated agriculture is theoretically possible if the necessary capital becomes available, because the utilisation of the water resources of India's major rivers is far from complete, with little more than ten per cent of their annual flow being withdrawn for irrigation.

Very large, multi-purpose schemes, either recently completed or under construction, are shown in Fig. 18. The Bhakra-Nangal project was begun in 1946 and is now almost finished. Its main structures are a 740-foot-high dam across the Sutlej at Bhakra, the 90-foot-high Nangal Dam, about 650 miles of canals and over 2,200 miles of distributaries. The project will eventually provide irrigation to 3·6 million acres annually, which are expected to yield great quantities of foodgrains, sugar cane, pulses and oil seeds.

The key structure in the Gandak project is the Gandak Barrage being built across the Gandak River on the Indo-Nepalese border in the Champaran district of Bihar. An associated canal network consists of two main canals, a western one 120 miles long and an eastern one 155 miles long, plus a number of branch canals. By 1968, the estimated completion date, the project was due to supply water for 2·65 million acres in the Saran, Champaran, Muzaffarpur and Darbhanga districts of Bihar, 592,000 acres in the Gorakhpur and Deoria districts of Uttar Pradesh and 144,000 acres in the Baraparsa and Rauthat districts of Nepal.

The Nagarjunarsagar project in Andhra Pradesh consists of a masonry dam near Nandikonda on the Kistna River, about one hundred miles from Hyderabad, and two canals, one on either side of the river, which were due to be completed in 1968-69 when they would provide water for an area of 2·06 million acres, to be devoted largely to the production of foodgrains. The Rihand project was formally inaugurated in January 1963 and requires the con-

---

* Forty-two per cent was irrigated by canals, twenty-nine per cent by wells, nineteen per cent by tanks and ten per cent by other sources.

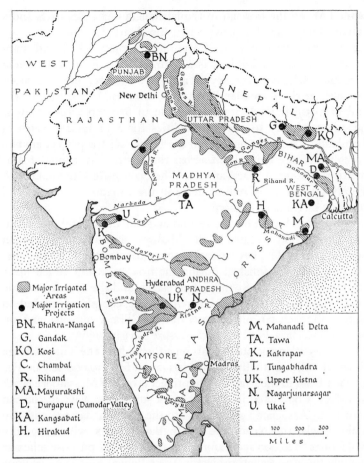

FIG. 18. Major irrigated areas and irrigation projects in India.

struction of a concrete gravity dam about 300 feet high and 3,065 feet long across the Rihand River in the Mirzapur district of Uttar Pradesh. The reservoir created by the dam will have a storage capacity of 8·6 million acre-feet and will provide irrigation facilities for 1·9 million acres of land in Uttar Pradesh and Bihar.

The main structure of the Hirakud-Mahanadi delta project is the Hirakud Dam on the Mahanadi River in Orissa. Claimed to be the world's longest mainstream dam, 15,748 feet long, it provides irrigation facilities for approximately 570,000 acres of land, while farther downstream in the Mahanadi delta a canal network is being constructed to provide irrigation water for another million acres. The Damodar Valley Corporation project, which will benefit West Bengal and Bihar, is a hydroelectric, flood control and irrigation scheme. Its key irrigation structure, the Durgapur Barrage on the Damodar River, was completed in 1955. By the end of 1959, it made water available to 620,000 acres and it is hoped eventually to provide facilities for 1·34 million acres of farmland. The main features in the Upper Kistna project are two dams which are being built across the Kistna River, one at Alamatti, the other at Narayanpur. When completed, the dams will supply water for 1·2 million acres in the Bujapur, Gulbarga and Raichur districts of Mysore.

Work has begun on the second stage of the Chambal project, which is a joint venture of the Madhya Pradesh and Rajasthan governments. The key irrigation structures are the Gandhi Sagar Dam, which was finished during the first stage and which has a storage capacity of 6·85 million acre-feet, and the Kotah Barrage. When the associated canal networks are completed, irrigation water will reach 1·1 million acres of land. The Tungabhadra Dam to serve Andhra Pradesh and Mysore was inaugurated in 1953. Together with associated canals on either side of the Tungabhadra River, it will eventually provide irrigation for 830,000 acres. The Canada Dam in the Mayurakshi project is on the Messanjore River in Bihar. Completed in 1955, it has a storage capacity of 500,000 acre-feet. Associated structures are the Tilpara Barrage and two main canals, the North and South Bank canals, which together will irrigate 720,000 acres annually. Other multi-purpose schemes include the Kangsabati project in West Bengal to irrigate 900,000 acres, the Tawa project on the Narbada River in Madhya Pradesh to irrigate 750,000 acres, and the Kakrapar and Ukai projects on the Tapti River in Gujarat to irrigate 543,000 and 392,000 acres respectively. At Harike on the Sutlej, the Great Rajasthan Canal is under construction; it will eventually be 425 miles long and irrigate considerable areas in the eastern part of the Thar Desert. The first ninety-mile section of the canal was completed by 1965, and small-scale irrigation was then being developed.

At present, India's largest areas of irrigated land are in the Northern Plain, especially in the Punjab and Uttar Pradesh, where natural precipitation is either almost absent or markedly seasonal, so that cultivation is impossible or very difficult without irrigation. In the Punjab, long known as the granary of India, the partition of the subcontinent caused considerable social dislocation, which inevitably affected the efficiency of its irrigated agriculture. The administration and maintenance of an elaborate water distribution system, not to mention the incidental activities of coping with such problems as the prevention of the illegal removal of water, demand a considerable degree of organisation, which in turn depends upon political stability. Such a period of stability will be guaranteed, it is hoped, by the signing of the Indus Water Treaty in 1960. The Punjab is primarily served by modern canal irrigation; wheat is the most important crop, followed by cotton, oilseeds, sugar and rice. Unfortunately, the canals are liable to considerable loss by seepage, and the prohibitive cost of lining them with concrete and the virtual impossibility of taking a section temporarily out of a main canal make it extremely difficult to deal with this problem.[18] Agricultural output in the Punjab depends mainly on the proportion of the total crop area under irrigation, the proportion of the crop area under improved seed varieties, the consumption of chemical fertilisers per acre and the weather. During the years between the wars, the growth in agricultural output was almost entirely the result of the expansion of irrigation. Since then, however, increased irrigation has accounted for only about a third of the growth rate. The rest is ascribed to improved varieties of some of the major crops, the growing use of fertilisers and a degree of mechanisation.

Uttar Pradesh has more than thirteen million acres of irrigated land, most of which is found along the Upper Ganges and its tributaries. Canals are the primary form of irrigation, and tube wells are becoming increasingly important; together they make water available for the cultivation of wheat, rice, barley, millet and sugar cane. This region has more rain than the Punjab, and consequently irrigation is less essential. But its use has become more extensive to enable crops to be grown during the dry season. Irrigation is also important along the Middle Ganges where it comes chiefly from canals. Rice is the chief crop, although maize, barley, sugar, wheat and jute are also grown.

In the southern half of India the major irrigated areas occur along the rivers which flow eastwards across the Deccan and into the Indian Ocean. On the plateau, tanks are particularly important, and Mysore contains about 37,000 of them, which provide irrigation for more than one million acres growing principally millet and cotton. Where the major rivers of the Deccan enter the coastal lowlands of Orissa and Madras, irrigation is used extensively. In the Mahanadi valley of north-eastern Orissa, a recently developed system of canal irrigation, together with wells, enables rice, pulses, linseed and wheat to be grown. Farther south, in the Kistna-Godavari delta region, more than two million irrigated acres are watered by canals and grow mainly rice. South of Madras, in the Cauvery delta, a modern canal network and an old tank system provide water for more than 1,300,000 acres on which rice, groundnuts and sugar are grown.

In Nepal, which has approximately 80,000 acres under irrigation, representing about one-fifth of the cultivated land, the major irrigated area is in the valley of Katmandu in the Terai Plain, which produces a summer crop of rice. On the higher ground, above the Katmandu valley, aridity is more marked and irrigation is essential for the cultivation of wheat, barley and maize. The most common type of irrigation in Nepal is carried out by means of dams between three and five feet high, which divert water from the rivers. Two large irrigation projects have come into operation in Nepal since the war: the Chandra Canal area on the Trijuga River, a tributary of the Kosi River, and the Judha Canal on the Manusmara River. The Chandra Canal is fifty-eight miles long and was completed in 1958 to irrigate 37,000 acres of paddy, while the Judha Canal, which dates from 1946, irrigates about 6,000 acres. Projects presently under construction to extend Nepal's irrigated lands include the Indian Kosi Dam on the Kosi River, which will provide some water for Nepal.[19]

Ceylon is divisible into two major geographical regions, the south-west 'wet zone' and the north and east 'dry zone'. In the former area, rice is the traditional crop, grown largely in fields irrigated by water brought down from the hills by diversion canals. Irrigation is easy there, and numerous small village works take water from local streams on a perennial basis. By contrast, the dry zone, which receives its rain from the north-east monsoon between November and February, has a seasonal shortage of water in the spring and summer, so that irrigation is essential for the greater part of the year. Unfortunately, there are few rivers and only a very limited supply of underground water. Use is made of the rivers by means of tanks, which have been common in this area from time immemorial, and in recent years many old tanks have been restored. One of the few areas in the north-east where much underground water is found is the Jaffna Peninsula, a karst area lying near sea level. Though very dry, it is fortunate in having ground-water supplies which can be reached by shallow wells, fifteen to thirty feet deep, and which permit the cultivation of rice, tobacco, and the palmyra palm. The dry zone undoubtedly has considerable agricultural potential, and there are plans to transfer surplus water from the wet zone and to increase the supply of underground water by deep pumping. If such plans are to be realised, however, much capital investment will be necessary. Some very large, multi-purpose projects have been undertaken, notably the Gal Oya project in south-east Ceylon, which is well on the way to completion. In 1966, Ceylon had slightly more than 980,000 acres under irrigation and intended to extend its irrigable area to over a million acres by 1968.

PAKISTAN

Pakistan had an estimated 27,400,000 acres under irrigation in 1963, representing approximately two-fifths of her cultivated land, and hoped to extend this to 30,000,000 acres by 1965.[20] By far the greater part of this land is in West Pakistan, where over considerable areas the almost total absence of rain makes irrigation essential. The best irrigated lands are on the alluvial plains of the Indus Basin, which support fairly dense rural populations exceeding 600 people per square mile in places. As in India, these high population densities are associated with small, fragmented holdings, cultivation which is intensive if relatively low in productivity, agricultural techniques which are largely traditional, and limited mechanisation. Water from the melting winter snows of the Himalayas is brought to the cultivated land largely by a modern system of diversion dams, canals and ditches constructed by British engineers since the eighteen-eighties. Where the water table is sufficiently close to the surface, it is tapped by shallow, hand-dug wells and more recently by modern tube wells, which provide water to irrigate land not reached by the canals. The main irrigated crop is winter wheat, which is grown both as a subsistence and a cash crop. Cotton and sugar cane are becoming increasingly important as cash crops, as are oilseeds, especially linseed and rapeseed. Rice is prominent in Sind both as a subsistence and a cash crop.

West Pakistan is fortunate in that the Indus and its tributaries provide abundant water,* and West Pakistan is as much the 'gift of the Indus' as Egypt is of the Nile. In 1947 the partition of the Indian subcontinent divided the Punjab, 'the land of the five rivers' (the Jhelum, Chenab, Ravi, Beas and Sutlej), into two halves. The western portion went to Pakistan and the eastern to India. Partition placed an artificial dividing line across one of the most remarkable networks of irrigation canals in the world, cut across major irrigation canals, and divided locks from their canals and headwaters from their locks. The control and equitable distribution of the waters of the five rivers have inevitably caused much disagreement between India and Pakistan. However, in September 1960 the two countries formally signed an agreement to share the waters: Pakistan was to have full control of the three western rivers, the Indus, Jhelum and Chenab; and India the three eastern ones, the Ravi, Beas and Sutlej (Fig. 19). As Pakistan on balance lost water by the agreement, she was to be compensated by the building of two great storage reservoirs, the Mangla on the Jhelum and the Tarbela on the Indus, six barrages and nearly 400 miles of link canals draining eastwards. Until the project is completed, by 1970 if all goes according to plan, India has agreed to limit water withdrawal from the eastern rivers, leaving a proportion for use in Pakistan. The Mangla Dam, which was completed one year ahead of schedule in 1967, at an estimated cost of twenty-six million pounds, will store 5·3 million acre-feet of water, create a reservoir forty miles long, feed canals that will irrigate three million acres, and generate large amounts of hydroelectricity. The second great dam, the Tarbela Dam on the Indus, which is presently under construction, will store 9·3 million acre-feet of water. The plan also provides for the construction of seven new link canals to carry water from the rivers and the dams eastwards across West Pakistan; three were completed in 1965, another in 1967, the fifth in 1968, and work is proceeding on the last two. In addition, four barrages have been constructed on the

* The average total flow of the Indus and its tributaries is in the order of 117 million acre-feet per annum, of which about 68 million acre-feet flow to the sea during the monsoon.

Indus, Jhelum, Chenab and Ravi, as well as diversion and drainage works and thousands of wells to overcome waterlogging and salinity.[21]

Although the Indus Basin as a whole contains the largest single stretch of irrigated land in the world, about twenty-three million acres, approximately one-fifth of this is severely damaged by

FIG. 19. The Indus Basin Plan.

salinity and waterlogging.[22] These conditions occur because of the farmers' excessive use of water and because of seepage from the canals. The Rohri Canal, the largest and most important canal in the Sukkur Barrage scheme, began leaking within a few months of completion, and by 1950 an adjacent area half a mile wide and about twenty-three miles long had to be abandoned.

Until fairly recently it was feared that the problem of salinity and waterlogging was insoluble, but since 1959 a counter-attack has been mounted with the construction of tube wells in the Rechna Doab, which lies between the Chenab and Ravi rivers. It had once been among the best irrigated land in the subcontinent, but some seventy years of irrigation was bringing the land back full circle and turning it once more into desert. The rising of subsoil water to within three to six feet of the surface had rendered one-fifth of the area sterile and uncultivable by 1958, and another one-fifth was on the way to being in a similar condition. Since 1959, however, thousands of tube wells have been sunk in an area of approximately 2,000 square miles. Powered by a new electrical supply system, they reach 200 to 300 feet below the surface and pump up water to be released into the irrigation canals. This has the effect of increasing the quantity of water available for cultivation, helping to leach the salts from the surface soil and simultaneously lowering the water table and draining the subsoil water. Since the operation began, there has been a marked lowering in the level of the subsoil water, a consequent decline in land sterility and an increase in the area under cultivation.

The success of the scheme has inspired similar projects developed by the West Pakistan Water and Power Development Authority in other parts of the Indus Basin, including those in the Chaj Doab and Khairpur areas. The Chaj project covers the area between the Chenab River and the Upper Jhelum Canal, and by means of 2,370 tube wells and the construction of 410 miles of drains, it aims to reclaim about 2·27 million acres of land. The Khairpur project area is by the Indus River between the Sukkur and Gudu barrages, and with 568 tube wells and 700 miles of drains, it is designed to reclaim 355,000 acres of land. The reclamation of vast areas of saline land will be a long and expensive business stretching many years ahead, but the urgency of the programme cannot be overestimated. While the decline of the land was unchecked, about 100,000 acres a year went out of production in Pakistan, whose population has been increasing at roughly a million a year. Several other countries are faced with these urgent problems, and the importance of the Pakistan programme lies partly in the fact that it is the first demonstration that what was thought an irreversible process of irrigation, saturation and sterilisation can be checked.

The best known of the major irrigation works on the Indus is the Sukkur Barrage in Sind, an enormous dam nearly a mile long and with more than 36,000 miles of main channels and distributaries. Completed by the British in 1932, it provides water for more than seven and a half million acres, on which cotton and wheat are the main crops. On the Indus above Sukkur, two new barrages at Gudu and Taunsa were completed in 1963, providing water for more than four million acres of irrigable land. Near the Indus delta, the Ghulam Mohammed Barrage has been completed to supply water to more than two and a half million acres. Other large projects in West Pakistan include the Jinnah Barrage and its canal system near Kalabagh, which when completed will irrigate more than two million acres of semi-desert between the Indus and Jhelum rivers, and the Warsak Dam on the Kabul River, recently completed to form a lake which backs up almost to the Afghanistan frontier and which provides water for 180,000 acres and hydro-electricity for Peshawar and its vicinity.[23] These recent developments all stress year-round irrigation.

The northern and western areas of West Pakistan have neither large areas of cultivable land nor considerable water resources. Instead, numerous small streams and seasonal torrents are the main sources of water, most of which goes to waste, often causing floods in the plains. To deal with this problem and to harness these limited resources, the West Pakistan Agricultural Development Corporation has set up a department called the Small Dams Organisation. The department aims to build multi-purpose small dams which will provide water for irrigation, promote fish culture in the reservoirs, and help to eliminate soil erosion and flood damage. To date, 300 prospective sites in the northern regions have been inspected; one dam at Misriot, about eight miles from Rawalpindi, has been completed, and nine more in adjoining areas are under construction.

In East Pakistan, about twenty-one million acres are cultivated in an average year, but of these only 600,000 acres or about three per cent are irrigated. It is estimated that some thirteen million acres could be made irrigable by a programme of extensive drainage, the construction of diversion works and canals, and the pumping of subsurface water, mainly to supplement rainfall during the winter season.[24] But there are considerable difficulties, because such a programme would be expensive and river control works are very hard to construct in the riverine lands of East Pakistan. Work has to be suspended for the five-month wet season, owing to extensive flooding. River alignments are apt to change from year to year, and there is a good chance that an expensive dam or barrage might be left high and dry by the breaking away of a major river during the annual inundation and its subsequent location in a new channel.

In order to overcome the problem of the seasonal nature of rainfall in East Pakistan, a number of new projects have been developed to provide water for year-round irrigation and especially during the period of severe drought from November to March. These include the Ganges-Kobadak scheme, which should supply water for the perennial irrigation of more than two million acres. Work began there in 1954, and large amounts of scarce investment funds were spent and much precious land was taken from thousands of farmers for a complex system of canals that were used only in part for the first time in 1963. Largely because the farmers were not educated to make use of this grand scheme, it has not proved as effective as was hoped, and many acres of potentially irrigable land have not been taken up.

More promising as a means of extending irrigated agriculture, both in East and West Pakistan, is the so-called small-pump scheme. A 'one cusec' diesel pump, lifting one cubic metre of water per second, can irrigate one hundred acres of dry-season paddy in Bengal with a great economy of labour, compared to the primitive equipment traditionally used by the Bengali farmer. As individual holdings are very small in this area, a number of farmers form a co-operative to use the pump, which is maintained by the Agricultural Department, which in turn levies an economic water charge based upon the area of irrigated land. It is estimated that about a thousand of these pumps were actually in use in 1962.[25] Such small-scale schemes have a great psychological advantage over the more impressive multi-purpose projects in that the farmer actually sees the pump in action and works in direct contact with the mechanic who maintains it, so that eventually he becomes intimately acquainted with the economic and technical problems involved in providing him with water. Moreover, small pumps are relatively portable and can be used in the dry season, when much of the land in East Pakistan is fallow, since only forty-three per cent is double cropped. Of the remaining fifty-seven per cent, much is sufficiently fertile to sustain double cropping because the silt left by the annual inundation restores the soil. If the whole of the fallow area could be brought under cultivation by the implementation of a small-pump scheme, and winter grains such as rice grown, then East Pakistan could be converted from a poor, food-deficient province into a moderately prosperous, food-surplus area.*

As has been clear from the foregoing descriptions, rice is the staple diet of the people of Monsoon Asia whose numbers have grown rapidly in the last decade or two. Fortunately, developments in rice-cultivation, particularly in the last five years, have enabled rice production to keep pace with population growth, at least for the present. Research has now produced new strains of rice such as H8, and IR8, the so-called 'miracle rice', developed in the Rice Research Institute at Los Banos in the Philippines, which yield over 2 tons an acre and may mature in 120 days. However, if the most effective use is to be made of such new species, then adequate water supply and drainage are essential. In other words, irrigation must be efficiently carried out.

Bibliographical References

1. Chae Kyung Oh, *Handbook of Korea* (Pageant Press, New York), 1958, p. 212.
2. Phillips, R. W. and Kuo, L. T. C., 'Agricultural Science and Its Application', *The China Quarterly*, No. 6, April-June 1961, p. 135.
3. *Farmer's World* (U.S. Department of Agriculture Yearbook, 1964), p. 81.
4. Chang-tu Hu, *China*, Survey of World Cultures Series (Hraf Press, New Haven), 1960, p. 351.
5. Hughes, T. J. and Luard, D. E. T., *The Economic Development of Communist China, 1949-58* (Oxford University Press), 1959, p. 168.
6. Snow, E., *The Other Side of the River* (Random House, New York), 1962, pp. 501-13.
7. *Ibid.*, p. 73.
8. Adler, S., *The Chinese Economy* (Monthly Review Press, New York), 1957, p. 121.
9. *Farmer's World, op. cit.*, p. 82.
10. Ekvall, R. B. and Downs, J. F., 'Notes on Water Utilization and Rule in the Sakya Domain-Tibet', *Journal of Asian Studies*, XXII, 1963, pp. 293-303.
11. Chiao-Min Hsieh, *Taiwan-ilha Formosa* (Butterworth, Washington, D.C.), 1964, p. 256.

* For a detailed regional examination of irrigation problems in Pakistan, *v.* J. R. Andrus and A. F. Mohammed, *The Economy of Pakistan*, O.U.P., 1958, pp. 77-104.

12. Shaaf, C. H. and Fifield, R. H., *The Lower Mekong : A Challenge to Cooperation in South-east Asia* (Van Nostrand, New York), 1963; Fisher, C. A., *South-East Asia* (Methuen, London), 1964, p. 513.
13. Trescott, P. B., 'Rice Production in Thailand', *World Crops*, September 1968, p. 56.
14. Pendleton, R. L., *Thailand*, American Geographical Society Handbook (Duell, Sloan and Pearce, New York), 1962, pp. 140-1.
15. Robequain, C., *Malaya, Indonesia, Borneo and the Philippines* (Longmans, London), 1961, p. 199.
16. George, P., *La Campagne* (Presses Universitaires de France, Paris), 1956, p. 187.
17. Sukhatme, P. V., *Feeding India's Growing Millions* (Asia Publishing House, London), 1965, p. 134.
18. Spate, O. H. K., *India and Pakistan* (Methuen, London), 1960, p. 472.
19. Karan, P. P., *Nepal* (University of Kentucky Press, Lexington), 1960, p. 37.
20. *Science and Technology for Development, III* (United Nations, New York) 1963, (E/CONF.39/1), p. 38.
21. Prentice, A., 'The Indus Basin Settlement Plan', *Geography*, XLIX, 1964, pp. 128-30.
22. *Farmer's World, op. cit.*, p. 89.
23. Wilber, D. N., *Pakistan, Yesterday and Today*, Contemporary Civilizations Series (Holt, Reinhart and Winston, New York), 1964, p. 169.
24. *The Second Five Year Plan (1960-5)* (Pakistan Government Planning Commission), June 1960, p. 194.
25. Johnson, B. L. C., 'Technology and the Economic Development of Pakistan', *Oriental Geographer* (East Pakistan Geographical Society, Dacca), VI, 1962, p. 76.

Additional Sources

Fisher, C. A., *South-east Asia* (Methuen, London), 1964.
Ginsburg, N. (Ed.), *The Pattern of Asia* (Constable, London), 1960.
Rawson, R. R., *The Monsoon Lands of Asia* (Hutchinson, London), 1963.
Tregear, T. R., *A Geography of China* (University of London Press), 1965.

1 TRADITIONAL METHODS OF IRRIGATION I:

A (*Left*) The shaduf, denkli or picottah. This primitive 'see-saw' water lift is operated by two men and is in use near Bangalore in Mysore, India.

B (*Below*) The sakia or Persian wheel. This wooden Egyptian water-wheel is operated by a blindfolded ox who turns the horizontal wheel which in turn moves the vertical wheel, so raising water from the river or well.

2 Traditional Methods of Irrigation II:
A (*Above*) Archimedes' screw or tambour. Like the shaduf, this is a primitive lifting device dependent on human power. Here, in Egypt, it is being used to raise water from the river into the irrigation ditches.

B (*Below*) Water-wheels or norias. These huge water-wheels at Lanchow, China, driven by the flow of the Yellow River, lift the water to be carried by a trough over the city wall to the fields beyond. Unfortunately, they operate only at high water seasons.

3 TRADITIONAL METHODS OF IRRIGATION III:

A (*Above*) The treadmill is still a common sight in China. A team of four pedals the axle moving an endless belt to which paddles are attached, and these lift the water from the Yangtse River to the the paddy fields.

B (*Right*) In areas where level land is limited, as here in Japan, terraces like enormous staircases are carved into the hillsides and are irrigated from mountain streams.

4 THE COLUMBIA BASIN PROJECT:

A (*Above*) Grand Coulee Dam, the key structure of the project. Water is stored in Lake Roosevelt behind the dam and is released through the sluices into the Columbia River.

B (*Left*) This photograph shows the level terrain typical of the irrigated farmlands in the project area. The West Canal, in the north-west part of the project, snakes across the area from the top right to the bottom left.

5 THE DISTRIBUTION OF IRRIGATION WATER:

A (*Above*) Water is distributed through a complex of canals leading from the Chu River in the Khirgiz Republic of Soviet Central Asia.

B (*Below*) In the Central Valley of California, water is diverted by means of control works known as headgates from the canals into secondary ditches at the highest points of the fields.

Contour
Lateral
Tube
Irrigated S

SECTION THROUGH DITCHES

6 THE APPLICATION OF IRRIGATION WATER I:

A (*Above*) Contour ditch irrigation. The water is spread across the field by flooding from contour ditches, and small outlets or siphons are placed at frequent intervals in the ditches so that water will spread evenly across the field when the water surface in the ditches is raised.

B (*Below*) Border irrigation. The field is divided into evenly spaced strips by means of earth borders and then flooded with water. Here, in southern Texas close to the Gulf Coast and the Mexican border, young citrus trees have been planted.

7 THE APPLICATION OF IRRIGATION WATER II:

A (*Above*) Furrow irrigation. From the secondary ditch in the foreground, the farmer leads water into the field ditches or furrows by making breaches in the earth bank.

B (*Below*) Sprinkler irrigation. Water is being applied to irrigated pasture in Hampshire, England, at the rate of about one inch in three hours, and yields are increased by as much as fifty per cent.

8 THE DRAINAGE OF IRRIGATION WATER:
A (*Above*) Waterlogging. This irrigated farmland in West Pakistan has become waterlogged by the rising water table and has turned into swamp.
B (*Below*) Salination. Spreading salt patches appear in wheat growing under irrigation in West Pakistan. On the white patches, the crop has been entirely killed. Although salination is less obvious in the surrounding fields which are lying fallow, it still affects the soil and will have a disastrous effect on subsequent crops.

9A THE TRANSPIRATION OF IRRIGATION WATER:

(*Right*) Water hyacinths have spread and choked this pond in East Pakistan and, by causing excessive transpiration, have reduced the water supply.

9B THE DESEDIMENTATION OF IRRIGATION WATER:

(*Below*) Three large desilting basins at the Imperial Dam on the Colorado River remove sediment from the irrigation water flowing into the All-American Canal.

A (*Left*) Thailand. The
photograph shows the
flat, featureless plain of
the Chao Phraya
(Menam) River, a land-
scape typical of the
alluvial rice-growing
plains of South-east
Asia. The land is sub-
divided into innumer-
able, small paddy fields
served with water from
the river and its
tributaries. A village
clusters on the banks
of the river and forms a
green, tree-framed island
in the sea of paddy.

B (*Below*) Ceylon. The photograph shows a typical tank landscape in northern Ceylon.
The tank in the background is situated near Anuradhapura and supplies water for the
network of paddy fields in the centre of the photograph.

11 IRRIGATED LANDSCAPES II:
A (*Above*) Egypt. This view across the Nile Delta, taken from the Great Pyramid, illustrates the sharp boundary between the irrigated land in the distance and the village, which stands on slightly higher ground. In the immediate foreground is the desert proper.
B (*Below*) The Tunisian Sahara. This photograph shows the nucleated character of the typical oasis, with its cluster of date palms in a hollow in the desert where water is at or near the surface.

12 Irrigated Landscapes III:

The Imperial Valley of southern California. This rectilinear landscape is divided into square quarter sections of 160 acres each by lateral canals (usually half a mile apart) and drains which run east to west, and by roads and paths which run north to south. The striking pattern of furrow irrigation shows up clearly.

13 MONSOON ASIA, INDIA:
A (*Above*) The Malabar Coast of southern India. Rice paddies in Kerala are watered by bucket lifts.
B (*Below*) The Nagarjunarsagar Dam under construction across the Krishna River in Andhra Pradesh. Most of the construction work is being done by about 30,000 Indian workers.

14 MONSOON ASIA, PAKISTAN:

A (*Above*) The Sukkur Barrage on the Indus River above Karachi.

B (*Below*) The Mangla Dam on the Jhelum River, West Pakistan, under construction. With its associated hydroelectric scheme, the dam is the first major undertaking authorised under the Indus Basin Plan between Pakistan and India.

5 CONTRASTING CANAL
SYSTEMS IN SOUTH-WEST
ASIA:

(*Above*) Inundation
canals running from the
Euphrates in Iraq fill
with water when the
level in the river rises
sufficiently high.

(*Right*) The modern,
concrete-lined canals of
the Israel National
Water Carrier carry
water from Lake
Tiberias in the north to
the arid lands of the
south.

16 MODERN COLONISATION SCHEMES IN EUROPE:
A (*Above*) Languedoc, France. In this state-directed scheme, farmers are settled on irrigated land in individual houses built on their holdings.

B (*Below*) By contrast, the modern Spanish colonisation schemes are based on nucleated villages like that of Guadiana del Caudillo in the Badajoz area of the Guadiana River. The rectangular pattern of holdings, main and secondary canals, and new roads is clearly shown.

17 AFRICA:

A (*Above*) Egypt. This photograph taken by the American Gemini IV astronauts shows the contrast between the cultivated irrigated lands of the fan-shaped Nile Delta and the barren desert on either side.

B (*Right*) The Republic of South Africa. The Jonzini Dam, shown here under construction, is the key structure of the Makatini Flats project designed to provide water for irrigating large areas in northern Natal.

A (*Above*) Canada. St. Mary's Dam stores water for irrigation in southern Alberta.

B (*Left*) United States. The Friant-Kern Canal supplies water for the cultivation of citrus groves in the dry, south-eastern part of the San Joaquin Valley in California.

LATIN AMERICA:
(*Above*) Peru. A modern irrigated cotton field in the Rimac Valley.
(*Below*) Chile. Irrigated vineyards in the valley of central Chile, near Llay Llay
tween Santiago and the coast.

20 AUSTRALASIA:
A (*Above*) Australia. Irrigated vineyards near Mildura, Victoria. This is an intensivel
farmed area with a distinctive rectangular pattern of fields, irrigation channels, drain
roads and shelter belts. The long, white buildings are drying sheds for the grapes.
B (*Below*) New Zealand. Irrigated farmlands of the Canterbury Plains show the can
leading to the Rakaia River.

CHAPTER 9

SOUTH-WEST ASIA

The broad sweep of land from Afghanistan to Egypt, generally known as South-west Asia, is, by contrast with South-east Asia, an arid zone with few and limited humid areas. As a consequence, irrigation is essential for cultivating crops at almost all times of the year. Like other arid regions, South-west Asia suffers from the absence of large, level areas with readily available supplies of water. The only region which comes into this category is the Tigris-Euphrates Valley. Moreover, primitive methods of carrying and lifting water are still very widespread, while evaporation and seepage are prohibitive in their consumption of valuable water. In the area as a whole, there is considerable variation in the proportion of cultivated land under irrigation. It is highest in the more arid areas, so that whereas only about eight per cent of the cultivated land of Turkey is irrigated, it is approximately seventeen per cent in Syria, forty per cent in Iran, sixty-five per cent in Afghanistan and virtually one hundred per cent in Saudi Arabia.

TABLE 4

Countries	Irrigated Areas ('000s of Acres)	Year
Afghanistan	509	1961
Iran	4,900	1960*
Iraq	9,081	1963
Israel	375	1965
Jordan	148	1964
Lebanon	178	1963
Saudi Arabia	400	1965
Syria	1,270	1965
Turkey	4,912	1957

South-west Asia: Irrigated Areas

(Based partly on figures cited in *F.A.O. Production Yearbook*, Vol. 21, 1967, p. 10.)

* Figuer issued by national government.

In South-west Asia as a whole, probably twenty per cent of the cultivated area is irrigated.[1]

The figures in Table 4 are only approximations. The United Nations publishes figures which are supplied by each country but makes no attempt at evaluation. In the absence of accurate surveys and precise data, it is impossible to judge the accuracy of the statistics. In addition, conflicting figures of the areas under irrigation are issued, frequently referring to the entire area which is occasionally supplied with water. The only countries in South-west Asia with considerable extents of irrigated land are Iraq, Turkey and Iran.

The most common methods of irrigating are by furrow and basin, although terrace irrigation is also found in places. Kanats or karez are also widespread, especially in Iran and Afghanistan, and although difficult to construct and restricted to certain types of terrain, they are more efficient than other methods of irrigation because they do not suffer loss by evaporation.

Afghanistan has approximately half a million acres under irrigation, of which about two-thirds are irrigated by water taken from rivers; one-eighth is irrigated by water from springs and the rest from underground water. At present, more than half of this irrigated land is in the northern piedmont, where rivers flowing north from the hills enter the plain to form irrigated tracts at levels generally between 1,200 and 1,500 feet, on which wheat, fruit and maize are grown. In the south-west desert area, kanats are common in oases like Farah, Girish and Kandahar, where they support a variety of field and market-garden crops; in the west, in valleys around Herat, rice and cotton are grown on narrow, irrigated strips along the riverbanks. In recent years Afghanistan has undertaken a number of large-scale projects, such as that in the Helmand valley where new construction, including the Kajakai Dam on the Helmand River and the Arghandab Dam on the Arghandab River, has led to a considerable extension of the irrigated area (Fig. 20). The forty-three-mile Jalalabad Canal east of Kabul will provide water for 75,000 acres in the Kabul valley.

In Iran only eleven per cent of the land is under cultivation, but since large tracts are constantly kept as fallow land, the actual land under various crops is less than four per cent, or approximately twelve and a half million acres. Of this, only about forty per cent, or 4.9 million acres, is irrigated, though it yields more than half the total agricultural products. In the next few years it is hoped to increase Iran's irrigated area to over six million acres. Most irrigated farming currently relies mainly on wells, kanats and crudely formed channels leading from rivers and streams. The most important agricultural area in the country is in north-central Iran, in the Elburz Mountains and Caspian Plain region, where

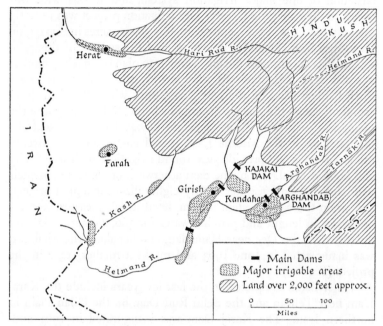

FIG. 20.   Irrigation in the Helmand Basin, Afghanistan.

irrigation is used principally to grow grains, cotton and rice. Farther to the north-west is the Azerbaijan region where irrigation is normally essential and where, fortunately, adequate supplies of water are available from streams. Wheat is the major crop there. The largest but least developed region of Iran is the arid Central Plateau, which supports very little agriculture except in a number of peripheral oases and irrigated alluvial fans at the base of the central Elburz Mountains, where cereals, fruit and vegetables are grown.

The most promising area in Iran for the development of large-scale irrigated agriculture is the Plain of Khuzestan in the south-west. Part of the Tigris-Euphrates lowland, it is the only plain of any size in the country and is approximately 16,000 square miles in extent. Formerly the site of an ancient, large-scale irrigation system, until recently it supported only a few irrigated areas along the riverbanks, in which rice, wheat, dates and fruit were grown. It was thought that the whole area could be irrigated by the construction of one major irrigation system, and it was with this object in view that the Greater Dez irrigation project was recently inaugurated. Since 1961, approximately 50,000 acres in this region have been brought under irrigation, and the success of this pilot scheme has encouraged the government to plan on making another 250,000 acres irrigable. In March 1963 the Muhammed Reza Shah Pahlevi Dam on the Dez River, built where the river flows rapidly through the Zagros Mountains before debouching into the plain, was dedicated. With a height of 647 feet, at present the highest dam in the Middle East, it will cost more than twenty million pounds and provide year-round irrigation, hydroelectricity and flood control. From the dam a network of concrete channels will release irrigation water to fifty-eight villages in a pilot project, and when the canal system is completed it will measure twenty-one miles in length and provide water for 360,000 acres. Higher upstream on the Dez near Hamadan, another dam, the Shahnaz, was inaugurated in June 1963 and marks a further stage in the project (Fig. 21).

Other dams completed in the last few years include the Karaj Dam near Tehran and the Sefid Rud Dam on the Gilan Plain in northern Iran. The Karaj Dam was inaugurated in 1961 and, with an associated diversion dam near Bilghan and a canal network, will help to alleviate Tehran's water shortage and make possible the irrigation of a considerable area. The Sefid Rud Dam, built at the confluence of the Sefid Rud and Ghezel Ozan rivers, was inaugurated in 1962 and will provide water for about 300,000 acres, mainly for the cultivation of rice. An associated canal system is under construction and is due for completion in 1967.

A government-sponsored scheme for drilling wells has also helped to increase the area of irrigated land. Between 1960 and 1964 almost 1,500 wells were drilled, and others are planned, especially in the Garmsar, Qazvin and Neishabour areas in the general region of Tehran. The normal irrigation capacity of these wells is between 175 and 250 acres of land, but as few peasants own more than between twelve and twenty-five acres, they are encouraged to form co-operatives to run the wells, which are developed with the aid of government loans. Although considerable progress is being made in some parts of Iran, yet the development of irrigation in the country as a whole faces many difficulties: water resources are unevenly distributed, much of the

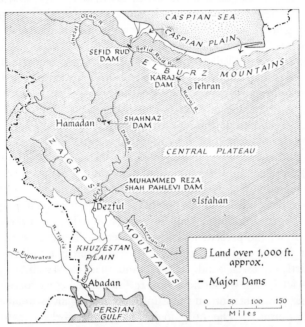

FIG. 21. Major dams in Iran.

terrain is unfavourable, and development schemes are costly. Further, insufficient technical knowledge on the part of both planners and farmers, such as their ignorance of soil types and the effect of irrigation upon them, has frequently resulted in short-sighted planning and inefficient irrigated farming. Consequently, the expansion of irrigated agriculture in Iran will be a slow and costly process.

In 1963, Iraq had more than nine million acres under irrigation, most of it in the plain of the Tigris and Euphrates rivers. Although the development of large scale perennial irrigation has gathered momentum in recent years, the older, more primitive forms of inundation and flood irrigation are still predominant. In the lower valleys, flood irrigation is most important, and annually the rivers inundate large areas devoted to rice-growing. Unfortunately, much of the land, particularly in the delta area, suffers from wasteful and inefficient irrigation farming and is subject to salinity. It is estimated that as much as twenty per cent of the cultivated land in this region has been made worthless in this way, resulting in 'long streches of poor barley, without apparent limits, alternating with long stretches of camel thorn, derelict salt-encrusted land and expanses of last year's flood water'.²

Higher up the valleys, primitive channels are dug to lead the water by gravity from the rivers into the fields, in which barley and wheat are grown. In many areas only one crop a year can be grown, as the summer level of the river may be too low. As an encouragement to double cropping, pumps are increasingly used to provide a more certain year-round supply, and they enable barley, millet and wheat to be grown in winter and rice in summer. The main factor limiting the use of such pumps is their high cost.

In recent years, strenuous efforts have been made to establish an over-all co-ordinated scheme of large-scale perennial irrigation on the Tigris-Euphrates plain to replace, for the first time in the modern era, the present makeshift system. The scheme requires a great deal of capital investment, provided partly by oil royalties and partly by foreign aid. It was announced in March 1965 that the Soviet Union would help Iraq to finance the construction of a dam and power station on the Euphrates costing an estimated fifty million pounds. The only major irrigation works constructed before the war were the Hindiya Barrage in 1913 and the Kut Barrage in 1939. During the last decade, three other major water-control schemes have been completed: the Wadi Tharthar flood-control scheme on the Tigris, the Habbaniya flood-control and irrigation scheme on the Euphrates, both inaugurated in April 1956, and the Dokan Barrage on the Lesser Zab, inaugurated in 1958 (Fig. 22.) The Wadi Tharthar scheme includes a new barrage at Samarra and the Habbaniya scheme has a new barrage at Ramadi. In addition, the Derbendi Khan Dam on the Diala River near the Iranian border was initiated in 1961 and, with a storage capacity of three million cubic metres, will control flooding on the Diala River, eliminate water shortages, and expand the area under summer cultivation. A number of drainage projects have also recently been inaugurated to reduce waterlogging and salinity in lands presently irrigated.

In December 1961 the Iraq government issued a detailed economic plan aimed at doubling the national income in about ten years. The plan envisages considerable expenditure on irrigation

FIG. 22.   Major irrigation works in Iraq.

and drainage projects, water storage and drilling. Among the major projects are (*a*) the Dibbis Dam on the Lesser Zab, presently under construction and the key structure in a scheme designed to irrigate large areas in the Kirkuk and Hawija region; (*b*) the Eski-Kalak project on the left bank of the Greater Zab River, half-way between Arbil and Mosul, now under construction and designed to irrigate more than 30,000 acres; (*c*) the Gharraf project and associated Shattra drainage west of Amara, on which work is under way and which, it is hoped, will eventually render more than 175,000 acres cultivable; (*d*) an artesian well programme in the northern and southern deserts, where over 800 wells had been drilled by 1962 and where an additional thousand are intended.[3]

While large areas of land could certainly be made cultivable if water could be stored for irrigation, possibly as much as five million acres in all, it is open to question whether the extension of cultivation is the most effective way of developing the country's agricultural potential. As Doreen Warriner writes in her excellent book, *Land Reform and Development in the Middle East*, 'The tendency to regard the extension of cultivation as the main aim of development derives from the engineer's approach which has dominated most thinking about the future of the country. Yet the immediate need is not to add to the area already cultivated but to get better cultivation on the land already in use.'[4] Lord Salter has argued that the present water storage works are sufficient and that no new, big dam scheme should be implemented. He advocates a complete change of policy whereby drainage would take priority and money would be invested not in new works but in increasing agricultural productivity on lands already farmed.[5]

Syria, unlike Iraq, has few extensive irrigation schemes but many small irrigated areas instead. A recent estimate places the extent of irrigated land at approximately one and a quarter million acres.[6] The most extensive and probably the oldest irrigated tract in the country is the Damascus oasis, comprising about 400 square miles, which is supplied with water from the Barada River and its tributaries flowing down from the Anti-Lebanon and Herman ranges to the west. Intensively cultivated, it produces vegetables, citrus fruit, cereals and cotton. Irrigation is also important along the Euphrates valley (Fig. 23), where it is hoped that water from the Euphrates will eventually provide for the irrigation of more than 800,000 additional acres.

A number of projects are in hand there, including that at Youssef Pasha where wheat, rice and cotton are the principal crops. Another recent project is that along the coast on the Sinn River near Latakia, where more than 13,000 acres are being brought under irrigation. Along the Orontes valley the area of irrigated land has been extended in the last thirty years by the construction of a barrage raising the level of Lake Homs and irrigating 60,000 acres by means of gravity channels running between Homs and Hama. A comparable area in this region is irrigated by private pump-schemes, which provide water for the cultivation of wheat, cotton and sugar beet, while the increasing use of pumps to tap deep artesian wells enables cotton to be grown around Aleppo. Below Hama in the Ghab, a government reclamation scheme that is well advanced will eventually make more than 170,000 acres irrigable. In February 1961 the Rastan Dam was completed there, making more than 60,000 acres irrigable, and in 1962 the Mahared

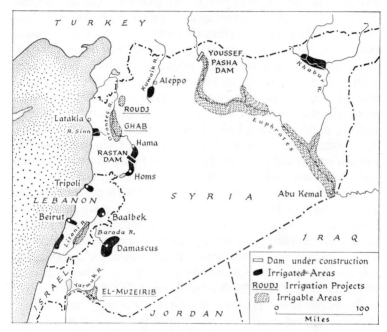

FIG. 23. Irrigated areas in Syria and Lebanon.

Barrage was inaugurated which will supply water for a similar area when completed. The Roudj project, south-west of Aleppo, was one-third completed by June 1963 and will eventually irrigate nearly 12,500 acres. Other state-operated schemes include those along the Khabur River, where some 10,000 acres are irrigable, and along the Kuwaik River, south of Aleppo, with over 30,000 acres. In southern Syria, along the Jordan border, a recent development that is part of the Great Yarmuk project is a headwater irrigation programme to provide controlled winter irrigation and expanded summer irrigation in the El-Muzeirib region; it is hoped eventually to make 16,500 acres irrigable. As Syria is predominantly an arid land, any considerable extension of agriculture will depend upon further irrigation developments; given substantial capital investment, Syria could conceivably triple her present irrigated area.[7]

Because of a more adequate supply of rainfall, Lebanon is less dependent upon irrigation than Syria and has a smaller irrigated acreage, estimated at slightly more than 90,000 in 1950 and 178,000 in 1963.[8] The most important agricultural area is the humid coastal plain, backed by limestone massifs which act as natural reservoirs and release water in the form of springs feeding perennial streams. These supplies of water make irrigation possible both on the coastal plains, where wheat, vegetables and fruit are grown, and at much higher levels where the occurrence of impervious beds brings the water near the surface, where it is led into a system of terraces on which vines, bananas and oranges are grown. Beyond the coastal range is the Bekka, a fault valley lying between the western ranges and the Anti-Lebanon and Herman ranges to the east. Because the climate is dry, cultivation is only possible where infrequent springs provide water for small, widely separated oases, but it is an area in which irrigation could be greatly extended. Lebanon has a number of schemes for extending her area of irrigated land, including the multi-purpose Litani project which is under construction and participation in a project for changing the courses of some of the headstreams of the Jordan River, a scheme which has caused considerable friction with Israel.

Israel has about 375,000 acres under irrigation, based chiefly on water derived from wells and pumps in the areas around Tel Aviv, in the upper Jordan valley, along the Kishon River and in parts of the southern Negev Desert. The major crop is citrus fruit, and sprinkler irrigation, using modern, Californian sprinkler equipment, is becoming increasingly common. As the southern two-thirds of the country is arid, it has been necessary to transfer water to it from the humid northern area. Unfortunately, Israel is nearing a point at which its water resources will be taxed to the limit, since apart from the Jordan the country is poorly endowed with rivers, and storage is often difficult because of the porous nature of the soils. Moreover, evaporation and transpiration cause considerable wastage of water, and excessive pumping of ground water in the Central Plain has brought about a decline in the water table and has accelerated salt-water intrusion near the coast. In an effort to conserve water, Israel has had to resort to reclaiming sewage effluent and to damming gullies to intercept floodwaters in the rainy months. For future demands, only two major sources of water are available, the salt water of the Mediterranean and Red seas and the fresh water of the River Jordan.

Mekorot, Israel's national water authority, has estimated that the country's water needs will rise by 500 million cubic metres by 1980, when the population is expected to be about four million. Three-fifths of this demand will be met by tapping remaining conventional and semi-conventional sources, including the Jordan River, Lake Tiberias, unused ground-water supplies, intercepted floodwaters and reclaimed sewage. For the rest, desalinated water will be required to make up the deficit and to dilute brackish waters which would otherwise be unfit for irrigation. There is little doubt that it is technically feasible to produce a desalination system extensive enough to provide the necessary water. The chief problem is to reduce production costs sufficiently to make such a system an economic proposition.[9]

Realising the urgency of the problem, the Israeli government, in partnership with an American corporation, has set up a de-salination demonstration plant at Eilat on the Red Sea, using a process by which water is frozen in a vacuum to produce salt-free ice crystals, which are then melted. At present, this is far too expensive to be economic, but it is hoped that substantial reductions will soon be possible.

Another joint study by technologists of Israel and the United States recommends the construction of a nuclear plant on the Mediterranean coast, south of Tel Aviv, to produce 200 megawatts of electricity and desalt 100 million cubic metres of sea water a year. Other proposals have been put forward to carry desalinated water inland to a reservoir of Israel's national water grid, so that it can then be delivered throughout the country.

Other research projects include an electrodialysis plant at the Negev Research Institute, where salt is separated from brackish water by drawing electrified particles through membranes by means of electric fields. Much work is also being done in the field of water conservation, including experiments to reduce evaporation in reservoirs and to store water underground. In the Negev Desert a new method of irrigation has been introduced whereby water is brought directly to the roots of plants by means of narrow, under-ground plastic pipes. In this way, there is little wastage of water, and it is estimated that this method will save up to thirty-five per cent of the water for further use in irrigation.

As far as a supply of surface water is concerned, Israel, like Jordan, will have to depend primarily on the River Jordan and its tributaries. Any scheme to utilise this source will also affect Lebanon and Syria, as some of the headwaters of the Jordan originate in these countries. The most effective use of the water resources of the Jordan would undoubtedly be achieved by devel-oping the valley as a whole. Several plans along these lines have been put forward, including the Jordan Valley Plan or the Unified Water Plan, drawn up in 1955 by Eric A. Johnston. Although his proposal was accepted by the Israelis, it was finally rejected by neighbouring Arab nations because of their intense hostility to-wards Israel. As a result, Israel and Jordan have decided to pro-ceed independently with separate aspects of the unified plan, with American financial assistance. The danger of open conflict over the water of the Jordan has grown more acute recently as a con-sequence of an Arab plan to divert several of the headwaters of the Jordan before they reach Israel.

Israel regards the development of the Jordan River as an integral part of her national water system, which at present con-sists of three main sections: (a) the Yargon-Negev section, com-pleted in 1955 and fed by wells east of Tel Aviv to provide irriga-tion for the Lakhish area south of the city, (b) water from north Galilean creeks to irrigate the inner portions of the Esdraelon valley, and (c) an area around Lake Huleh, which has been drained and reclaimed. In order to link these and other existing systems together as well as to extend irrigation south into the Negev Desert, Israel has begun the construction of a trunk line, the National Water Carrier, to take water directly from Lake Tiberias, which is fed by the Jordan, and to carry it 125 miles south into the Negev (Fig. 24). As Lake Tiberias is below sea level, the water has to be lifted by three electrically driven intake pumps 812 feet through a penstock 1·3 miles long. It then enters a canal eleven and a half miles long and so into a storage reservoir, from which it passes into the pipeline. When the system becomes fully operational in 1970, it is intended to carry an average water flow of 320 million cubic metres annually. Because Lake Tiberias features prominently in

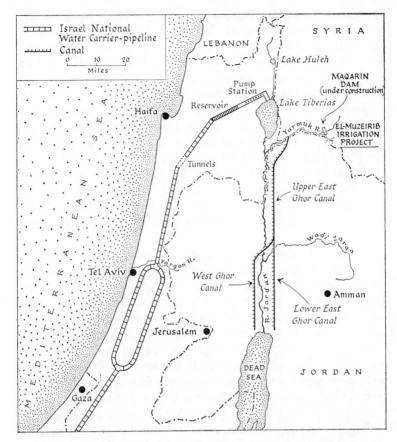

FIG. 24. The Israel National Water Carrier and Jordan Valley Plan.

this scheme as a means of water storage, it will be necessary to reduce its present high degree of salinity by capturing saline springs which now flow into the lake and diverting them into the Dead Sea.

Jordan is currently using the waters of the Jordan's main tributary, the Yarmuk, in her Great Yarmuk project which she is carrying out in co-operation with Syria. It has three main components: (a) a headwater irrigation programme to provide irrigation for the El-Muzeirib region of southern Syria, (b) the Upper East Ghor Canal system, presently under construction, to divert water from the Yarmuk along the foothills of the eastern Jordan valley, in order to irrigate some 30,000 acres of previously marginal and undeveloped land between the Yarmuk and the Wadi Zarqa, about forty miles to the south,* and (c) the Maqarin Dam, to be constructed across the Yarmuk on the Jordan-Syria border to store and control the total winter flow of the river (Fig. 24). The scheme will lead to the generation of hydroelectricity, to be shared by Jordan and Syria, and the provision of irrigation water, mainly for Jordan, to irrigate 125,000 acres along the lower Jordan valley. By the end of 1965 the first stage of the East Ghor Canal was completed and was reputedly providing water for the cultivation of 40,000 acres. It is interesting to note that the separate endeavours of both Jordan and Israel are largely in tune with the Unified Water Plan, whose provisions have been very closely followed because of the physical realities upon which they were based.[10]

In 1958, Jordan had approximately 120,000 acres under irrigation,[11] the bulk of which was along the east bank of the Jordan in valleys formed by perennial streams flowing into the main river. In these relatively small tracts, highly specialised, intensive fruit-farming is carried on, involving a heavy application of capital and labour to the land in order to obtain maximum yields. The water is brought to the orchards through concrete and masonry conduits and flumes. Vegetables, planted in terraces, are double-cropped and intercropped, and bananas and citrus fruit are produced to be marketed all year round. In the past ten years, private well-boring in the Jordan valley around Jericho has led to the intensive cultivation of about 40,000 acres, also for orchard and market-garden crops. This kind of agricultural economy provides a complete contrast with the bulk of Jordanian agriculture, which is non-irrigated and extensive, lacking in mechanisation and the use of fertilisers and giving relatively low yields. Other small irrigated areas include an interesting project of the Arab Development Society, a private, philanthropic society which has succeeded in irrigating and cultivating 6,200 acres of salt desert land near Jericho.[12] The government has sponsored a number of small-scale projects, including one for the proper control of run-off water in the more humid north, a scheme that has made consider-

---

* As a result of the June war of 1967, Jordan lost almost half her irrigable land to Israel. The future of the Upper East Ghor Canal scheme is in doubt as Israel now occupies part of the northern bank of the Yarmuk.

able amounts of water available for livestock in areas where it has not previously been available. In addition, a number of schemes have been proposed for wadis leading into the Jordan valley and near springs and wells farther inland. Several such operations have been carried out, making 12,800 acres of irrigable land available for cultivation, while others have been abandoned either because they could not be put into effect successfully or because it was found advisable to consider them as integral parts of the Jordan valley scheme.

In the Arabian peninsula, cultivation is based very largely on oases like Medina, near the Red Sea, and Riyadh and Anaiza farther north. Saudi Arabia, a true desert country, has less than two per cent of its area under cultivation, of which eighty per cent is entirely under irrigation.[13] Three main types of irrigation are in use: (a) perennial irrigation, by far the most common, in which water is lifted in skin bags from pits and wells by donkeys and camels, though a number of turbine and centrifugal pumps are currently in use, (b) the drawing of water from springs through tunnels in the hillsides, and (c) the construction of earthen diversion dams to divert occasional floodwaters through ditches into prepared bordered or dyked areas. Cultivation is based mainly on tree crops, including dates, deciduous and citrus fruits and coffee; and grains, principally millet, wheat and rice. Dates are by far the most important single crop and occupy a sizable percentage of the total irrigated area. A number of large-scale projects have been planned, including the Akramah Dam which was completed in 1959 and the Wadi Jiza Dam which has been under construction since 1960 and which, when completed, will supply water to 50,000 acres of newly irrigated land near the Yemen border. It is also intended to reclaim many ancient dams which have fallen out of use. Unfortunately, methods of irrigation are too often rudimentary and inefficient, and it is not uncommon for the Arabian farmer to use far more water than is necessary to grow his crops, with the result that waterlogging and salinity have already become very evident and some areas have degenerated into malaria-infested bogs. Proper drainage exists in only a very few areas, and there is an urgent need for adequate drainage systems. Moreover, the indiscriminate pumping of wells at Riyadh has caused a serious lowering of water tables.[14]

Irrigated agriculture is very limited in the sheikdoms of the

Persian Gulf. Bahrain is best supplied with water, and free-running springs promote the cultivation of date palms, fruit, cereals and fodder crops. In Qatar a few wells support gardens and date palms, and in Trucial Oman artesian water supplies are used for irrigation in a few oases like Sharjah and Buraimi. Muscat and Oman are more favoured and use water from springs and wadis running down the north and east slopes of the Jebel Akhdar Mountains, and in the Yemen wells and tanks allow some cultivation at higher levels, usually above 4,500 feet.

Until recently, irrigation in Aden was restricted to a few limited areas in valleys, using water from laboriously dug wells worked by animal power. Kanats are also found in some places, and cultivation in the Wadi Hadhramaut relies partly on springs which emerge from the base of the cliffs. Traditional crops are largely subsistence and include sorghum, millets, sesame and dates, with wheat, barley and some coffee at higher altitudes. Since the end of the war, efforts have been made to extend and improve irrigation by the establishment and development of farmers' co-operatives, which now undertake major irrigation works. The pilot scheme for such associations was begun in the nineteen-forties in the Abyan Plain, utilising the floodwaters of the Wadi Bana and the Wadi Hasan. Earth dams were constructed and long-staple cotton was introduced as the principal crop. The irrigated area was gradually extended and it now covers more than 50,000 acres. Since then, a similar association has been set up in the Lahej area to use the floodwaters of the Wadi Tiban, and cotton is now being grown there. In other parts of the Protectorate, particularly in the Wadi Hadhramaut, sakia are gradually being replaced by oil pumps, and a number of tube wells have been installed near Zinjibar. Further extension of the irrigated area is possible, and a survey has been undertaken at Beihan with a view to using the floodwaters of the Wadi Behan.

Turkey has an irrigable area of approximately five million acres, representing ten per cent of the cultivated land. It is doubtful, however, if the whole of this area is utilised, since inadequate drainage and salination in some places have discouraged farmers from changing from dryland to irrigation farming. Moreover, where irrigation farming is practised, it is often done by means of unsuitable crop rotations and the wasteful use of water with primitive techniques. Nonetheless, in the last fifteen years the government has invested considerable capital in the development of Turkey's abundant water resources. In recent years a number of large dams have been completed, including the Seyhan Dam near Adana, the Sariyar Dam on the Sakarya River near Ankara and the Gediz Dam in western Turkey (Fig. 25). Some doubt has been expressed as to the wisdom of using Turkey's scant financial resources on a few large projects, and a recent report of the International Bank recommends that the government should restrict itself to a programme of small-scale irrigation based on earthen dams and the use of underground water.[15]

FIG. 25. The water resources of Turkey.

The largest irrigated area in Turkey is along the southern coast in the Seyhan Plain, where the recent systematic irrigation of an area of 30,000 acres, based upon a dam constructed just north of Adana, has resulted in the cultivation of cotton, maize and rice. There are plans to reclaim and irrigate further sections of the Seyhan lowlands and to extend irrigation to about 350,000 acres. Along the western Aegean coast, irrigation canals are under construction to provide water for an area that will eventually exceed that of the Adana irrigation scheme. At present, however, irrigation is more common in the northern coastal valleys, where rice, cotton, sugar beet and vines are grown. Farther inland, two dams have been constructed on the Menderes River below Danizli, which provide water for over 100,000 acres, and there is a scheme to build a dam on the Porsuk River above Eskesehir to water an interior valley on the margins of the plateau. On the Central Plateau itself, large-scale irrigation is most difficult and has not been very successful mainly because many of the rivers are heavily charged with silt, so that storage reservoirs fill up rapidly and become useless, and also because few of the rivers are suitable for irrigation, being deeply incised into the plateau. As a consequence, small-scale irrigation is more common. One of the few large barrages is the Sariyar Dam near Ankara, which provides water for the cultivation of cereals and vegetables. In eastern Turkey, the Malatya region on the upper reaches of the Euphrates is an important fruit-producing area, where it is hoped eventually to irrigate 250,000 acres. Higher up the Euphrates, thirty miles north-west of Elazig, is the site of the proposed Keban dam and hydroelectric project. The cost of the project will be at least £125 million, and Turkey has recently been trying to raise money in Western Europe to finance the scheme. Although it is primarily designed to meet increasing power needs and to lay a basis for the creation of heavy industry in eastern Turkey, it will also provide irrigation for a large area of arid land.

Of a total of 1,300,000 acres of cultivated land, Cyprus has only 233,000 acres under irrigation, and most of these are irrigated seasonally, in winter and spring. Although perennial irrigation is therefore very limited in extent, it is much more important than seasonal irrigation and promotes the cultivation of cereals, market-garden produce, especially citrus fruit and vegetables, and vines. Mechanical devices for lifting water have been increasingly used in recent years, including water-wheels, windmills and pumps. Also common in Cyprus are chains-of-wheels, some of which have been in use for centuries and which are similar to the kanats of Iran and Afghanistan. They tap shallow aquifers and commonly lead water down conduits which are constructed at a gentler inclination than the fall of the surface above so that the water will eventually reach the surface. Many chains-of-wheels were constructed in the latter half of the nineteenth century and in the early years of the twentieth. Springs are also important local sources of water, notably in the Kyrenia Range. Undoubtedly, irrigation practice in Cyprus could be more efficient but there are considerable difficulties, including complicated land tenures and water rights, the common practice of flood rather than furrow irrigation, with its wasteful use of water, water losses due to leaky, silted and overgrown channels, and a general lack of technical knowledge.[16] Moreover, underground water has been pumped so enthusiastically that there are growing dangers of seawater intrusion. To counter this, a new law is being introduced to forbid random drilling and impose economy in the use of irrigation water.[17]

Bibliographical References

1. Cressey, G. B., *Crossroads, Land and Life in Southwest Asia* (Lippincott, Chicago), 1960, p. 159.
2. Warriner, D., *Land Reform and Development in the Middle East* (Oxford University Press), 1962, p. 115.
3. *The Iraqi Revolution in Its Fourth Year* (High Commission for the Celebrations of 14th July, Baghdad), 1962, p. 176 *et seq.*
4. Warriner, *op. cit.*, p. 116.
5. Lord Salter, *The Development of Iraq, A Plan of Action* (Caxton, London), 1955, p. 49.
6. Walker, D. S., *The Mediterranean Lands* (Methuen, London), 1962, p. 442.
7. Fisher, W. B., *The Middle East* (Methuen, London), 1961, p. 418.
8. Ginsburg, N. (Ed.), *The Pattern of Asia* (Constable, London), 1960, p. 807.
9. 'Finding Water for the Promised Land', *The Times*, London, March 24, 1965, p. 13.
10. Garbell, M. A., 'The Jordan Valley Plan', *Scientific American*, CCXII, No. 3, March 1965, pp. 23-31.
11. Pateau, R., *The Kingdom of Jordan* (Princeton University Press, New Jersey), 1958, p. 121.
12. Harris, G. L., *Jordan*, Survey of World Cultures Series (Hraf Press, New Haven), 1958, p. 154.
13. Twitchell, K. J., *Saudi Arabia* (Princeton University Press, New Jersey), 1958, p. 21.
14. Lipsky, G. A., *Saudi Arabia*, Survey of World Cultures Series (Hraf Press, New Haven), 1959, p. 214.
15. Eren, N., *Turkey, Today and Tomorrow* (Pall Mall Press, London), 1963, p. 118.
16. Christodoulou, D., *Cyprus: The Evolution of the Rural Land Use Pattern* (Geographical Publications, Bude), 1959, p. 114 *et seq.*
17. Kent, W., 'Drought is Still the Foe', *The Times*, London, June 19, 1968, p. vii.

Additional Source

Bryce, W. C., *South-West Asia* (University of London Press), 1966.

CHAPTER 10

EUROPE AND RUSSIA

Estimates of the total area under irrigation in Europe (excluding the Soviet Union) in the early nineteen-sixties vary from 21·8 to 26 million acres. Even the latter figure, which is based on figures extracted from United Nations publications (Table 5), may be too low, as it does not include the irrigated lands of a number of countries such as East Germany and Czechoslovakia, for which figures are not available.

TABLE 5

Country	Irrigated Land ('000s of Acres)	Percentage of Arable Land under Irrigation	Year
Austria	67	0·63	1960
Belgium	30	0·61	1960
Bulgaria	2,335	21·0	1966
Denmark	110	—	1960
England and Wales	266	1·0	1965
France	6,180	7·20	1960
Greece	1,420	16·1	1965
Hungary	566	—	1964
Italy	6,900	13·37	1960
Poland	400*	0·80	1963
Portugal	1,040	10·16	1960
Rumania	818	—	1966
Spain	5,610	10·30	1965
West Germany	840	2.30	1965
Yugoslavia	277	0·75	1966

The Major Irrigated Areas of Europe

(Based on figures cited in *F.A.O. Production Yearbook*, Vol. 21, 1967, and elsewhere.)
* Based on figures cited by International Commission on Irrigation and Drainage, 1963.

The way in which irrigation is organised varies greatly from country to country. Where it is extensive and elaborate, farmers' irrigation co-operatives are quite common. In Italy, for example, there are many 'Associations of Landowners', which are compulsory in certain areas and recognised by law as public corporations. In all, they administer some sixty per cent of Italy's irrigated lands. In addition, a number of voluntary associations of groups of farmers have been set up to administer reclamation schemes, including irrigation installations which serve several farms. These 'Associations of Land Betterment' serve thirty per cent of Italy's irrigated lands. In England and West Germany, on the other hand, where irrigation is largely supplemental, installations are owned and administered privately by individual farmers.

SOUTHERN EUROPE

The largest and most important irrigated areas are in southern Europe. In these regions, most irrigation is carried out by furrow methods and is applied to only a small proportion of the cultivable land, on average, about ten per cent. However, given sufficient capital, irrigation could likely be extended to almost a quarter of the arable land. Irrigation is important in southern Europe because it makes possible the cultivation of a wide range of crops and crop rotations and, as in the market gardens of southern Spain, frequently promotes a diverse and intensive agriculture. It is little used for winter crops because normal precipitation is available, but it is very important for spring and summer crops. It also gives considerably greater crop yields; in the North Italian Plain, for example, seven or eight cuts of forage crop can be obtained each season with irrigation, but only two or three without.

Italy had almost seven million acres under irrigation in the early nineteen-sixties, representing over thirteen per cent of the total cultivable land but accounting for more than twenty-five per cent of the value of agricultural output. The ratio of irrigated land to arable land varied greatly from region to region. It was highest in Lombardy where it was almost half and least in the south where, in places, it was little more than one per cent. In recent years, however, there has been a considerable extension of the irrigated acreage in Southern Italy, particularly in the coastal regions of Apulia and Lucania where the government-sponsored *Cassa per il Mezzogiorno* (The Southern Development Fund) has invested large sums of money in colonisation and irrigation. These provinces have considerable potential and it is estimated that some 1,750,000 acres are irrigable.[1] Most irrigation here is based on rivers and groundwater while, elsewhere, notably in Latium and Tuscany, sprinkler irrigation has increased recently.

The important irrigated areas in the northern lowlands are generally found on impervious soils, above the floodplains of the River Po and its tributaries but on land sufficiently low to be served by irrigation channels which run from tributary rivers across the interfluves. A great deal of water is obtained from springs (*fontanili*), especially along the northern edge of the plain where impermeable beds of clay force the water to the surface in long lines of springs (Fig. 26). This water is particularly valuable in

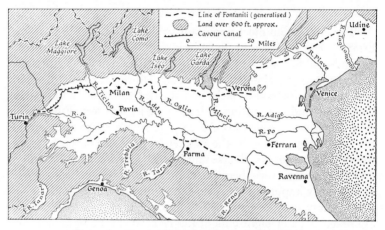

FIG. 26.   Fontanili in the North Italian Plain.

that its flow and temperature remain remarkably constant, and it has been used for growing crops for well over two thousand years. A similar line of springs, less frequent and less continuous, is also found on the southern edge of the plain. In addition, artesian wells (*pozzi modenesi*) are used locally, as at Ferrara. The ready availability of water, the favourable climate and a highly developed and complex network of irrigation channels and wells have promoted a rich agriculture of great variety. Although irrigation has been used there for several millennia, its greatest expansion has taken place since the eighteen-fifties, when Cavour initiated the construction of new, major canals, including the Marzano Canal, the Naviglio Grande and the Cavour Canal. These made possible the perennial irrigation of very large areas. The principal crops are rice, which is grown in the Piedmont around Turin and in the lower Po floodplain, sugar beet, hemp and cereals. Dairying is also of considerable importance, especially in southern Lombardy and western Emilia, where it is based on hay grown in irrigated water-meadows.

In central Italy, irrigation is important in the Perugia-Terni area of Umbria. There, water is obtained from Apennine streams and wells to grow olives, mulberries, vines and wheat. In southern Italy, irrigation is of considerable and growing importance, particularly for market gardens, where intensive cultivation produces citrus fruit, vines and early vegetables. These are to be found in limited areas where water and soil conditions are favourable, in Campania, Apulia, along the west Sicilian coast and around the large towns such as Naples, Bari and Brindisi. The Cassa per il Mezzogiorno has provided considerable impetus for extending the irrigated acreage by supplying money to build numerous small dams along Apennine streams. Thousands of wells are also under construction, and it is hoped to double the area under irrigation in the south within a few years. Irrigation is also locally important in the islands, particularly Sardinia, where a recent project financed by the Cassa per il Mezzogiorno is the Flumendosa scheme. A number of dams are under construction on the Flumendosa River and its tributaries, and it is intended to irrigate about 150,000 acres of the Campidano and to provide hydro-electricity for the Cagliari area.

As the precipitation in the greater part of France is fairly adequate, irrigation is less vital than in Italy and is used mainly to supplement the natural rainfall. As one would expect, it is primarily found in southern France, which experiences a summer drought over much of the region. Development has taken place in certain special areas, notably the lower Rhône Valley, the Durance valley and the Basin of Aquitaine.

In the country as a whole, irrigation is virtually indispensable for garden crops and flowers and is usually provided by sprinklers, which are also used to irrigate tobacco. Some areas of grassland are irrigated by flood and furrow methods. As elsewhere in Europe, the use of irrigation is growing rapidly, largely because it enables greater yields to be obtained. For example, Table 6 gives a general idea of the increased yields of irrigated crops grown in the lower Rhône-Languedoc area of southern France.

Irrigated farming is particularly important in the middle and lower Rhône Valley (Fig. 27). In the fertile and frequently dry

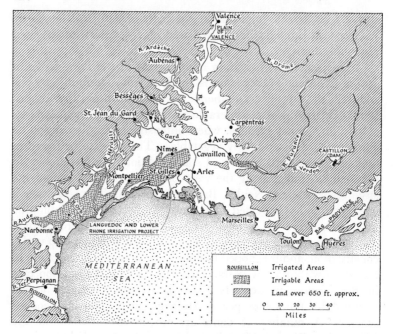

FIG. 27.   Irrigation in the lower Rhône Valley, France.

TABLE 6

Crop	Maximum Regular Yield of Non-Irrigated Crops	Output Obtained with Irrigation	
		Normal	Maximum
Potatoes	200	300	350
Apples	100	200	500
Cauliflower	100	200	250
Rice	34	45	91
Maize	30	65	93
Lucerne	20	60	80
Wheat	20	40	55
Barley	18	35	—

The Lower Rhône-Languedoc Area: Crop Yields
(In Quintals per Hectare)

(Based on figures cited in *Agricultural Mechanization—Irrigation by Canals and Sprinklers*, United Nations, New York, 1962, p. 29.)

It will be seen that the normal yields of irrigated crops are generally twice as high as the maximum yields of non-irrigated crops. Under the most favourable conditions, irrigation can increase yields three times in the case of grain crops like wheat, maize and rice and as much as five times for orchard crops like apples.

plain of Valence in the middle Rhône, it is especially useful on the accessible lands just above the wet water-meadows, where it supports market gardening and the cultivation of wheat and maize. Although irrigation has been used for centuries in the lower Rhône Valley, it has been developed on a large scale only in the last hundred years by the construction of canals using water mainly from the Rhône and Durance. These include the Canal de Carpentras, which serves the Carpentras and Cavaillon districts; the Canal de Craponne, which serves Arles and the area to the east; and the Canal de l'Isle, which supplies the Avignon area. The total region served by these and similar canals and, to a lesser extent, by water obtained from underground sources, is more than 75,000 acres, devoted largely to market gardening.

In recent years, irrigation has helped to reclaim parts of the Camargue area of the Rhône delta, where rice is the chief crop, being grown on more than 80,000 acres supplied by a system of canals, syphons and aqueducts. With the aid of seasonal Spanish labour, 130,000 tons of rice are grown annually, making France self-sufficient in this commodity. Wheat, fruit and early vegetables are also cultivated. Water is obtained from the Rhône and some is pumped back into the river after use, but most drains off into the marshes, where it causes salination in places. The diminution of marshland and prairie in the Camargue, resulting from the spread of irrigation, has caused concern to those interested in the preservation of wildfowl, for which this area is famous. Attempts are being made to secure wildlife-protected areas in the remaining unused land and to preserve the whole area as a national park.

Parts of the Crau, to the east of the delta, have also been improved by irrigation, and fodder crops, principally lucerne and sanfoin, and market gardening are important there. Small-scale developments have brought about a gradual extension of irrigated farming in this region, especially during the last five years. In 1960, for example, 6,000 acres beyond Moulès were made irrigable. A number of canals, including the Canal de Langlade and the Canal d'Istres, have been opened up and divided into branches. By these means, the area under irrigation was increased to an estimated total of 38,500 acres by 1965, and the value of some of the land in the Crau has multiplied tenfold in the last five years. Fruit-growing has been expanded with the introduction of plum, apricot, cherry, peach and fig trees from Italy. Fodder crops are of growing importance, and a recent interesting experiment in this direction involves the use of liquid nitrogen, which is put into the irrigation canals serving meadows in order to increase the nitrogen content of the grass.

Farther east, in lower Provence, one of the principal irrigated areas is the plain of Hyères near Toulon, where fruit and flowers are intensively cultivated.

Recently, a multi-purpose, government-sponsored scheme has been under development in lower Provence and lower Languedoc, where a number of dams have been built, including the Castillon Dam on the Verdon. In Languedoc, a vast irrigation scheme is transforming the region from one of relative poverty, based upon the cultivation of olives and vines, to what has been called 'a French California',[2] based upon fruit orchards and market gardens. It is hoped that the region will gradually become highly productive, exporting fruit, vegetables and meat to other European countries. A wholesale market covering over 600 acres has already been built outside Nîmes, and it is planned to transport high-quality produce abroad by air. The scheme is divided into two zones, an eastern one using water from the Rhône and a western one using water from barrages on the rivers Orb and Hérault and their tributaries. The construction of pumping stations and canals and the installation of underground pipes and water-sprinklers to feed the water to the crops are both proceeding, and it is hoped eventually to irrigate over 600,000 acres. At present, only the section between Nîmes and St. Gilles, comprising about 80,000 acres, is extensively equipped with piping, but the intention is to make land available for cropping at the rate of 25,000 acres a year from 1965 onwards.

This project is the largest irrigation scheme in Europe and is due for completion by 1980. It may be said to have got under way in 1955, when a development company was set up by the French government to construct and operate the entire irrigation network. The company is non-profit-making and its capital has been subscribed chiefly by the French government. The Common Market, through the European Investment Bank, is also backing the scheme, and locally, farmers, banks and industries have also invested capital. The project is part of a grand government scheme to diversify the economy of the region and includes land consolidation, farm modernisation, new industries and modern transport facilities.

Another project, presently under construction in the Durance Basin, will provide supplemental irrigation for about 150,000 acres.

Other irrigated areas in southern France are the dry plain of Roussillon at the foot of the eastern Pyrenees, parts of the Cevennes on the eastern edge of the Massif Central and parts of the Aquitaine Basin. In Roussillon, water is obtained from rivers and wells to promote intensive cultivation similar to the huertas of south-east Spain. Vegetables are the chief crop, and vines, fruit and fodder crops are also important. Streams flowing down the eastern edge of the Massif Central supply water for market gardening in a string of small towns at the foot of the Cevennes, including Aubenas, Bessèges, Alès and St. Jean du Gard, which are situated in fertile valley pockets. In the Aquitaine Basin, irrigation is important around Agen in the Garonne valley, where water is raised by electric pumps for the intensive cultivation of vegetables. In Charentes and in the Couteaux de Gascogne in the south, irrigation is extensively used for the improvement of water-meadows. In the Adour Basin in the south-west, swiftly flowing Pyrenean streams are tapped by lateral canals which carry water along river terraces for the cultivation of irrigated fodder crops, especially lucerne.

As a result of a government regional plan started in 1957, irrigation is being developed on the eastern coastal plain of Corsica, especially for the cultivation of citrus fruit. New dams are being built in the mountains, and farms established on the plain. It is hoped to make 80,000 acres irrigable.[3]

Spain had just over five and a half million acres under irrigation in 1965,[3a] of which the majority was devoted to huerta (market garden) cultivation and new, large-scale systems. In addition, there are three other less important categories of irrigated land: (a) the citrus groves of the Levante, specialising in cash-crop farming developed in the last hundred years with the aid of pumps lifting water, (b) the areas in north-west Spain using the well and spring irrigation system, a skilful means of providing for the short period of summer drought, and (c) the land supporting cereal crops, inefficiently irrigated, in south-east Spain, especially in the Lorca area.[4]

The regional distribution of irrigated agriculture in Spain and the area and value of irrigated crops are shown in the following table:

TABLE 7A

Regions	Area ('000s of Hectares)
Ebro	480
Guadalquivir	292
Jucar	235
Duero	186
Segura	165
Guadiana	125
Sur	97
Norte	95
Tajo	89
Pirineo Oriental	67
Subtotal	1,831
Canary Islands	28
Balearic Islands	17
Total	1,876 or 4·6 million acres

Spain: Major Irrigated Areas by Regions, 1960

(Based on figures cited in International Bank for Reconstruction and Development, *The Economic Development of Spain*, Johns Hopkins Press, Baltimore, 1963, p. 271.)

TABLE 7B

Crops	Area ('000s of Hectares)	Value (Billions of Pesetas)
Cereals (except rice)	541	6·5
Vegetables/Condiments	143	6·0
Sugar beet	119	3·4
Alfalfa	113	1·6
Potatoes (except early potatoes)	112	2·2
Cotton and other textiles	110	2·2
Olives	95	0·6
Citrus	85	6·6
Forage and artificial pasture	70	0·8
Rice	67	1·8
Melons	61	1·5
Tomatoes	50	2·9
Others	220	—
Total	1,786 or 4·4 million acres	

Spain: Area and Value of Irrigated Crops, May 1959

(Based on figures cited in International Bank for Reconstruction and Development, *The Economic Development of Spain*, Johns Hopkins Press, Baltimore, 1963, p. 271.)

The main areas of huerta cultivation are along the Mediterranean coast of Spain. In the Valencia area, water is obtained mainly from the rivers Mijares, Turia, Júcar and Serpis to grow fruit and vegetables, cereals, tobacco and rice. Crops have been grown there under irrigation for more than two millennia, and ancient customs still rigidly control the use of communal water: the occupation of a holding usually carries with it the right to share in the available water. The control is maintained by the Water Tribunal, which meets every Thursday at the Apostles' Door of Valencia Cathedral to rule on irrigation disputes. The tribunal was created during the Moorish occupation and has been so useful that it has continued to the present day. It consists of eight judges who are agricultural workers, one for each of the main canals which serve the region. They wear the traditional black smock and conduct hearings in regional dialect. In addition, there are watchmen for each canal who report on infractions such as stealing or contaminating water, or altering the course of part of the canal network. They also confirm complaints against those brought before the court. The complainant states his case before the court, and usually the verbal account, supported by the testimony of the watchman, is sufficient for the tribunal to reach a decision. The work of the tribunal is considered a model of its kind and has attracted delegations from all over the world.

To the south and west of Valencia are the more arid areas of Murcia and Alicante, whose huertas produce crops all the year round. Tropical in summer and temperate in winter, they include vines, vegetables, fruit, sugar cane, groundnuts, cotton and dates. Water is obtained from the rivers Vinalapo, Segura and de Velez. Farther west, the coastal huertas of Almería and Málaga produce dates, sugar cane, cotton, tobacco, citrus fruit and vegetables.

The large-scale projects sponsored by the government differ from the coastal huertas in two main ways: cultivation is on a much more extensive scale, and it concentrates on increasing the production of cereals and industrial and fodder crops, as part of a national plan to make Spain self-sufficient in basic foodstuffs, textile fibres and dairy produce. Cereals occupy by far the largest acreage of any irrigated crop, though their value per acre is considerably less than the huerta-cultivated fruits and vegetables.

Among the best established of these schemes are the Guadalquivir and Ebro basins. In the past, the Guadalquivir Basin has suffered from the latifundia system (*latifundismo*) and has been the scene of considerable efforts by the government at colonisation and rehabilitation based upon irrigated agriculture, notably in the Jaen province, where a series of dams is being constructed on the upper Guadalquivir and its tributary the Guadiana Menor. The chief crops are cereals, groundnuts, cotton, tobacco and rice. In the Ebro Basin, the Ebro and its tributaries are tapped by a large-scale network of barrages and canals to provide water for the dry steppes of Cinca, Bardenas and Los Monegros. As the growing season is shorter, irrigation is used principally to ensure good yields.

The main hope of increasing Spain's agricultural production lies in the extension of schemes such as these, which at present cover less than ten per cent of the total arable land. The Spanish government has embarked upon a large and costly programme which should in a few years extend the irrigated area by a further two and a half million acres, and plans have been drawn up for making an additional three million acres irrigable at a later stage.

The programme consists of a series of regional plans for Estremadura, Aragon, Cáceres, Salamanca, Seville and Granada (Fig. 28). Typical of these agrarian projects is the Badajoz Plan based on about one hundred miles of the Guadiana valley in Estremadura, between the towns of Orellana and Badajoz (Fig. 29). 'El Plan', as it is called in Spain, involves the controlling of the Guadiana River, until recently the most perverse in the country, liable to dry up in the summer and cause disastrous floods in the winter. The project began in 1953 and was originally scheduled for completion by 1965. However, it has since been amplified and the completion date extended to 1970. The plan is designed to harness the waters of the Guadiana, render irrigable two, forty-mile-long, lozenge-shaped areas along its banks and establish new farming communities and local industries. The key structure is the Cijara Dam.

By the middle of 1964, about thirty new villages had been built with a total population of around 17,000; by 1970, nearly 50,000 people will have been resettled in the area and nearly 200,000 acres brought under intensive cultivation. Each independent farmer, who in almost all cases used to be an agricultural labourer, has been given twelve acres, which the government considers to be an economic holding. The land has been expropriated from the great landowners who owned that part of Spain and who have been compensated at the value of the land at the time of expropriation. Modest charges have been levied on the new farmers for houses, land and equipment, and undoubtedly the value of the land will have multiplied many times before repayment is due.

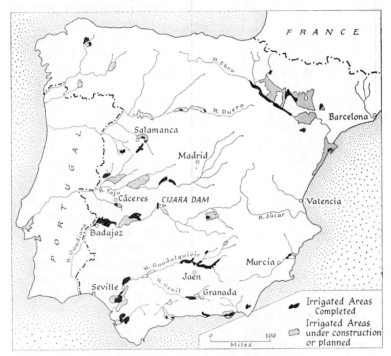

FIG. 28. Major irrigation projects in Spain.

Two crops a year are commonly grown, chiefly maize, pimentos, barley, cotton, hemp and rice, on what was largely a barren waste a few years ago. Most of the crops are marketed by village co-operatives, and a number of factories, including vegetable-canning plants, have been built to process local produce. In addition, 200 miles of new roads and a 110-mile-long railway from Villanueva to Talavera la Real have been constructed. In these ways, a new landscape, as well as a new way of living for the Spanish farmer, is being created.

The development of these and similar plans will depend upon considerable expenditure, and a recent report issued by the

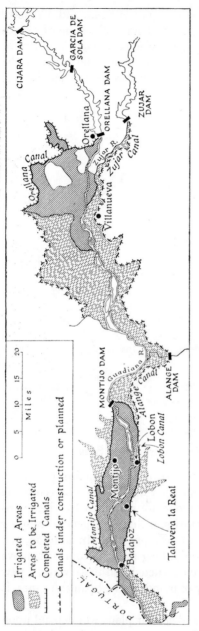

FIG. 29.   The Badajoz Plan.

International Bank for Reconstruction and Development, at the request of the Spanish government, urges that consideration should be given to less costly ways of achieving increased agricultural production.[5] It recommends that capital should be spent on a limited number of projects that can all be completed on a normal construction schedule, so that the benefits may be secured many years earlier than if the limited money available were spread over a large number of ambitious projects. It further stresses the need to make a careful economic analysis to determine in advance the most appropriate scale of the projects and to decide which are the most suitable to be financed. Efforts should be made to obtain maximum yields from existing irrigation projects, by providing suitable farming equipment and expert technical assistance, before embarking upon new ones. The report recommends that while irrigation technique in Spain is of a high order, some immediate small-scale improvements might be considered, for example, the wider use of sprinklers, especially in the south, in the Levante and the Canaries, where water is expensive; the use of piped supplies instead of open canals to save water and maintenance costs and to avoid tunnelling, bridging and land-levelling; and the need to pay more attention to salinity, which is threatening some coastal areas. In conclusion, the report recommends that the Spanish government should give high priority to a fresh appraisal of its whole irrigation policy.

Portugal has slightly more than one million acres under irrigation and is currently devoting considerable capital expenditure to extend this acreage. These schemes frequently combine irrigation and reclamation projects, as in the lower Tagus valley, where the lowest areas are flooded each February but where for much of the year the neighbouring higher land receives insufficient water. Perhaps the most extensive irrigation undertaking presently being developed in Portugal is the Alentejo Irrigation Plan, which covers a project area of 420,000 acres (Fig. 30). Other state schemes completed in recent years include dams to provide irrigation water for farmlands along the lower courses of the Sado and Sorraia rivers. Elsewhere, there has been some development of irrigated farming by the private modernisation of large estates and the establishment of small irrigation schemes.

In northern Portugal and farther south in the area east of Coimbra, small-scale irrigation based on local springs is an essential feature of the agricultural system. On the low coastal plains of the Algarve in southern Portugal, there are many irrigated *hortas* (market gardens) producing early vegetables, and in lower Alentejo, well irrigation promotes intensive polyculture. Over much of the country, primitive methods of lifting are still in use, including the shaduf and donkey-driven water-wheels, though petrol pumps are becoming increasingly common.

The extension of irrigated agriculture in Greece is hampered above all by lack of water. The country has few permanent rivers, suffers from summer drought when the evaporation rate is high, and has extensive areas of porous limestone through which water sinks rapidly. In some areas the construction of dams is made hazardous by the threat of earthquake damage. For these reasons, Greece is still largely dependent for irrigation water upon springs, seasonal streams and wells. However, during the last fifty years, there have been a number of large-scale irrigation and reclamation projects, and the area under irrigation has increased considerably

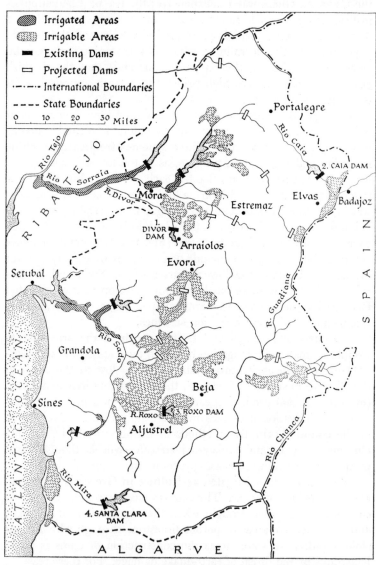

FIG. 30. The Alentejo Irrigation Plan, Portugal. The first stage of the plan, due for completion in 1966, provides for an irrigable area of 62,000 acres based on four sites: (1) Divor Dam, (2) Caia Dam, (3) Roxo Dam and (4) Santa Clara Dam.

since 1945. This land is devoted mainly to the cultivation of annual crops, especially cotton and market-garden produce, and to fruit, olives and vines.

Of the 1,420,000 acres which were being irrigated in 1965, about two-thirds were supplied with surface water from rivers,

FIG. 31. Major irrigation projects in Greece.

streams, springs and lakes, and one-third was supplied from underground sources, from both shallow and deep wells. Mechanical lifting devices are widespread, including windmills, which are a familiar feature of the Greek islands. As elsewhere in Europe, sprinkler irrigation is increasing, and between 1957 and 1964 the area under sprinklers had increased fourfold to almost 100,000 acres.

A long-term programme for the extension of irrigation is taking place in three main areas (Fig. 31), and it is hoped eventually to make more than 850,000 acres irrigable.

Irrigation is less vital in Yugoslavia than in Greece and is used mainly to supplement the nearly adequate natural precipitation. On the plains, water is derived mainly from wells, though a number of irrigation projects have been developed in recent years using river water, particularly on land adjacent to the Danube-Tisza-Danube Canal. In the southern part of the country, in Macedonia, a number of fertile valleys and basins, notably the lower Vardar valley, are irrigated to produce maize, wheat, fruit and vines.

In Turkey-in-Europe, irrigation farming has developed considerably in recent years in the plain of Thrace. The soils are generally fertile, and where water is available from rivers or underground sources, wheat, barley and vegetables are grown. In the lower Maritsa valley, rice is grown under irrigation.

NORTH-WESTERN EUROPE

In north-western Europe, irrigation is used mainly as a safeguard against occasional droughts and to increase crop yields. Sprinkler irrigation is chiefly used and can be particularly valuable in areas of high winds, heavy evaporation or pervious soil, where some crops, especially vegetables, require more than the normal amount of precipitation.

It has been estimated recently that irrigation by sprinklers or by other methods may increase grain yields by twenty to fifty per cent, sugar-beet yields by as much as seventy to eighty per cent and potato yields by sixty to one hundred per cent.[6] This is particularly true of England and Wales, where although the climate is such that a reasonable level of crop production can be maintained by rainfall alone, it is nonetheless unreliable and varies both from year to year and from place to place.[7] It has been estimated that in the area approximately south-east of a line joining Hull and Torquay, there is insufficient natural rainfall to ensure optimum growth for many crops in one year out of two, while in the London area and south-east England, irrigation is likely to be required for nine years out of ten.[8] It has become apparent that the need for irrigation is far greater than even an experienced farmer might expect and that the rewards in the form of increased crop yields to be derived from skilful irrigation are considerable.

Until quite recently, the most common form of irrigation was the water-meadow, and its use dates back to the eighteenth century. By this method, an area of flat land adjoining a river or stream was laid out in a more or less irregular system of ridge and furrow with water supply channels running along the ridges and open drainage channels along the furrows. The near-by stream supplied the water which promoted the cultivation of good crops of early grazing and later of hay. However, the high cost of maintaining water-meadows, which require a considerable amount of labour and whose layout prevents the use of modern haymaking machinery, has led to their gradual disappearance, and now very few remain in operation.[9]

At present, the irrigated area in England and Wales is increasing at the rate of approximately 15,000 acres a year. This increase is largely determined by the rate at which suitable equipment can be manufactured, and it is likely to accelerate significantly in the near future. If cheap water supplies could be produced, an estimated 500,000 acres might be under irrigation by 1980 and one and a half million acres some time after that. But if the latter figure is ever to be reached, it will require a peak supply of about 2,700 million gallons of water daily, which is more than half the present total for all needs.

According to a recent estimate, there were 266,000 acres under irrigation in England and Wales on 7,000 farms in 1965,[9a] while an agricultural census conducted by the Ministry of Agriculture in June 1962 suggested that in a dry season the area usually irrigated by sprinklers was then about 210,000 acres. According to this census, the main irrigated crops were as indicated in Table 8.

TABLE 8

Grass	67·5	Orchard fruit	6·5
Potatoes (early and late)	46·5	Small fruit	4·0
Vegetables	37·5	Hops	2·5
Sugar beet	24·5	Other crops	21·0

England and Wales: Acreage of Crops Usually Irrigated by Sprinklers in a Dry Season
('000s of Acres)

These crops were grown on 6,819 holdings, whose total area was about 1·1 million acres. The approximate dates of installation of sprinkler equipment were as follows:

Before 1950:	1,008 holdings	1956 to 1963:	4,216 holdings
1950 to 1955:	1,463 holdings	Unspecified:	132 holdings

It is apparent from these figures that the past decade has seen a great increase in the installation and use of irrigation equipment. Such equipment is in operation on a great variety of lands from heavy clays to light sands, primarily for the cultivation of grass, vegetables, fruit and sugar beet. It is also increasingly used for greenhouse crops.

Although irrigation results in heavier yields, it also removes greater quantities of plant nutrient from the soil than would otherwise be the case. Irrigation therefore makes heavier demands on fertilisers, which can often be supplied by applying them in solution in irrigation water. For example, on grassland, sulphate of ammonia may be dissolved in irrigation water before application.

In addition, irrigation is used as a means of fertilising market-garden crops by applying diluted chemical fertilisers, which are commonly alternated with pure water. The recent intensification of English agriculture, especially the increase in farm animals associated with factory farming, has created a serious problem of the disposal of dung. As the traditional methods of carting the dung for distribution on the fields are slow and expensive, a growing number of farmers are using the dung in the form of organic irrigation. The animal pens are sluiced with high-pressure hoses, thus converting the dung into slurry, which is carried through special pumps and pipes and deposited on the fields by high-pressure sprinklers. This procedure eliminates handling of the dung in the normal way and results in a very even distribution on the fields.[10]

The use of sprinkler irrigation as a protection against frost has also grown in recent years. Two methods are commonly employed: wetting the soil in advance and so releasing warmth from the ground to combat frost; and forming a continuous, protective ice-coating on leaves and buds to prevent their temperature from falling to danger level. The former method is based on the fact that a wet, compact soil conducts heat better than a dry, loose one. Consequently, if the land is irrigated during the day, it will release more of the ground's heat on a cold night than dry soil. In this way, the air immediately above the soil is warmed by one or two degrees Fahrenheit, sufficient during periods of light frost to give protection to low-growing crops like early potatoes and straw-berries.

Continuous sprinkling as a means of frost protection is based on the fact that when water changes to ice it releases latent heat. Provided that water is applied quickly enough to ensure that it freezes continuously on trees and bushes, it will prevent the temperature from falling below freezing point. Ice will accumulate on the foliage, but its weight will not be sufficient to break the branches, though it may bend them. As large quantities of water are required for this method of frost protection, the capital costs of permanent installation are high and it is only used on a limited scale in Britain.[11] At present, its use is restricted to small areas of orchards and fields of early potatoes, which are affected by radiation frosts during dry spells in late spring.

This picture of supplemental irrigation applied to a highly sophisticated agriculture is repeated elsewhere in western Europe. Sprinklers are becoming increasingly important, and the crops they support vary with local physical and economic conditions. In West Germany the growth of the area under irrigation from 590,000 acres in 1958 to 840,000 in 1965 was entirely due to an increased use of sprinklers. The main crops are fruit and vegetables, beet, maize, tobacco and vines. In Belgium, sprinklers are widely employed for the cultivation of flowers and market-garden produce, and in Denmark they support fodder crops and cereals.

CENTRAL AND SOUTH-EASTERN EUROPE

Few countries of central and south-eastern Europe have large irrigated areas. Supplementary irrigation to offset local dry periods or to control frost is practised in Switzerland and Austria, but these countries generally have sufficient natural rainfall to make irrigation unnecessary. In Poland and Hungary, limited irrigation based on water from the main rivers and their tributaries is associated with drainage schemes. Most of the irrigation is accomplished by gravity flow, and nearly all the irrigated land is under grass, since crop irrigation is insignificant.

Only in Bulgaria and, to a lesser extent, in Rumania is irrigation extensive where it is used in summer when there are regular, very hot, dry periods lasting for two or three months. The main Bulgarian irrigated areas are in the Central Basin east of Sofia and in a similar enclosed basin to the east, drained by the upper part of the Tunja River. The most common method of irrigation is by means of long ditches, though in the last ten years a number of dams have been built, like the Dimitrov Barrage on the upper

Tunja, as well as many small pumping stations connected with reservoirs to raise water mechanically. Throughout these areas wheat, beet, maize, vines, mulberries, temperate fruit and tobacco are grown.

THE SOVIET UNION

The Soviet Union has considerably increased its irrigated agriculture in recent years and, in 1966 an estimated 23·5 million acres were under irrigation, representing an increase of over forty per cent in thirteen years. As Table 9 shows, the irrigated lands were devoted to 'technical crops' (principally cotton), cereals, potatoes, feed crops, fruit and vegetables, hay, and pasture.

TABLE 9

Irrigated Lands
(Millions of Acres)

	1953	1957	1960	1962	1966
Total irrigable area	27·2	27·7	28·7	29·4	—
Area actually irrigated	16·6	17·8	—	19·3	23·5

Acreage of Irrigated Croplands, 1966

Technical crops	6·7	Orchards and vineyards	2·3
Cereals	5·5	Potatoes	1·4
Feed crops	4·8	Other crops	2·8
		Total	23·5

The Extent of Irrigation in the Soviet Union

(Based on figures cited in *Economic Survey of Europe in 1963*, Pt. 1, p. 23, and *Economic Survey of Europe in 1967*, Pt. 1, p. 23, United Nations, New York.)

The considerable discrepancy between the irrigable lands—one estimate suggested that these exceeded 30 million acres in 1963[12]—and the land actually under irrigation is due partly to the inefficient use of existing irrigation facilities and partly to the fact that in areas of marginal rainfall, farmers have preferred to rely upon natural precipitation. Other handicaps to the more widespread application of irrigation include the great shortage of experts in the field, the growing demand for relatively scarce irrigation equipment and the long-standing problem of inadequate supplies of spare parts.

Of the total irrigated area, the four Central Asian republics of Uzbekistan, Kirgizia, Tadzhikistan and Turkmenistan contain forty-six per cent; the Transcaucasian republics, nineteen per cent; the Kazakh Republic, eighteen per cent; the Russian Republic, thirteen per cent; and the Ukrainian and Moldavian republics, two per cent.[13] The Central Asian republics and Kazakhstan, commonly called the Middle Asian republics, contain almost two-thirds of Soviet irrigated lands, and nearly all the cultivated land is under irrigation. Their rivers rise in the mountains to the south and flow north across the desert and steppe into three great

FIG. 32.   Major irrigated areas in Soviet Central Asia.

inland drainage basins, the Caspian Sea, the Aral Sea and Lake Balkhash, or dry up in salt lakes in the middle of the desert. The two most important rivers are the Amu Darya and the Syr Darya. Other rivers supporting irrigated agriculture include the Ili and Chu in the east, the Zeravshan between the Syr Darya and the Amu Darya, the Murgab and Tedzhen in Turkmenistan and the Vakhsh in Tadzhikistan (Fig. 32). They provide water for a dis-continuous belt of irrigated regions along the northern slopes of the Tien Shan from Taldy-Kurgan in the east through Alma Ata, Frunze and Tashkent to Samarkand and Bukhara, and then west across the Kara Kum Desert and along the northern foothills of the Hindu Kush and Kopet Dag mountains, through Mary and Tedzhen to Ashkhabad. Other important areas include the Fergana Basin, which lies between two arms of the Tien Shan and which is the largest continuous irrigated area in Central Asia; and irrigated oases along the lower courses of the Syr Darya and the Amu Darya. The most important irrigated crop is high-quality cotton, and about seventy per cent of the Soviet Union's cotton production is located there. Other irrigated crops include sugar beet, wheat, rice, fruit and vegetables. Vineyards are found in some areas, and recently tobacco and *kenaf*, a fibre crop used to make ropes and sacks, have been introduced.

Modern systems have been developing in Soviet Central Asia for nearly forty years and are growing at an accelerating rate. The particular form of irrigation varies from place to place, from the intensively farmed cotton fields of the Fergana valley, divided into small plots by irrigation channels, to the large, extensively farmed lands of southern Kazakhstan, formerly devoted to dry farming and only recently brought under irrigation. The costs of development are met by the government, which is responsible for the construction of the large distribution canals, while individual collective farms pay for the construction of the distribution system from the main canal to the farm. Each year individual farms submit cropping plans and water needs to a 'water master', who examines these in relation to the total supply and notifies each farm of the quantity it is allowed. One of the advantages of large collective farms is that they can organise their water distribution systems so as to reduce the area of land devoted to canals and permanent ditches. Like other dry lands, this region is faced with the problem of excessive loss of irrigation water because of seepage and evaporation; an estimated forty-five per cent of the water flowing along the Great Fergana Canal is lost in these ways each year.[14]

It is estimated that, properly utilised, Central Asian rivers could triple the present irrigated area,[15] and much greater use could be made of the ground water which underlies large sections of Central Asia, Kazakhstan and the Caspian Depression. The largest irrigation project presently under construction is the Kara Kum Canal, which leads water westwards from Kelif on the Amu Darya through Mary and Tedzhen to Ashkhabad. This section was completed in 1962, and when an associated network of canals is constructed the project will make water available for a large area in southern Turkmenistan. It is hoped eventually to extend the canal as far west as Krasnovodsk on the Caspian, but financial and physical difficulties make this a somewhat doubtful prospect.

The Kayrak Dam, across the Syr Darya on the western edge

of the Fergana Basin, was completed in 1957 and will eventually provide water for about one million acres, three-quarters of which lie in the Golodnaya (Hungry) Steppe to the west of the Fergana Basin in Uzbekistan. Irrigation in the Fergana Basin itself will be extended by more than 250,000 acres by a series of improvements including the widening of the Great Fergana Canal. Another important project is the construction of the Amu-Karakul Canal begun in 1959. It runs from the Amu Darya to Karakul on the western end of the Zeravshan River and will provide water for a large area between Samarkand and Karakul when completed. In September 1965, work was begun on a very large irrigation project to dam the Amu Darya at Takhia Tash. By 1970, the estimated completion date, it should increase the irrigable area in the lower reaches of the river to more than three million acres. More than a thousand miles to the north-east, a canal is under construction to divert water from the Siberian River Irtysh to Karaganda in Kazakhstan. The first section of the canal, stretching for more than sixty miles from the river to the mining town of Ekibastuz, was finished in August 1965. When the first stage of the project is fully operating, in the very near future, it should provide water for almost 500,000 acres of irrigable steppe. Also under construction is the Nurek Dam on the Vakhsh River in south-east Tadzhikistan, which should eventually provide water for 250,000 acres of cotton-growing land. In addition to these major irrigation schemes, a number of smaller projects are in hand. Together they should extend the irrigated area in the Central Asian republics by two to three million acres.

Other, equally ambitious schemes have been mooted but their future development will depend very largely upon the emphasis that the Soviet government chooses to place on the expansion of irrigated agriculture. The failure of Krushchev's 'Virgin Lands' programme, in which irrigation figured prominently, led him to put forward a new plan in December 1963 to devote capital to the expansion of the Russian chemical industry in order to produce fertilisers which would increase yields on the best lands, rather than to extend the acreage of virgin lands by irrigation. In any case, by February 1964 it had become clear that large areas of land which had been provided with irrigation canals were not in fact being irrigated. Yet by August 1964 Krushchev was urging the adoption of a large new programme of capital investmeut in irrigation facilities for the corn-growing areas of southern European Russia, and this was one of the proposals which helped to increase the opposition that finally brought about his downfall two months later.[16] At the present time, the Russian government seems likely to treat with some caution any large-scale schemes for the extension of irrigated agriculture in the Middle Asian republics and elsewhere.

While in the drier areas of Middle Asia canals are used almost exclusively for irrigation, in other areas such as the region of the Volga-Don Canal navigation and power are more important, and irrigation plays only a secondary role. The Volga itself is being transformed into a series of reservoirs along its entire course, with dams to provide hydroelectricity, and main and lateral canals to provide irrigation for millions of acres in the fertile Caspian-trans-Volga regions. Progress has not been as rapid as was hoped, and unforeseen difficulties have been encountered. For example, the construction of large dams along the Volga has produced lakes of relatively still water, and during summer these bodies of water become fairly hot, so that evaporation increases considerably. In addition, the waves are much higher on these stationary bodies than formerly and have in some cases flooded valuable land on the low-lying left bank of the river. As a consequence of storing vast quantities of water upstream, the level of water at the Volga delta and in the Caspian Sea has declined, with adverse effects on fishing villages. However, irrigated agriculture is of growing importance in this area, especially along the Volga floodplain between Volgograd and Astrakhan, where melons, fruit, rice, vegetables and a little cotton are grown.

The other major irrigated areas in the Soviet Union are in Caucasia and the Ukraine. In Caucasia the most important region is the great valley which extends over 300 miles west from Baku. It is drained by rivers flowing from the Caucasus Mountains into the Black and Caspian seas, notably the Kura and the Rioni rivers, which promote irrigated agriculture along the foot of the ranges (Fig. 33). In the Kura lowland, cotton and alfalfa are the most important crops, and fruit and vegetables are also grown in large quantities. This is the second most important cotton-growing area in the Soviet Union after the Middle Asian republics. The irrigated area was extended to approximately 500,000 acres when the Mingechaur Reservoir on the Kura was opened in 1953. In the Colchis lowland, at the mouth of the Rioni River, corn, tobacco, fruit and vegetables are all grown under irrigation. In the Armenian Republic in the extreme south, approximately 650,000 acres were under irrigation in 1963, of which slightly more than sixty per cent were in the Aratskaya valley, the principal lowland area.[17] Water from Lake Sevan and from many small mountain

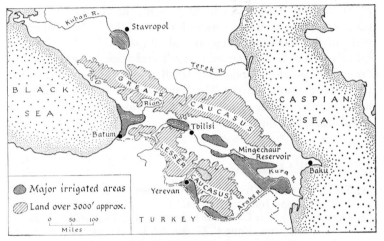

FIG. 33. Major irrigated areas in Caucasia.

streams promotes the growth of cotton around Yerevan, the capital of Armenia, where alfalfa, vegetables and fruit are also grown.

Some extension of irrigated agriculture is proposed in this area, and in October 1965, preliminary surveys were completed for a joint Soviet-Iranian project to harness the waters of the border river Araks (Araxes). The project includes the construction of two dams and a hydroelectric station. At present, the river floods its lower reaches in early spring when the water is not needed and becomes shallow in the summer when water is required. If it can be controlled and its waters stored in reservoirs, it will be possible to make large sections of the dry Murganskaya and Milskaya steppes irrigable. Along the northern edge of the Caucasus, in the North Caucasian Foreland, some irrigated agriculture is carried on along the Kuban River, especially along its eastern section, where sugar beet is the main crop.

Irrigation is important in the southern Ukraine, an area where rainfall is marginal and irregular. There, plans to divert water from the Dnieper and Don rivers should ensure irrigation for several million acres in the Don and Dnieper basins and northern and eastern Crimea. Some construction work has begun, including the Crimea Canal, of which the first eighty miles were completed by 1964. However, difficulties have arisen similar to those encountered along the Volga, and it may be many years before the plans are fully implemented. At present, the Kakhovka Dam on the lower Dnieper supplies water for several thousand acres on the plain of the Black Sea Steppes and across the Perekop Isthmus into the Crimea. Farther east, the Tsimlyansk Reservoir on the lower Don provides a relatively small amount of water for irrigation. To the west, in the Moldavian Republic, the middle and lower sections of the Dniester River provide irrigation along the broad floodplain for the cultivation of fruit, vegetables and vines.

Bibliographical References

1. Zagni, A. F. E., 'Irrigation Development in south-eastern Italy', *World Crops*, June 1967, p. 22.
2. Graves, N. J., 'Une Californie Française. The Languedoc and Lower Rhône Irrigation Project', *Geography*, L, 1965, pp. 71-72; Dupuis, A., 'Europe's Biggest Irrigation Project', *Span* (Shell International Chemical Company Limited), VII, No. 2, 1964, pp. 92-93.
3. Thompson, I., 'The Revival of Corsica', *Geographical Magazine*, April 1966, pp. 898-908.
3a. Naylon, J., 'Irrigation and Internal Colonization in Spain', *Geographical Journal*, 133, 1967, p. 179.
4. Houston, J. M., *The Western Mediterranean World* (Longmans, London), 1964, pp. 216-17.
5. International Bank for Reconstruction and Development, *The Economic Development of Spain* (Johns Hopkins Press, Baltimore), 1963, p. 266 *et seq.* and p. 320.
6. *Farmer's World* (U.S. Department of Agriculture Yearbook, 1964), p. 79.
7. Ministry of Agriculture, *Irrigation*, Fisheries and Food Bulletin No. 138 (Her Majesty's Stationery Office, London), 1962, foreword.
8. Penman, H. L., 'Irrigation in Britain', *Journal of Royal Society of Arts*, March 1963, pp. 272 and 289.
9. Watson, J. A. S. and More, J. A., *Agriculture* (Oliver & Boyd, Edinburgh), 11th ed., 1962, p. 66.
9a. Weller, J., *Modern Agricultural and Rural Planning* (Architectural Press, London), 1967, p. 255.
10. MacBean, J., *The Soil* (Faber & Faber, London), 1961, pp. 73-75.

11. Laverton, S., *Irrigation: Its Profitable Use for Agricultural and Horticultural Crops* (Oxford University Press), 1964, pp. 117-21.
12. *Farmer's World, op. cit.*, p. 80.
13. *Soil and Water Use in the Soviet Union* (U.S. Department of Agriculture Report), June 1959, p. 51.
14. *Ibid.*, p. 38.
15. 'Soviet Geography: Review and Translation', *American Geographical Society*, December 1962, p. 7.
16. Schwartz, H., *The Soviet Economy since Stalin* (Gollancz, London), 1965, pp. 161-75.
17. Greenwood, N. H., 'Developments in the Irrigation Resources of the Sevan-Razdan Cascade of Soviet Armenia', *Annals of Association of American Geographers*, LV, 1965, pp. 291-307.

Additional Sources

Natural Resources (Technical) Committee, *Irrigation in Great Britain* (Her Majesty's Stationery Office, London), 1962.

Lydolph, P. E., *Geography of the U.S.S.R.* (Wiley, London), 1964.

Monkhouse, F. J., *The Countries of North-Western Europe* (Longmans, London), 1965.

Monkhouse, F. J., *The Regional Geography of Western Europe* (Longmans, London), 1961.

Shackleton, M. R., *Europe* (Longmans, London), 7th ed., 1964.

Walker, D. S., *Italy* (Methuen, London), 1962.

Walker, D. S., *The Mediterranean Lands* (Methuen, London), 1962.

CHAPTER II

AFRICA

In 1963 Africa had approximately fourteen million irrigated acres representing only 3·8 per cent of the world's total irrigated acreage Although there are large tracts of land which are arid and semi-arid and which would consequently benefit from irrigation, Africa is unfortunate in having few alluvial valleys whose river regimes or surface contours are as favourable as those in the Nile Valley. Nor, apart from the Nile Valley, is there any long-standing, traditional irrigated agriculture. Therefore, the Nile Valley is by far the most important single irrigated area in Africa, with more than eight million irrigated acres, three-quarters of them in Egypt

TABLE 10

Country	Irrigated Land ('ooos of Acres)	Year
Algeria	677	1964
Egypt	6,869	1965
Ethiopia	74	—
Ghana	30	1964
Kenya	35	1961
Libya	361	1965
Madagascar	1,700	1966
Mali	150	—
Mauritania	7	1964
Mauritius	30	1966
Morocco	655	1965
Niger	10	1963
Rhodesia	84	1965
Senegal	188	1964
Somalia	50	—
South Africa	1,500	1962
South-west Africa	25	—
Sudan	2,500	—
Swaziland	60	1964
Tanzania	99	1966
Tunisia	195	1964

Africa: Major Irrigated Areas

(Based partly on figures in *F.A.O. Production Yearbook*, Vol. 21, 1967, and in Richard M. Highsmith, Jr., 'Irrigated Lands of the World', *Geographical Review*, LV, 1965, pp. 385-86.)

and the rest in the Sudan. Elsewhere irrigation is relatively limited and sporadic, with the main areas being along the Mediterranean coast of North-west Africa, along parts of the Niger and Senegal rivers in West Africa, in Rhodesia, in the Union of South Africa and in Madagascar (Table 10).

It has been estimated that the extent of irrigation in Africa could be tripled, partly by extending the present irrigated areas and partly by bringing new areas under irrigation. The latter are mainly the perennial and seasonal swamps, which are a striking feature of Africa, covering about 125,000 square miles and including the Niger delta, Lake Chad, the freshwater swamps of Nigeria, the Congo Basin and the Kafue Flats in Zambia. But if such immense areas are ever to be reclaimed, vast pumping and drainage schemes will be required, at great cost.

Other areas of potential development are in the vast desert and semi-desert regions of Africa, where water is frequently available from underground sources, which most usefully occur in troughs between fixed sand dunes, in alluvial fans at the foot of mountains and in the beds of seasonal streams. Although sand-dune water is frequently used by pastoral tribes, alluvial fan water remains, in the words of G. H. T. Kimble, 'probably the one underexploited source of ground water in arid Africa. It is not every society that has acquired the knack of tapping this underground supply at its most rewarding points or of using what it taps with efficiency.'[1] In these parts of Africa the so-called dry streams or wadis are probably the most widespread source of water. However, many wadis are unreliable and may either dry up entirely or are subject to occasional flooding, though they frequently retain water in the subsoil, which can be reached by digging shallow wells. In the true desert the only major sources of water are either rivers, which rise in wetter areas and may, like the Nile, sustain their courses across the desert; or underground water, which moves beneath the desert from distant sources. Where the water-bearing rocks are sufficiently close to the surface, the water can be obtained by wells and boreholes, frequently in sufficient quantities to support oases. While it is almost certain that the underground water resources of the African deserts are considerable, their development faces certain problems. Firstly, it is often very difficult to locate the water, which being underground may leave no clue on the surface of a featureless desert. Besides, once it has been located, the ground water may be too hot for use with growing plants; some of the water from the deeper Nile Valley wells exceeds 100°F. in temperature.[2] Finally, if ground water is to be utilised on a large scale, a great deal of capital will be required. In spite of these difficulties, the desert and semi-desert areas of Africa are not without their promise for the future, and Egypt, for example, has begun to explore the possibility of tapping the vast water table of the Sahara. As the demand for water grows in these areas, similar projects are likely to become more common elsewhere.

Perhaps just as important as finding new supplies of irrigation water is managing to conserve and use efficiently the water presently available. In too many areas, both in Africa and elsewhere, water is used wastefully, and salinity and waterlogging have resulted. Nor are large irrigation schemes by themselves any guarantee of increased agricultural productivity. In Morocco, instead of bringing about much needed agricultural expansion, such schemes have further favoured speculation and large land-holdings, and in the newly irrigated lands of Imfout, farmers have simply cultivated less land better, leaving the rest fallow, thus keeping the same standard of living at considerable expense to the state.[3] A more successful way of extending and improving irrigated agriculture in many areas might be by installing simple, small-scale, water-conserving dams rather than constructing large, expensive projects. One of the most common simple devices is the 'subsand dam', consisting of a cement barrier placed across the sand bed of a river which is underlain at no great depth by an impervious formation. The barrier retains some of the water, which is then drawn off through pipes and similar devices. In addition, as the water percolates through and lies below the surface of the sandy bed, the sand will rise in time to the top of the barrier, so that the loss due to evaporation from the surface will be less than in the case of the conventional dam and reservoir. Since 1954, hundreds of these dams, which are cheap and simple to build, have been constructed in the former British territories of East and Central Africa.[4]

EGYPT AND THE SUDAN

In Egypt, which has a total irrigated area of about 6·9 million acres, virtually the entire agricultural economy is dependent on irrigation based on the Nile waters. Modern Egypt is largely the creation of irrigation engineers, who maintain a highly complicated and efficient system of water distribution and who plan and execute its further development on behalf of the government. Each year, plans for seasonal water budgets and programmes for water control at the various dams and barrages are drawn up, taking into account the acreages under the principal crops, the particular needs of these crops and the amount of water available at any given time. These plans are co-ordinated by two inspectors-general, one in Upper Egypt and one in Lower Egypt.[5]

However, if the methods of storing and distributing water on a large scale are complex and efficient, irrigated farming as practised by Egyptian peasants remains primitive compared with the highly mechanised and scientific agriculture of the developed countries. Crop rotations are practised and large quantities of fertiliser are used, but equipment is primitive or lacking, holdings are usually small, and crop yields are often low.

There are two main forms of irrigation along the Nile Valley, basin irrigation and perennial irrigation. Basin irrigation is now confined to little more than 700,000 acres, largely restricted to Upper Egypt. It has few mechanical requirements, but being dependent on flooding, it is largely devoted to single cropping. Exceptionally, oil pumps have been installed in a few basins to raise water for use in the dry season. Perennial irrigation, on the other hand, involves a complex, large-scale system of storage reservoirs, barrages, regulators and canals (Fig. 34), and is preferred to basin irrigation for a number of reasons. It enables a wider range of crops to be produced, including those which require a constant supply of water throughout their growing season, and it increases crop yields considerably. The completion of the Aswan High Dam should enable those areas in Upper Egypt at present given over to basin irrigation to be converted to perennial irrigation. Among the consequences of the introduction of perennial irrigation into Egypt by British engineers during the past century have been the reintroduction and rise of cotton, rice and sugar cane, the introduction of maize, and the decline of wheat, flax, indigo and saffron. In general, summer cash crops have become dominant at the expense of food crops.

The development of perennial irrigation has not been without its problems, however. Overcropping and consequent soil exhaustion, salinity and waterlogging, and declining fertility result-

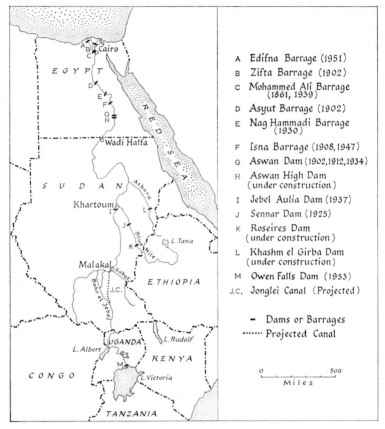

A   Edifna Barrage (1951)

B   Zifta Barrage (1902)

C   Mohammed Ali Barrage (1861, 1939)

D   Asyut Barrage (1902)

E   Nag Hammadi Barrage (1930)

F   Isna Barrage (1908, 1947)

G   Aswan Dam (1902, 1912, 1934)

H   Aswan High Dam (under construction)

I   Jebel Aulia Dam (1937)

J   Sennar Dam (1925)

K   Roseires Dam (under construction)

L   Khashm el Girba Dam (under construction)

M   Owen Falls Dam (1953)

J.C.   Jonglei Canal (Projected)

‑   Dams or Barrages

······   Projected Canal

FIG. 34.   Major control structures in the Nile Basin.

ing from lack of silt have all followed in its wake. Salinity and waterlogging are perhaps the most pressing and immediate problems and can only be reduced by an efficient drainage system. This is not necessary in basin irrigation, as the water is allowed to drain back into the river of its own accord, but it is essential with perennial irrigation because the silt is clayey and not sufficiently permeable to allow the water to seep quickly down to its lowest layers. The problem is most acute in the low-lying delta, where the canal system is relatively old and where perennial irrigation was introduced before the importance of a proper drainage system was fully realised. The greater part of the delta is still drained by a series of wide ditches; this wastes both time and water and is expensive to maintain. Experiments are being made with small-bore tile drains of porous cement, which are laid below root level and are inclined very gradually in the direction of the main drains. But since their use involves a considerable capital outlay, they are not as yet very widespread.

In areas where canal irrigation is not provided or where water cannot be guaranteed throughout the year, various methods of lifting and pumping water from rivers and wells are used. These include primitive lifting devices as well as modern pumps driven by steam, diesel or electricity, which are usually owned by the wealthier landowners or the government. Such lifting devices are found either in small areas bordering the river, which are often too high to be reached by canals except at the height of the floods, or in the delta on land normally watered by canals from gravity flow. In the latter case, pump irrigation is usually limited to the early part of the flood, when the demand is so great that not all the canals can be supplied with enough water to reach all parts of any particular section of the system. It is anticipated that when all the new barrage and drainage projects have been fully developed, lift and pump irrigation will practically disappear.

The urgent need to expand Egypt's irrigated agriculture in order to feed her rapidly growing population has led the government to inaugurate a long-term development programme for irrigation. How best to achieve this expansion has been a matter of considerable debate, involving problems of both a technical and a political nature. As Egypt contributes none of the Nile floodwater, international co-operation, particularly with the Sudan, is essential. Under normal conditions, the flow of the Nile is insufficient to irrigate even the present acreage of cultivated lands, while during the flood period there is much more water than can be used. At present, the Egyptian barrages provide only annual storage, and if the area under irrigation is to be extended and basin irrigation replaced by perennial irrigation, then long-term storage facilities will have to be provided. An international, long-term plan for the storage and control of the water of the Nile Basin has been in existence for some time, and measures in accordance with this plan include the Owen Falls Dam in Uganda, completed in 1953 to control the outflow of Lake Victoria and generate hydro-electricity, and the Jebel Aulia and Sennar dams in the Sudan. The Jebel Aulia Dam, completed in 1937, is operated largely for the benefit of Egypt; the Sennar Dam, finished in 1925, provides a reservoir and barrage to raise the level of the Blue Nile sufficiently to allow the water to flow into the Main Gravity Canal of the Gezira scheme, for the benefit of the Sudan. In November 1959 a new agreement was signed by Egypt and the Sudan allocating to the Sudan a greater share of the water stored behind the Sennar

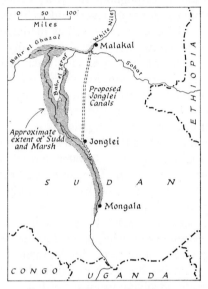

FIG. 35.   The Jonglei scheme.

Dam. To complete the harnessing of the Nile waters, the co-operation of the Congo, Tanzania and Ethiopia as well as that of Uganda, the Sudan and Egypt would be essential, since complete water control would involve the regulation of lakes Albert and Victoria in East Africa, Lake Tana in Ethiopia and the Bahr el Jebel swamps in the Sudan.

The most feasible and rewarding of these measures would probably be the one regulating the swamps of the southern Sudan, where large quantities of water are now lost to evaporation in the Sudd between Mongala and Malakal. Much of this water could be conserved and the flow of the White Nile increased by implementing the project known as the Jonglei scheme (Fig. 35). This consists of two major, interdependent phases: (a) the use of Lake Victoria as a reservoir for long-term storage, with sufficient water being held in it by means of the Owen Falls Dam and other regulating devices to make up for any deficiencies in the annual flow; and (b) the improvement of the existing Nile channel between Mongala and Jonglei by dredging and excavating and by the construction of a duplicate Jonglei canal. The storage capacity of Lake Victoria could be greatly increased by raising its maximum level about four feet, which would also increase the volume delivered to Bahr el Jebel. By building the Jonglei canal, from Jonglei to a point downstream between the mouths of the right-bank tributaries of the Bahr el Zeraf and the Sobat, about half the water which normally goes into the Sudd would be directed into the White Nile, and evaporation would be enormously reduced. The scheme would be a complicated and expensive one, calling for co-operation between the countries concerned. Moreover, although it is estimated that it would increase the water available by an amount equal to the expected loss due to evaporation from the Aswan High Dam, the scheme is not without its social and economic difficulties. For example, it would likely result in a loss of pasture and fisheries that would directly affect 600,000 Nilotic pastoralists and indirectly another 400,000.[6] In any case, general political considerations have led Egypt to set aside indefinitely this more comprehensive scheme in favour of the national project at Aswan. It may be, however, that the enormous cost of the Aswan project and the uncertainty concerning its ability to provide sufficient storage capacity to keep pace with Egypt's mushrooming population may at some time in the future cause the Egyptian government to reconsider the wider Jonglei scheme.

In the meantime, the Aswan High Dam (*Sadd-el-Aali*) (Fig. 36) has become the cornerstone of the Egyptian government's plans for extending the country's cultivated area. Situated four miles upstream from the present Aswan Dam, it will be 364 feet high and 11,480 feet long. When full, its reservoir, to be called Lake Nasser, will be 282 miles long. It will flood much of Nubia, including important archaeological sites, as well as the Wadi Halfa region of the Sudan, and will have a total capacity of 127 million acre-feet and a usable capacity of 62 million acre-feet annually. In 1960 work began on the dam, which will take at least ten years to complete, though the first and perhaps most difficult stage was finished in May 1964 when the Nile was diverted from its original

course by the sealing of the barrier across the river. It is difficult
to estimate the total cost of the project but it will probably exceed
£400 million. It is intended to store sufficient water to irrigate as
much as two million additional acres and to convert the present
700,000 acres under basin irrigation to perennial irrigation. In
addition, the dam will both provide the total cultivated area with
supplemental water during periods of low-water supply and store
sufficient reserves of water to meet deficits in years of low flood.

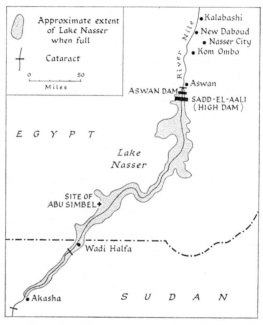

FIG. 36.   The Aswan High Dam project.

The controlled flow of the Nile will make it possible to distribute
the proper amounts of water to the various crops at the right time,
and the enormous storage capacity of the reservoir will eliminate
the possibility of periodic overflooding. By curtailing the free
flow of water at the height of the flood season, the dam should also
lower the ground-water table and reduce the dangers of waterlogging. Last but by no means least, power stations on the site
will provide great quantities of hydroelectricity primarily to power
Egypt's industrial development. On the other hand, there is no
doubt that a dam of this sort, situated in the middle of the Sahara

Desert, will lose a great deal of water by evaporation, estimated at almost twice that of the capacity of the present Aswan Dam reservoir.[7]

The project has also caused an enormous social upheaval. Almost the entire Nubian population, some 60,000 people, has been dispossessed of its ancient home, which will disappear under the waters of Lake Nasser. In order to rehouse the Nubians, evacuated from more than forty villages, about seventy-five government townships have been built on the land soon to be irrigated, including Kalabashi, New Daboud and Nasser City, which will be the new Nubian capital to replace the old one, Ineiba. These developments represent the construction of a new Nubia on an area of about 170,000 acres in the vicinity of the sugar-refining town of Kom Ombo.

Another way in which the Egyptian government hopes to increase the cultivated area is by the reclamation of desert lands away from the immediate vicinity of the Nile. In the pre-Christian era the Mediterranean coast of Egypt was celebrated for its grains and wines. But since then, the southern limit of Mediterranean rain has moved north, and the water table is now much lower than it was two thousand years ago. Nevertheless, reclamation possibilities exist in the desert areas, and the government has established a number of experimental stations in the Western Desert and the Sinai Peninsula. In the former region, 54,000 acres were set aside for irrigation in 1954, east of the old Cairo-Alexandria road, where fruit and vegetables are grown with the aid of Nile water brought by means of a specially built canal. This project labours under a number of difficulties, however, including the high cost of production and the fact that not enough water will be available until the Aswan High Dam is completed. Another scheme is designed to reclaim lands on the sites of present and former oases in the Western Desert by drilling for underground water, but its success will depend partly on the availability of such water and partly on the amount of capital invested in pumping equipment. The great cost of the Qattara Depression scheme, estimated at more than £100 million, is also likely to bring about its eventual postponement. This scheme entails boring and operating wells on the floor of the Qattara Depression in order to tap the Saharan water table. The depression, which is only 120 miles west of the delta, occupies an area of about 7,000 square miles and has a bed averaging 150 feet below sea level. It is estimated that by drawing in Mediterranean water by means of a canal leading to the northern tip of the depression, sufficient electricity could be generated to make deep pumping a practicable, if expensive, proposition.[8] In the Sinai Peninsula a number of reservoirs have been built to capture as much as possible of the meagre supply of rainfall. Together with auxiliary supplies from wells, sufficient water is available to enable fruit to be grown around El Arish. In the north-western part of the peninsula, 50,000 acres may be made irrigable by the transfer of fresh water from the Ismailia Canal under the Suez Canal.

In these various ways, Egypt could probably double her present cultivated area. But even if the most ambitious projects are realised, it is likely to be a long, slow and costly business. In the near future, the conversion of areas presently under basin irrigation to perennial irrigation will likely lead to greater productivity.

In 1959 the Sudan had approximately 2·5 million acres under irrigation, representing only five per cent of an estimated fifty million potentially irrigable acres. Since then, a number of extensions have taken place and others are planned. The most important irrigated area is the celebrated Gezira scheme (Fig. 37), based on the triangular plain between the White and Blue Niles. The Gezira is supplied with water by a main canal which leads from the reservoir above the Sennar Dam, completed in 1925. When the scheme first came into operation, the irrigable area was 300,000 acres; with the opening of the north-west extension in 1952, the total became nearly one million acres. The Gezira is especially well suited to irrigation because it consists of heavy clay soil, which retains the water at the surface and supports the growth of long-staple cotton, the major crop of the area. Developed under the British administration, the Gezira has become the model for similar agricultural developments in other countries.

Since Sudanese independence in 1959, a number of extensions to the Gezira have been planned to increase the Sudan's agricultural productivity and to relieve overpopulation in the northern part of the country. An important extension is the Manaqil project to the south of the Gezira, which is a product of the Nile Waters Agreement of 1959. By this agreement, which reallocated the waters of the Nile, the Manaqil area now receives twenty-five per cent of the water with an additional margin for evaporation.

In return, the Egyptian government received an eighteen-year 'loan' of unused Sudanese water and permission to flood the Wadi Halfa region consequent upon the backing up of water behind the Aswan High Dam. Other important extensions are the Kenana project, based upon the new Roseires Dam on the Blue Nile, 132 miles upstream from the Sennar Dam, which was made possible

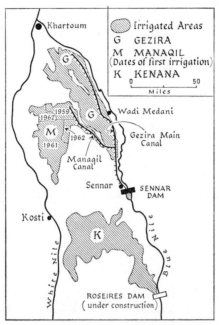

FIG. 37. Irrigated areas between the White and Blue Niles, Sudan.

by the Nile Waters Agreement and a loan of thirty-two million dollars from the World Bank; and the dam at Khashm el Girba on the Atbara, which is designed primarily to provide cultivable land for farmers dispossessed by the flooding of Wadi Halfa. In addition to these large-scale, government-sponsored schemes, there has also been considerable private investment in irrigation facilities in recent years.

A number of schemes for irrigating alluvial terraces with the aid of diesel pumps have been developed in recent years along the Nile below Khartoum, and in central Sudan along both the Blue and White Niles.[9] In Kassala Province in north-eastern Sudan, floodwaters of the Gash and Baraka rivers enable cotton to be

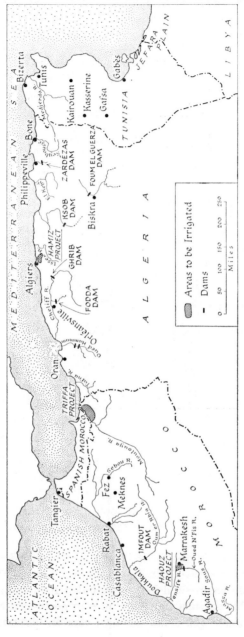

Fig. 38.   Water resources in North-west Africa.

grown on approximately 150,000 acres in the Gash and Tokar deltas.

In North-west Africa, irrigation has been most important and successful in the Mahgreb, the Mediterranean coastal region of Morocco, Algeria and Tunisia, where it has been practised for thousands of years. In Morocco, which at present has an irrigable area of about 655,000 acres, a very small proportion of the total cultivated area is under irrigation, and the government is making great efforts to increase the irrigated acreage by sponsoring a number of large-scale schemes based on the construction of dams along some of the rivers flowing down from the High Atlas into the Mediterranean, notably the Sebou, Moulouya and Oum er Rbia rivers (Fig. 38).[10]

In all these areas the irrigation water is used for the cultivation of cereals, vines and citrus fruits. However, reclamation has been difficult and expensive, as the low-lying coastal areas suffer from waterlogging and salinity, especially in the late spring and early summer when the snow melts from the mountains and floods the lower courses of the valleys. Consequently, irrigation has hitherto been restricted to the zone along the junction of the mountain and plain above the coastal marshes; with water taken from wadis, farmers cultivate olive groves and citrus orchards.

Even more difficult to bring under cultivation are the semi-arid steppes between the High and Anti Atlas, where the flow of wadis is too capricious to support a stable agriculture on a large scale, though there is some limited cultivation. It may be possible to exploit underground water supplies in these regions, such as those which underlie the Tadla Depression between the Meseta plateau and the Middle Atlas. It is estimated that the present irrigated area of approximately 50,000 acres could be enlarged five times, but such a project would be very expensive. Along the southern desert margins of the Saharan Atlas, there are a number of oases which utilise artesian waters located in Tertiary and Cretaceous aquifers. This area of the northern Sahara has considerable potential, as a number of aquifers have recently been found which could support considerable agricultural development. Perhaps the most important of these is the one in the Inter-Calary Continental Albienne Nappe, the most prolific aquifer yet discovered.

Algeria also has a relatively limited irrigated acreage, probably about 700,000 acres. Future development will be very expensive, and the Algerian government has apparently decided to invest its limited capital resources in industrial expansion. As in Morocco, the most important irrigated areas are in the coastal foothills above the poorly drained coastal plains. There, water is available from wadis and springs and is used by peasant farmers to cultivate olive groves and citrus fruit orchards, largely with the aid of primitive devices. In addition, there are a few fairly large-scale irrigation projects, based on barrages and dams constructed by the French. These include the Oued Hammam Basin south-east of Oran, the Cheliff valley around Orléansville based on the Ghrib and Fodda dams, the Hamiz project east of Algiers designed to serve an area of more than 35,000 acres, the Ksob Basin based on the Ksob Dam, the coastal area east of Philippeville supplied by the Zardézas Dam and, in the interior, the Biskra area served by the Foum el Guerza Dam.

Tunisia, with a total of approximately 195,000 irrigated acres, has only a very small proportion of her cultivated area under irrigation but is planning a considerable development of irrigated agriculture in the next few years. The only river capable of dnsplying large amounts of water for irrigation is the Medjerda, and a large-scale scheme on the lower Medjerda is now nearing completion. Furthermore, work is expected to begin shortly on an irrigation and drainage project in the Lake Ichkeul area near Bizerta. The key structure will be the Oued Kasseb Dam across the Rhazala River, and in 1970, the estimated completion date, it will provide water for about 50,000 acres. As Tunisia is unsuited to the construction of large dams, underground water is generally more important at present, and a number of pumping schemes are planned, notably in the Kairouan Plain, on the coast near Gabès, at Gafsa and at Kasserine.[11] The most important irrigated areas at present are the coastal plains behind Bizerta, where citrus fruit is the chief crop.

Irrigated agriculture is also very limited in Libya. About 360,000 acres are under irrigation in three main areas: the Jefara Plain in Tripolitania, the Barce Plain in Cyrenaica and a number of scattered oases in the desert to the south (Fig. 39). The most important of these is the Jefara Plain between Misurata and the Tunisian border in the north-western part of the country. There, in irregular line of coastal oases produces dates, olives and oranges. In the plain backing the coast, farmers have in recent years switched from dry to irrigated farming with the aid of pumps which tap excellent supplies of underground water. The emphasis is on cash crops, mainly groundnuts, which have become the

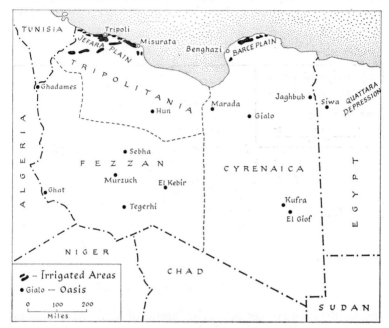

FIG. 39. Main irrigated areas in Libya.

leading agricultural export of the country, potatoes and citrus fruit. As these crops consume a great deal of water, excessive pumping has taken place, causing a serious drop in underground water levels.[12]

WEST AFRICA

The major irrigated areas in West Africa are based on the Niger and Senegal rivers in the semi-desert, or Sahel, zone between the savanna to the south and the Sahara proper to the north. There, large-scale irrigation projects installed by French engineers have had some success in redeeming land for sedentary agriculture.

The Niger River project (Fig. 40) in the north-central part of the
Mali Republic is an ambitious scheme begun by the French in
1932. The key structure consists of the barrage at Sansanding.

Originally, the French planned to develop the enormous inland
delta of the Niger primarily for irrigated cotton and secondarily
for rice, but despite considerable expenditure, these objectives
have never been attained. Even by 1960 fewer than 150,000 acres
were actually irrigated and fewer than 50,000 people were settled
on the project area, though they were enjoying an income far

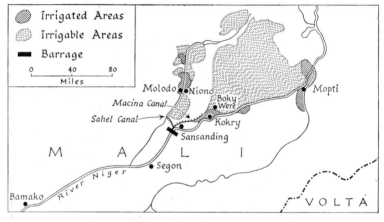

FIG. 40.   The Niger River project, Mali.

greater than the average per capita income of Mali. According to
Sir John Russell, this 'disparity between expectation and achievement' was the result of a lack of basic knowledge arising from
inadequate preparatory surveys; excessive overhead charges
owing to the proliferation of European staff; and the reluctance of
African natives to move to new sites as well as their lack of industry
and knowledge of irrigation farming.[13] The French administration
of the Niger River project had little understanding of the problems
of the Mossi tribe, whose indigenous culture they seemed to regard as 'little more than a compendium of savage rites upon
which European usages need only be imposed in order to prevail.
Such an approach reveals a failure to comprehend both the complexity and tenacity of the Mossi cultural heritage.'[14] On the other
hand, a recent sociological study of the resettlement of some 5,000
members of the Mossi tribe concludes that the Mossi adapted

themselves fairly easily to their new environment and in time
mastered the new technology of irrigation farming. But acute
social problems arose as a result of their removal from a cultural
setting which had been relatively undisturbed by the influence of
European civilisation to one in which the economic situation was
formed and directed by Europeans.

Perhaps a more fundamental reason for the disappointing
results of the Niger project is that over much of the area the soil

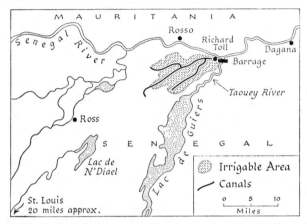

FIG. 41. The Richard Toll project, Senegal. The barrage
stores water in Lac de Guiers, and a pumping station lifts the
water into canals, from which it is led into the irrigated area.

is poor. The project has also suffered from aerial attacks by locusts
and swarms of birds. Consequently, only a small proportion of
the original project area has come into full operation, with rice
being a more important crop than cotton.

Another costly regional development scheme sponsored
originally by the French government is the Richard Toll project
(Fig. 41) on a large inland delta at Richard Toll in north-west
Senegal. Work began in 1946 but by 1957, after the expenditure
of a great deal of money, only 14,000 acres had been brought under
cultivation, mainly for rice. Since independence, the project has
been taken over by Senegal.

Both the Niger and Senegal rivers could support considerable
extensions of irrigated agriculture if the necessary capital were
available for the construction of dams and canal networks. A study

of the potential of the Senegal River has been in progress since July 1962, sponsored jointly by Senegal, Mali, Mauritania and Guinea, and in October 1963 a draft agreement to undertake the economic development of the Niger River throughout its length was signed by Mali, Niger, Upper Volta, Guinea, the Ivory Coast, Dahomey, Cameroun, Chad and Nigeria. The agreement provides for the development of the river's resources, including fishing, irrigation, power and navigation. If these schemes are ever to be converted into reality, they will require expenditures far beyond the means of the West African countries, and thus considerable foreign financial assistance will be essential.

The only other irrigated areas of any note in former French West Africa are quite small, based on more than 600 wells and some 200 irrigation dams built by the French between 1949 and 1954 in Mauritania, Sudan, Upper Volta and the Niger. One of the by-products of this venture was the outbreak of sporadic fighting between the sedentary settlers for whom the water was intended and the nomads who coveted it. The governments of the newly independent territories hope that the progressive settling down of the nomadic tribes will eventually result in peace with the sedentary farmers.

In former British West Africa the only major potential area of irrigated agriculture is the Accra Plain in Ghana, a gently undulating area of open scrub between the Akwapim Hills and the sea, with an unusually dry climate for that part of the world. A pilot scheme has been established on a small tract near Kpong to test the suitability of the area for intensive irrigated farming, and it is hoped that the Volta River scheme will render irrigable hundreds of thousands of acres of savanna that are unused at present. There are few irrigated areas in Nigeria, except along streams in the Sudan zone around Kano, where together with easily accessible ground-water supplies, they provide water for the cultivation of foodgrains and groundnuts. Such areas in north and central Nigeria could be considerably expanded and could make possible both the cultivation of specialised crops such as rice, sugar cane and vegetables and the extension of dry-season cropping.

Another area of potential development is the Lake Chad region, and a scheme has been mooted to dyke the dry-season shoreline of the lake and utilise the impounded water for irrigating 10,000 acres of land south of the lake.

EAST AFRICA

Irrigation is of limited importance in Kenya, Uganda, Tanzania and Ethiopia, though in each country there are considerable areas that are potentially irrigable. In Kenya, irrigation is used on some of the European farms, while a number of intensive irrigation schemes are in operation in some of the areas farmed by Africans, notably on the Masai Reserve in the south, in the Mwea-Tebere area of Mount Kenya, where some 5,000 acres are under paddy, and along the lower Tana River. The last two schemes together comprise the Tana River irrigation project. The Mwea-Tebere scheme, which is on a tributary of the upper Tana, on the southern side of Mount Kenya near Embu, sixty miles north-east of Nairobi, has an irrigable potential of about 20,000 acres. To date, about 5,400 acres have been developed for rice cultivation. An important aspect of the scheme is that it absorbs large numbers of landless and unemployed people. Between 10,000 and 12,000 people are living within the cultivated area and benefiting directly or indirectly from the scheme.

The lower Tana area is at present being surveyed by a team from the United Nations Food and Agriculture Organisation. It is hoped to launch a large scheme of 10,000 irrigated acres to grow cotton and sugar, as a prelude to the development of the main lower Tana area. Another potentially irrigable area is at Taveta, where springs flow from the eastern and southern slopes of Mount Kilimanjaro. As in other developing countries, the lack of knowledge of irrigation farming is one of the major obstacles to any great extension of the irrigated area.

In Tanzania, irrigation is at present very limited in extent, applied to not more than 100,000 acres, and is found both on large estates growing sugar cane and on small African farms on the slopes of Mount Kilimanjaro and Mount Meru. Typical of the Africans farming on the mountain slopes are the Arusha, the agricultural Masai of northern Tanzania. On the slopes of Mount Kilimanjaro and Mount Meru, which are divided by many swift-flowing streams, they cultivate fields in narrow strips along the valleys. Water is led from irrigation channels on the higher ground via subsidiary channels which run down through the fields to the streams. According to the Arusha, these narrow fields are easier to irrigate.[15] About 25,000 acres in Tanga Province and a similar amount in Western Province are irrigated by African farmers to cultivate coffee, paddy, maize and onions. Several million acres are probably potentially irrigable in the country as a whole, notably in the Rufiji Basin south and west of Dar es Salaam and in the Ruvu Basin about forty miles north-west of Dar es Salaam. However, such development would be expensive, and the most suitable areas are very sparsely populated and fairly remote. A recent development is the Pangani River project, whose key structure, the Nyumba Ya Munga Dam, is being constructed on the Pangani River about fifty miles south of Moshi. When completed, it will provide irrigation facilities for more than 50,000 acres in the Pangani valley.

In Uganda, as the rainfall is generally adequate, irrigation is relatively unimportant, being restricted largely to supplemental irrigation on estates growing sugar cane.

Although Ethiopia has at present only about 75,000 acres under irrigation, a number of large-scale schemes are under construction. The plains along the Red Sea are most suitable, with their black, alluvial soils. There, recent undertakings include those on the Haddas and Alighede rivers and adjacent streams. The first stage is the construction of the Zula Dam on the Haddas River near Massawa, which will make some 25,000 acres irrigable for the cultivation of cotton, corn and sorghum. In other parts of the country, some terrace and well irrigation is found.

Irrigation in Somalia is very limited, and little more than 50,000 acres are irrigated. In the north along the gulf of Aden, a number of coastal orchards produce dates, and farther south between Mogadishu and the Kenya border, some irrigated agriculture is found along the Uebi Scebeli and Giuba rivers, where sugar and bananas are the main crops. Cotton and vegetables are grown in places along these rivers, which offer the main possibilities for extending irrigation.

SOUTHERN AFRICA

The possibilities of developing large-scale irrigated agriculture in southern Africa are at present limited, though there are some areas of potential development which are drained by rivers from well-watered areas. These include the Orange River Basin and north and east Transvaal in the Republic of South Africa; the

Swaziland lowland; parts of Zululand; the Sabi-Lundi and Zam-
besi valleys of Rhodesia; the lower valleys of rivers crossing the
Mozambique coastal plain, including the Incomati, Limpopo,
Pungwe and Zambesi rivers; and the floodplains of the Kafue and
Shire valleys in Malawi.[16]

At present, the major irrigated areas in Rhodesia are small,
comprising some 84,000 acres, including the Mazoe citrus estates

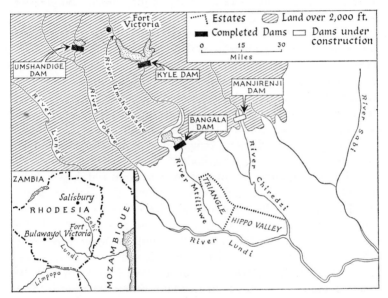

FIG. 42.   The Sabi and Lundi valleys, Rhodesia.

on the Mazoe River north of Salisbury, and sugar estates and
farms in the Sabi and Lundi valleys, south-east of Fort Victoria.
Only recently have large-scale developments taken place, notably
in the low veld, where the Sabi-Limpopo Irrigation Project is
being undertaken by the government-sponsored Sabi-Limpopo
Authority. This is one of the most spectacular of the present
irrigation projects in Africa. Its first dam, the Kyle Dam, was
constructed in 1961 at the junction of the Mtilikwe and Umshagashe
rivers, and in the same year the Bangala Dam was completed
farther down the Mtilikwe River (Fig. 42). Together they supply
water which is used by overhead sprinkler and furrow irrigation in
the Triangle and Hippo Valley estates. A new estate north of

Hippo Valley will be supplied with water from the Manjirenji Dam, presently under construction on the Chiredzi River. It is hoped that the project will stimulate Rhodesia's economic development, promote the establishment of new townships and industry, and greatly increase the country's agricultural productivity by diversifying an economy hitherto largely dependent upon the export of tobacco.[17] Elsewhere in Rhodesia the government and private enterprise have sponsored the sinking of innumerable boreholes to tap supplies of underground water.

In Malawi, work has begun on the Shire Valley project, where an estimated 400,000 acres could be made irrigable as well as a smaller acreage in neighbouring Mozambique. At present, there is a little irrigation on tea estates and on peasant farms, where it is used in a primitive and almost accidental manner for growing rice. The development of irrigated agriculture is hindered by the small size of African agricultural holdings and by the migratory habits of many people, and where irrigation is practised, it tends to be by primitive and wasteful methods.[18]

In the Portuguese colonies of Mozambique and Angola, some irrigation projects are under construction. The most important in Mozambique is the Limpopo valley irrigation project, which has been in the planning stage for a quarter of a century.[19] The key structure is a barrage built across the Limpopo River fifteen miles above Giuja, and it is intended to provide water for approximately 150,000 acres. Fourteen new villages have been built to house about 1,300 farmers, of whom 1,000 are Europeans resettled from the poorer parts of Portugal and the Azores. Each settler is given between ten and twenty-five acres of irrigated land as well as sixty acres of dry-farming land, which is devoted to ordinary cropping and pasture. The chief irrigated crops are rice, wheat, cotton, maize, vegetables and lucerne, which are marketed through a co-operative. A similar project is under construction in Niassa Province near Vila Cabral.

In Angola the most important irrigation scheme is located in the very dry south along the middle Cunene valley, where a dam at Matala provides water for the growing of tobacco, wheat and vegetables. Another important irrigation scheme is planned for the lower Cuanza valley about twenty miles south-east of Luanda. The key structure is the Cambambe Dam, which is under construction across the Cuanza River. It is hoped eventually to irri-

gate an area of more than 200,000 acres, much of which will be
devoted to the production of sugar.

Only a small proportion of South Africa's cultivated land is
irrigated, about one and a half million acres, most of which is in
the maize triangle of southern Transvaal, northern Orange Free
State, coastal Natal, the mixed-cropping areas of central Transvaal, and in south-west, south and east Cape Province (Fig. 43).

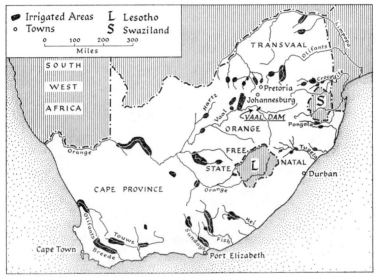

Fig. 43.   The major irrigated areas of South Africa.

In the Mediterranean region of the south-west Cape, irrigated
vineyards are important along the Little Karoo, and citrus fruits
are grown under irrigation in the Olifants and Breede valleys.
Citrus orchards are also important in the Fish and Sundays valleys
of the south-east Cape, and there they are irrigated regularly during
dry periods at intervals of three to six weeks, depending on soil
type and time of year. The most common forms of irrigation are
by sprinklers and shallow basins, which are dug round the base of
each tree and filled with water from furrows between each two
rows of trees. In the Transvaal, cotton is an important irrigated
crop, and citrus fruits and lucerne are grown there under irrigation,
the latter being made into hay and sold as animal feed to the dairy
farmers of the Rand.

The country has several major water undertakings, of which the largest is the Vaal River development scheme, whose key structure is the Vaal Dam. Besides providing water for the dense concentration of population, mining and industry in the Witwatersrand complex, it supplies many irrigation areas, including the largest irrigation settlement in the republic at Vaal-Hartz, where there are 87,000 irrigable acres. Although the Vaal Dam was enlarged to double its size in 1956, its resources are becoming

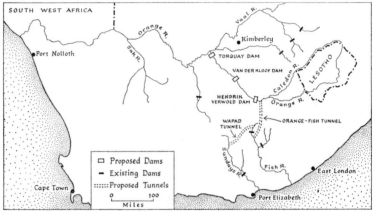

FIG. 44.   The Orange River project.

severely taxed, and the Vaal River is already fully harnessed. The Orange River is the country's only major water resource which has so far been little used, and it is now the site of the multi-purpose Orange River project (Fig. 44). This will cost an estimated £225 million, and its first stage is now under way, with the main works consisting of two large dams and a tunnel fifty-one and a half miles long. The total of 116,000 acres to be served at the end of the first phase will make the scheme the largest in South Africa so far. After 1970, five succeeding phases of the project will be undertaken according to the needs of the country, and by the nineteen-nineties, when the project is scheduled for completion, 750,000 acres will be brought under irrigation, and vast quantities of hydroelectricity made available for industrial and urban development.

A project of this magnitude and expense has not been without its critics. Doubts have been expressed about the country's ability to absorb the vast amounts of agricultural produce which the project should yield. It has been argued that since the project area will be divided into small holdings, cheap production will be difficult. The only way to reduce agricultural prices would be to consolidate holdings and run farms on a 'factory' basis. Farmers and soil experts have criticised the routes that some of the canals will follow on the grounds that in many cases they have been planned with little regard for the potential of the soil. Finally, the loss of water through evaporation will be great.

Another irrigation scheme presently under development is the Makatini Flats project, designed to irrigate about 137,000 acres in northern Natal with water from the Jonzini Dam. It is proposed to allocate plots of about fifty acres each to settlers, on which it should be possible to grow such subtropical crops as sugar cane, coffee, citrus fruit and rice, and it is hoped that the agricultural development will provide the basis for future large-scale industrial and commercial development.

Professor Cole has emphasised the need to examine the whole question of the utilisation of water resources and the economic status of irrigation farming in South Africa as a whole, before embarking on expensive projects like the Orange River scheme.[20] In general, the agricultural productivity of South African irrigation settlements has been disappointing, largely because a high proportion of the irrigable land has been used for the cultivation of cereals which bring in a low annual return. If a great deal of money is to be poured into the extension of irrigated agriculture, it will be necessary to obtain the maximum return of which the land is capable, and horticultural crops and dairying based on irrigated pastures and fodder crops would likely offer the best prospects.

Elsewhere on the mainland of southern Africa, irrigation is limited either by inadequate water resources or by lack of capital. It is only locally significant on a number of small estates producing rice, sugar cane and citrus fruits, notably in Swaziland, which is relatively rich in water resources and which has several irrigable areas (Fig. 45).

Madagascar has a considerable area under irrigation, claimed to be 1,625,000 acres in 1962.[21] This figure, issued by the Malagasy Ministry of Agriculture, is a very optimistic one, and in any case, the area consists mostly of riceland, where much of the irri-

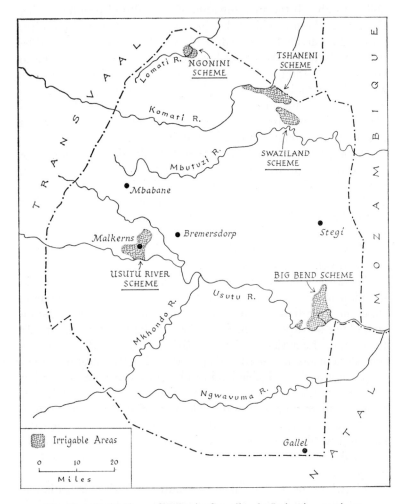

FIG. 45. Irrigation schemes in Swaziland. Irrigation projects developed in recent years include the Swaziland and Tshaneni schemes where nearly 10,000 acres produce sugar cane, and smaller areas are under citrus fruit and rice; the Big Bend scheme where there are 9,500 irrigated acres of which one-third are under sugar cane; the privately-run Usutu River scheme where an irrigated area of about 10,000 acres containing 35 European farms grow rice, citrus fruit, bananas and vegetables; and the smaller Ngonini scheme producing bananas and citrus fruit.

gation is uncontrolled. In the central highland region of the
country, stretching south from Tananarive, the capital, irrigated
rice is grown in interior basins and valleys in terraces which
occasionally resemble those of South-east Asia. In general, irrigation is inefficient and uncontrolled, and consequently yields are
low. Irrigation is also locally important in the drier western and
southern regions of the island. In the north-west, for example, in
valleys near Majunga, irrigated rice, tobacco and sugar are grown.
By far the greater part of the cultivated land in Mauritius is
devoted to sugar cane. Much of it is grown in large, efficiently
organised estates which have obtained greatly increased yields
with the aid of irrigation.

Bibliographical References

1. Kimble, G. H. T., *Tropical Africa*, I, *Land and Livelihood* (Twentieth
Century Fund, New York), 1960, p. 241.
2. *Ibid.*, p. 241.
3. Zartman, T. W., *Morocco: Problems of New Power* (Atherton Press,
New York), 1964, p. 149.
4. Kimble, *op. cit.*, p. 245.
5. Harris, G. L., *Egypt*, Country Survey Series (Hraf Press, New Haven),
1957, p. 202.
6. Church, R. J. H. and others, *Africa and the Islands* (Longmans,
London), 1964, p. 156.
7. Barbour, K. M., *The Republic of the Sudan* (University of London
Press), 1961, p. 127.
8. McBride, B. St. C., 'The High Dam', *Geographical Magazine*, July
1965, pp. 169-83.
9. Barbour, *op. cit.*, pp. 269-70.
10. Houston, J. M., *The Western Mediterranean World* (Longmans,
London), 1964, p. 161.
11. *Ibid.*
12. Hill, R. W., 'Underground Water Resources of the Jefara', in S. G.
Willimott and J. I. Clarke (Ed.), *Field Studies in Libya* (University
of Durham), 1960, pp. 10-25.
13. Russell, Sir E. J., *World Population and World Food Supplies* (Allen
& Unwin, London), 1961, p. 315.
14. Hammond, P. B., 'Economic Change and Mossi Acculturation', in
W. R. Bascom and M. J. Herskovits, *Continuity and Change in
African Cultures* (University of Chicago Press), 1959, pp. 252-56.
15. Gulliver, P. H., *Social Control in an African Society* (Routledge &
Kegan Paul, London), 1963, pp. 17-18.
16. Green, L. P. and Fair, T. J. D., *Development in Africa* (Witwatersrand
University Press, Johannesburg), 1962, pp. 69-70.

17. Hussey, D. E., 'The Rhodesian Lowveld', *Geographical Magazine*, August 1965, pp. 249-62; *Overseas Review, 1965* (Barclays Bank D.C.O., London), p. 75.
18. Pike, J. G. and Rimmington, G. T., *Malawi, A Geographical Study* (Oxford University Press), 1965, p. 203.
19. Church, R. J. H., 'The Limpopo Scheme', *Geographical Magazine*, July 1964, pp. 212-27.
20. Cole, M. M., *South Africa* (Methuen, London), 1961, p. 152.
21. Hance, W. A., *The Geography of Modern Africa* (Columbia University Press, New York), 1964, p. 595.

Additional Sources

Fitzgerald, W., *Africa* (Methuen, London), 1964.
Jarrett, H. R., *Africa* (MacDonald & Evans, London), 1962.
Mountjoy, A. B. and Embleton, C., *Africa* (Hutchinson, London), 1965.

CHAPTER 12

NORTH AMERICA

THE UNITED STATES

In 1964 the United States had approximately thirty-seven million acres under irrigation, of which by far the greater part was in the seventeen western states (Fig. 46).[1] Only a small proportion of the total irrigated area, about seven and a half million acres, has been developed by federal projects; the remainder is the responsibility of private enterprise. The figure of thirty-seven million acres represents an increase of more than ten million acres in fifteen years, and an official projection estimates that by 1975, forty-five and a half million acres of cropland will be irrigated.[2]

At present, California has the largest irrigated area, with 7·5 million acres; Texas comes next with 6·4 million acres; and Colorado, Idaho and Nebraska have more than two million acres each. A substantial proportion of this acreage, probably almost half, is in need of some degree of conservation and is liable to damage by erosion, excess water, unfavourable soils or adverse climate.[3] In the higher and more northerly parts of the country, the short growing season limits the variety of crops, so that it is frequently necessary to grow early-maturing crops or grasses and legumes for hay and pasture. Increasing emphasis is being placed on the more efficient use of irrigation water, and in areas of low precipitation, this often means cultivating crops that make their growth when water is available. In some parts of the south-west, dependable supplies of surface water are almost completely appropriated, resulting in an increasing demand for ground-water supplies, which in Arizona, for example, are now used to twice the extent of surface water for irrigation. This growing demand brings about a steady lowering in water tables, particularly marked in the most important agricultural areas, where demand is greatest. In the Maricopa-Stanfield area of Arizona, about eighty miles northwest of Tucson, the water table fell more than seventy-five feet between 1946 and 1955, and in the area between Picacho and the Casa Grande Mountains, pumping has been so great that land subsidence has occurred. In general, the rapid fall in water tables in parts of Arizona, southern California and Texas has led to increased pumping costs, prohibitive in some areas, and decreasing yields of water.[4]

Despite these problems, as well as the higher costs of irrigation works and tighter limitations on the use of available water resources,

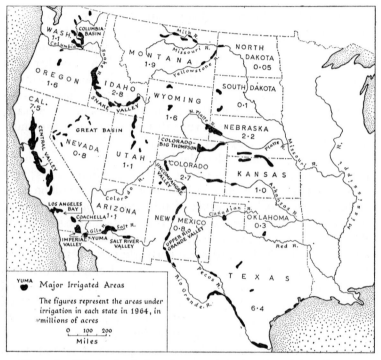

FIG. 46.   The major irrigated areas of the western United States.

the area under irrigation is steadily growing. There are two major types of irrigation project. One is the innumerable small-scale schemes which owe their inception to the work of individuals, co-operatives, irrigation companies or local governments; these consist mainly of stream diversion works and wells, and are usually simple and relatively cheap but suffer from a lack of storage facilities and are more likely to be affected by pollution and falling water tables. Secondly, there are large-scale, federal irrigation

projects which involve considerable capital expenditure and major
engineering; these are frequently liable to loss of water through
evaporation and sedimentation. Contrary to popular belief, the
small-scale schemes serve by far the greater amount of irrigated
land. It should be noted, however, that the amount of irrigated
land may vary from year to year depending on the quantity of water
supplies in the west, economic considerations and the adequacy of
rainfall in the east, where irrigation is used largely to supplement
natural precipitation in times of drought.

As mentioned previously, California has more land under
irrigation than any other state. In addition to a substantial number
of widely dispersed, small-scale, private irrigation enterprises, the
state has three major areas where irrigation is of outstanding importance: the Central Valley, the Los Angeles area and the Imperial-Coachella Valley area. Agriculture in the Central Valley is
based largely on the Central Valley project, a plan of the United
States Bureau of Reclamation for the over-all development of the
water resources of the basins of the Sacramento and San Joaquin
rivers. It involves the transfer of an overabundant water supply
from the northern part of the Sacramento Valley to the southern
part of the San Joaquin Valley, where a deficiency exists. Construction was begun in 1937, and the main task of water transfer
has since been achieved by means of the Delta-Mendota Canal,
which carries water from the lower Sacramento to Mendota on the
San Joaquin. The canal, 115 miles long, with its associated
facilities, was completed by 1951, and in 1962 delivered more than
three million acre-feet of water to approximately 900,000 acres of
the most productive land in the state. The canal, which has never
been put to maximum use, will carry more water when the San
Luis unit of the Central Valley project comes into use in a few
years' time. These and similar facilities are making possible the
delivery of an irrigation supply throughout the Central Valley
from Shasta Dam in the north, the major control structure on the
Sacramento, to the vicinity of Bakersfield, nearly 500 miles to the
south. The surplus waters of the San Joaquin are controlled by
the Friant Dam and diverted into the Friant-Kern Canal for consumption in the arid lands in the southern part of the valley. The
Central Valley as a whole is served by numerous projects, and
with more than three million acres comprises the largest single
irrigated area in the United States. Water is obtained both from

canals and by pumping from wells; rice, alfalfa, sugar beet, cotton, oranges and grapes are the main crops.

In the Los Angeles area the growing of citrus fruits is particularly important. To the east and south-east of Los Angeles, for a distance of between forty and fifty miles, more than 300,000 acres of lowland drained by the Santa Ana and San Gabriel rivers produce oranges, lemons, peaches, apricots and olives. In recent years, however, the urban sprawl of Greater Los Angeles has begun to encroach on the citrus orchards of the aptly named Orange County. The majority of farmers in this area obtain water by pumping, and natural ground-water levels have dropped alarmingly in recent years. The other major source of water for this region is the Colorado Aqueduct, which brings water from Parker Dam on the Colorado River. Growing rivalry between California and Arizona for the use of Colorado River water has provoked a series of legal battles, which resulted in a Supreme Court decision in 1963 limiting California to 4,400,000 acre-feet of water out of the annual supply of 7,500,000 acre-feet of main-stream water in the Lower Colorado Basin. In addition, the development of projects on the Upper Colorado is likely to lead eventually to a reduction in the flow of the Colorado River Aqueduct, so that southern California will become critically short of water within the next twenty-five years unless alternative supplies are found. The problem is intensified by the fact that one of the greatest westward migrations of population in the history of the world is now taking place in the United States, and California is absorbing this influx at the rate of over a thousand people a day. The population of California has more than doubled in the last twenty years and by the end of 1962 reached an estimated seventeen and a half million. As development is greatest in southern California, it will be necessary to develop water resources as rapidly as possible, and to meet this emergency the comprehensive California Water Plan has been drawn up (Fig. 47).[5] Among other things, this envisages co-operation with the federal Central Valley project, whereby a series of aqueducts will be constructed by the early nineteen-seventies to carry water the length of the Central Valley to be pumped over the Tehachapi Mountains for use in the southern coastal regions. The key structure in this scheme is the Oroville Dam recently completed on the Feather River, a tributary of the Sacramento. With its subsidiary dams and canal networks,

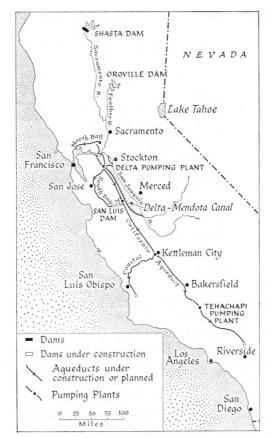

FIG. 47. The California Water Plan.

it will play a significant role in regulating and supplying water from northern California to the water-short areas 600 miles to the south.

Another recent development in this scheme is the construction of the San Luis unit, which will connect the facilities of the Central Valley project to those of the California Water Plan, enabling the waters of the Sacramento and its tributaries to be used as far south as San Diego. The unit is being constructed by the federal Bureau of Reclamation, and the state of California is paying a proportionate share of the cost. The key structure is the San Luis Dam, south-west of Merced on the western slopes of the San Joaquin Valley. Completed in 1967, 320 feet high, its reservoir which is

WGI P

now filling with water, will store more than two million acre-feet of water. Pumps will lift the water from the federal Delta-Mendota Canal and the state California Aqueduct into the San Luis Reservoir for storage. When required, water will be allowed to flow back into the California Aqueduct, where it will run 103 miles south to Kettleman City, where approximately half the water will enter the southern section of the California Aqueduct to be lifted over the Tehachapi Mountains for use in the southern coastal regions. About twenty-five miles above Kettleman City, a pumping plant will lift the water 138 feet into the Pleasant Valley Canal. When it is completed, the San Luis unit will provide water for more than 250,000 irrigable acres. It is designed to be the first of a number of such units transferring water from the northern part of the Central Valley to southern California.

This is one of the three main ways in which the long-range answer to the supplemental water needs of southern California is being sought. The others are the desalination of ocean water, which is not likely to become an economic proposition for some time, and the diversion of water from the Pacific North-west, particularly from the Columbia and Snake rivers. This last project is currently the subject of controversy between the states of the Pacific South-west and those of the Pacific North-west, who, although they have a surplus of water at present, envisage a time in the not too distant future when they will also need the waters of the Columbia-Snake. Even more grandiose schemes have been proposed, such as those to transfer water thousands of miles by huge aqueducts and canals from the Yukon and Canada to California and Arizona. The cost of such schemes would be astronomical, and as yet they exist only in the realm of ideas.

The third major irrigated area in California is that of the Imperial and Coachella valleys with almost one million acres under irrigation, drawing their water from the Colorado River via the All-American Canal and the Coachella branch which leads to the east and north. Some lifting of water is necessary, but great use is made of gravity flow. There, crops are grown almost all the year round, principally citrus fruits, cotton, dates and vegetables. Southern California's use of the waters of the Colorado has roused considerable enmity both in Arizona and among the Upper Colorado Basin states of Colorado, New Mexico, Utah and Wyoming. In the words of D. E. Mann, 'The people of Arizona have come to look upon the officials of California and particularly those of the Imperial Irrigation District and the Metropolitan Water District of Los Angeles as diabolical schemers who are dedicated to the robbery of Arizona's birthright,'[6] a sentiment shared by the Upper Basin states. This attitude is largely the result of southern California's uncompromising opposition to any and all proposals for the development of the Upper Colorado Basin.

Californian opposition notwithstanding, development of the water resources of the Upper Colorado and its tributaries is slowly taking place under the aegis of the Colorado River Storage Project (CRSP) (Fig. 48). To supplement its three large dams on the Lower Colorado, the Hoover, Davis and Parker dams, the Bureau of Reclamation has recently built three large storage dams in the Upper Basin: Glen Canyon Dam on the Colorado in northeast Arizona, Flaming Gorge Dam on the Green River in northeast Utah and the Navajo Dam on the San Juan River in northwest New Mexico. The most spectacular of these is Glen Canyon Dam, whose 580-foot-high concrete arch retains the slowly filling Lake Powell, 186 miles long, whose surface area will equal that of Lake Mead behind Hoover Dam. In addition to these major storage facilities, three smaller dams are being built on the Gunnison River in western Colorado. Together they will eventually permit a considerable extension of irrigable lands, generate large quantities of hydroelectricity, and allow a far greater degree of control over the Colorado than is at present possible. Other potential sites are being investigated along the Colorado in northern Arizona, principally at Bridge and Marble canyons between Hoover Dam and Glen Canyon, and proposals have been submitted to build multi-purpose dams there and so complete the stairway of dams on the Colorado. Arizona wants federal assistance to build these dams as part of her Central Arizona project, a complex scheme to relieve water shortage by pumping water from the Colorado through aqueducts to the Phoenix and Tucson areas. The project is fiercely opposed by southern California, unwilling to be deprived of its share of Colorado water, and by conservationists, who are enraged at the idea that the construction of Marble Canyon Dam would reduce the Colorado to a small stream through the Grand Canyon, a prospect which they consider the desecration of a national treasure.

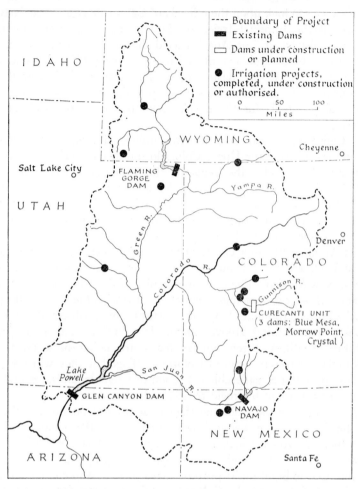

FIG. 48.   The Colorado River Storage Project.

Other important irrigation schemes in the intermontane region include the Columbia Basin project and the Colorado-Big Thompson project. The former scheme is based upon the Grand Coulee Dam and provides water for irrigation in the Big Bend of the Columbia River in south-central Washington. The Colorado-Big Thompson project diverts some of the headwaters of the Colorado under the Continental Divide by lifting them 186 feet through a tunnel thirteen miles long to be stored in reservoirs on the eastern slope. The water is then released during the irrigation season into a number of east-flowing rivers, including the Big Thompson, and thence by irrigation canal systems or private reservoirs into the irrigable area, which lies east of the Great Divide on the Rocky Mountain piedmont north of Denver, Colorado. The project has had its problems: it has become more important for the provision of supplemental water than for permanent irrigation and it has not greatly extended the irrigated area, while the cost of the scheme has considerably exceeded the original estimates. Nonetheless, it provides additional benefits in the form of hydroelectricity and makes possible the cultivation of sugar beet, potatoes, corn, vegetables and dairy produce.

Elsewhere in the vast area of the intermontane region are many irrigated areas varying greatly in size and productivity, including the Yuma area and the Salt River Valley of Arizona, the Upper Rio Grande Valley in New Mexico, the Uncompahgre Valley of Colorado, the Great Basin of Utah and Nevada, the Snake River Valley of Idaho and the apple-growing valleys of the Columbia Basin. The Yuma area on the eastern side of the Colorado River has more than 10,000 irrigated acres, where cereals and market-garden produce are grown. The Salt River Valley runs through Phoenix, Arizona, where 465,000 acres are served by water from Roosevelt Lake impounded behind the Roosevelt Dam. A year-long growing season enables alfalfa, cotton, citrus fruits, figs and melons to be grown, while an elaborate pumping system prevents waterlogging. Along the Upper Rio Grande Valley a number of irrigated strips, particularly those around the Mesilla and Estancia valleys, based on the Elephant Butte Reservoir, grow principally cotton and alfalfa. Along the Uncompahgre River in south-west Colorado, some 20,000 acres of flat, irrigated lands along the river produce onions, sugar beet, potatoes and alfalfa. In the Utah section of the Great Basin the most important irrigated areas are those in the Salt Lake Oasis, watered by westward-flowing streams descending from the Wasatch Mountains. A number of discontinuous irrigated areas, together comprising more than a million acres to the east and south of the Great Salt Lake, contain two-thirds of the population of Utah. There, the Mormons first began irrigated farming in 1847 and established what has been called 'the cradle of American irrigation'. The area under irrigation has been extended greatly in the past century, and recent federal projects include those at Bear River, Ogden and Strawberry Valley. The main crops are sugar beet, potatoes, wheat, vegetables and fruit; in addition, irrigated forage crops are grown for beef and dairy cattle. Other important oases in the Great Basin include those on its western edge along the Truckee, Walker, Carson and Humboldt rivers in Nevada, where alfalfa, dairy products, wheat and vegetables are important.

The Snake River Valley of southern Idaho is fortunately endowed with many tributary streams and wide areas of relatively flat land suitable for irrigation. As a result, there are many irrigation projects along the river growing alfalfa, beans, potatoes and wheat, while fruit is important along the western end of the valley. In central Washington and north-central Oregon a series of small rivers in the eastern, rain-shadow side of the Cascades drains into the Columbia. There, narrow, level strips along the valley are used primarily for growing irrigated crops of apples. The largest of these projects is at Yakima in south-central Washington, where irrigable land totals approximately 460,000 acres.

East of the Continental Divide, the most important irrigated areas are in Texas and in the Missouri Basin. Texas has the second largest area of irrigated land in the United States, more than half of which is found on the High Plains, where it is largely dependent on wells to grow cotton, corn and vegetables. Much development has taken place in this area during the last fifteen years, but the increasing difficulty in finding adequate supplies of ground water casts doubt on the possibility of extending it further. The Canadian River project is being developed to supplement these supplies. The Sanford Dam on the Canadian River near Amarillo in north-west Texas is designed to store water to be carried by an aqueduct system extending into the Gulf Basin area. The second largest irrigated area in Texas is along the Rio Grande River and its tributary the Pecos River. More densely settled and more intensively farmed than the High Plains, it consists of a series of irrigated oases producing citrus fruits and vegetables. Most of the water is derived from the Rio Grande and Pecos, but their variable flow has led to an increasing use of ground water to supplement it. The construction of the Falcon Dam, completed in October 1953, has helped to provide more dependable supplies of water for the Lower Rio Grande irrigated areas.

The principal irrigated areas within the Missouri Basin are

found along the right-bank tributaries of the Missouri, notably
the North Platte River in Nebraska and Wyoming, where corn,
tomatoes, peas and sugar beet are grown on 500,000 irrigated
acres. Nebraska has witnessed a rapid development in well
irrigation in recent years due to a comparative abundance of
relatively good ground-water supplies which are subject to frequent recharge by precipitation and stream flow. Consequently,

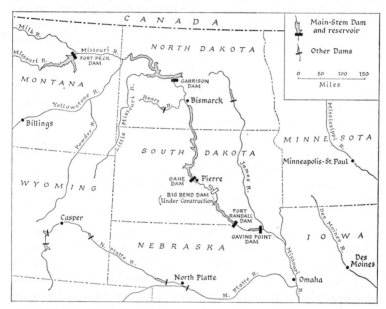

FIG. 49. The major control works of the Missouri Basin project.

there is little danger of ground-water reserves being depleted.
This area has been notable, too, for the use of gas engines for
pumping up the water; the cheap cost of gas has made deep-well
irrigation a practical proposition for many Nebraska farmers.

The Missouri Basin project is a large-scale federal scheme
designed to irrigate about six million acres. Main-stem dams al-
ready completed on the upper Missouri include Fort Peck in
Montana with a hundred-mile-long reservoir, Garrison in North
Dakota, Fort Randall, Big Bend and Oahe in South Dakota and
Gavins Point on the South Dakota-Nebraska border (Fig. 49).
In all, thirty-four multi-purpose dams have been built since 1946
and nine more are under construction. Federal projects alone have

provided water for almost 300,000 acres in the northern Missouri Basin, and almost 200,000 more irrigable acres are being developed. Farther south, in Kansas, the Tuttle Creek Reservoir and Dam on the Kansas River now cover 16,000 acres and provide flood control besides supplying water for irrigation.

East of the Mississippi River, irrigation is almost entirely of a supplemental nature. Florida, for example, despite being one of the wettest of American states, uses large and growing amounts of water annually for irrigation, especially during the dry autumn and winter seasons. In 1963 more than 400,000 irrigated acres produced principally citrus fruits and vegetables.

CANADA

The major irrigated areas of Canada are all in the western half of the country. Compared to the United States, there has been little irrigation development, largely because over much of the country the natural water supplies have generally been adequate. Out of approximately three million acres of potential irrigable land, between one and a half and two million acres have been or are in process of being developed. The principal irrigation areas are southern Alberta with approximately 870,000 acres (Table 11), southern Saskatchewan with 450,000 acres and British Columbia with 220,000 acres. Large-scale irrigation in the Prairie Provinces dates from 1935, when, as the consequence of a series of disastrous 'dust bowls', the Prairie Farm Rehabilitation Administration (PFRA) was set up by the Dominion government and given responsibility for the provision of a number of irrigation projects. According to J. Wreford Watson, the chief problem of prairie irrigation is one of economics rather than geography.[7] The rivers which flow eastwards from the Rockies can supply sufficient water to promote large-scale irrigation, but as is common in other areas of marginal rainfall, the productivity of irrigated land does not at present sufficiently exceed that of non-irrigated land to make many large-scale projects worthwhile. Consequently, most irrigation systems are relatively limited in extent and are used on small plots to produce very high yields of specialised crops like early vegetables, potatoes, sugar beet and alfalfa.

Typical of such farming is the Lethbridge area of southern Alberta, which contains the greater part of Alberta's irrigated farmlands and where the principal crops are sugar beet, potatoes

TABLE II

Name of District	Irrigable Area ('000s of Acres)	Receiving Water in 1966 ('000s of Acres)	Source of Supply
St. Mary-Milk Rivers	177	165	St. Mary's River
Magrath	8·5	4	,,
Raymond	21	16	,,
Taber	54	26	,,
Western Irrigation District	150	3	Bow River
Eastern Irrigation District	200	196	,,
Bow River	119	40·3	,,
Mountain View	3·7	2·8	Belly River
Leavitt	4·5	4·5	,,
Aetna	6·6	2·5	,,
United Irrigation District	34	12·7	,,
Lethbridge Northern	89·7	19·2	Oldman River
Ross Creek	2	1	Gros Ventre Creek
Total	870	493	

Alberta: Major Irrigation Districts, 1966

(Based on figures cited in Alberta: *Annual Report of the Department of Agriculture for 1966*, Edmonton, 1967, p. 222.)

Alberta's irrigable acreage has gradually increased during the last few years; for example, it has risen from 745,000 acres in 1963 to 870,000 acres in 1966. However, the area actually receiving water has fluctuated considerably from year to year, depending largely upon the amount of annual rainfall. Thus, in 1962, 632,000 acres received irrigation water, while in 1966 only 493,000 were supplied with water. However, in general, irrigation water is being used more efficiently, resulting largely from a government-sponsored land development programme which has placed emphasis on an ever-increasing use of sprinklers.

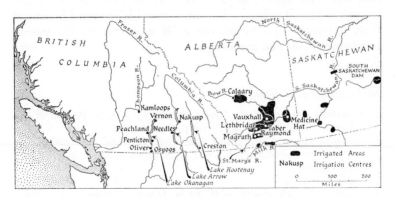

FIG. 50. Major irrigated areas in Canada.

and legumes. Other important schemes are found at Calgary, Vauxhall, Magrath and Raymond (Fig. 50). These areas face the same problems of seepage and drainage as the irrigated tracts farther south in the United States. However, irrigation in the Prairie Provinces is being extended to new areas, and projects presently under construction include the Bow River scheme west of Medicine Hat in Alberta, with a potential of 240,000 irrigable acres; the St. Mary's River scheme near Lethbridge, which should make more than 200,000 acres irrigable; and the South Saskatchewan River scheme in central Saskatchewan, the largest irrigation project currently under construction in Canada. The key structure of this project, which is being developed under the auspices of the Prairie Farm Rehabilitation Administration, is the South Saskatchewan River Dam. Although it will generate considerable quantities of hydroelectricity, its main purpose is to provide irrigation water. Together with a network of pumping stations, canals and secondary reservoirs, it should eventually make about 500,000 acres irrigable. Some of this new land will support more than a thousand existing farms, and an additional thousand new farms will be created.

Irrigation in southern British Columbia, as in the Prairie Provinces, is used to promote intensive cultivation. However, the provision of irrigation in this area is fairly straightforward, since numerous perennial streams flow from the mountains into broad, warm valleys. The streams can be easily dammed and led by flumes into the flat valley tracts, and expensive, large-scale irrigation works are unnecessary. Moreover, the valley floors are flat enough to permit irrigation but sufficiently high to provide natural frost drainage.[8] Fruits are the chief crop, principally apples, peaches, apricots and cantaloups.

Bibliographical References

1. *Statistical Abstract of the United States: 1964* (U.S. Bureau of the Census, Washington, D.C.), 1964, p. 623.
2. *Soil and Water Conservation Needs—A National Inventory*, Miscellaneous Publications No. 971 (U.S. Department of Agriculture), 1965, p. 49.
3. *Ibid.*, pp. 49-52.
4. Mann, D. E., *The Politics of Water in Arizona* (University of Arizona Press, Tucson), 1963, pp. 3-4.

5. *The California Water Plan*, Bulletin No. 3 (State of California Department of Water Resources, Sacramento), May 1957.
6. Mann, *op. cit.*, p. 81.
7. Watson, J. W., *North America, Its Countries and Regions* (Longmans, London), 1963, p. 398.
8. *Ibid.*, pp. 433-35.

CHAPTER 13

LATIN AMERICA

Irrigation is little developed in Latin America, which has approximately twenty-four million acres, representing just over three per cent of the total irrigated acreage of the world. Mexico, Chile, Peru and Argentina contain over eighty per cent of the total.

MEXICO

Unlike most of Latin America, Mexico has in recent years experienced a substantial growth in agricultural productivity due largely to the extension of irrigated areas. These have grown from approximately two million acres in 1946 to an estimated 10·6 million in 1964.[1] Of this amount, 6·9 million acres have been developed by government action and 3·7 million by private enterprise. In addition, a government-sponsored programme to rehabilitate older irrigated areas rendered useless by salination is under way, as are other large-scale projects; together, they should provide an additional three million irrigable acres.

This great increase in irrigated agriculture is part of a massive government-sponsored 'hydraulic programme', one of the largest of its kind in the world and certainly the largest in Latin America. The programme, which represents an enormous investment of public funds, has been successful on the whole and has served as a model for technicians and engineers in other developing countries. The large-scale projects under construction or developed in recent years as part of this programme are planned to irrigate more than one million acres (Fig. 51).

One of these schemes, the Raudales Malpaso complex now being constructed in the Grijalva-Usumacinta Valley east of Minatitlan, is claimed to be among the five largest hydraulic works in the world and will generate enormous amounts of hydro-electricity besides irrigating a considerable area. Because of uncontrolled flooding and bad drainage, this area has hitherto been largely marsh and liana-tangled forest.

The more successful of these projects have generally been those

located in the arid parts of the country, like the Rio Fuerte. By
contrast, an attempt to develop the wet tropical coastlands of the
Papaloapan Basin has met with only limited success (Fig. 52).
The Papaloapan Commission was set up as long ago as 1947, and
a recent assessment of its achievements concludes that although
considerable progress has been made in flood control, in the construction of dams and in the building of roads, its agricultural

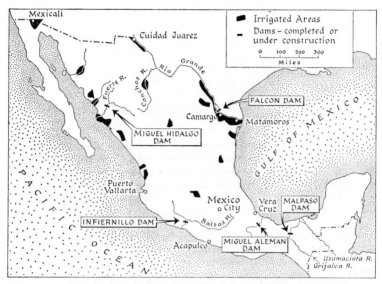

FIG. 51.   Major irrigated areas in Mexico.

programme has met with few successes and numerous dismal
failures.* The over-all failure of the scheme to develop a stable
irrigated agriculture is attributable to a number of reasons: the
excessively paternalistic attitude of the commission towards the
colonists, the failure to precede colonisation with adequate surveys
and a preliminary period of agricultural experimentation, the
failure of successive presidents to support the commission with a
continuing policy and adequate finance, and the refusal of the
local cattle farmers to have their holdings broken up into small
irrigated farms of questionable productivity. It remains to be seen

* For a detailed account and appreciation of the scheme, *v.* Thomas T.
Poleman, *The Papaloapan Project: Agricultural Development in the Mexican
Tropics*, Stanford U.P., 1964.

whether the Grijalva-Usumacinta project, another tropical scheme, will fare any better. In addition to these massive schemes, the government has sponsored innumerable small-scale projects of vital importance to Mexico's agricultural economy. These minor irrigation works have been built in almost every state and territory,

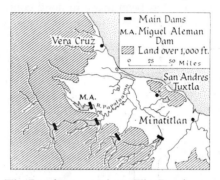

FIG. 52. The Papaloapan project. The Papaloapan and its tri-butaries carry great volumes of water, and the vast summer run-off brings floods and malarial swamps. A number of dams have been built, including the key structure, the Miguel Aleman Dam, and some cut-offs have been constructed across meanders in the lower course of the Papaloapan to facilitate run-off.

usually in co-operation with the states and municipalities concerned, and have led to a steady growth of about 70,000 irrigable acres annually.

Irrigation, allied with improved techniques of cultivation, has made possible considerably larger yields than is the case on the non-irrigated farmlands. This is well illustrated by the following figures, quoted in a recent United Nations publication (Table 12):

TABLE 12

Crops	Irrigated Lands	Non-Irrigated Lands
Sugar cane	67,553	51,655
Potatoes	8,170	5,087
Rice	2,839	1,736
Wheat	1,972	1,037
Maize	1,512	913
Beans	1,077	430

Mexico: Crop Yields
(Per Kilogramme/Hectare)

(Based on figures cited in *Economic Bulletin for Latin America*, *VIII*, *No. 2, October 1963*, United Nations, New York, 1964, p. 162n.)

At present, Mexico's major irrigated areas are in the north-west in the state of Baja California, in the states of Sonora and Sinaloa, and in the Gulf Coast Lowlands (Fig. 51). In Baja California the Colorado River supplies water to some 400,000 acres in the vicinity of Mexicali, where cotton, vegetables, olives and vines are grown. In Sonora and Sinaloa, the Mexican government has been engaged for the past decade in the most extensive programme of irrigation in its history. Gravity-flow systems have been constructed or are under construction in the coastal lowlands, rendering almost two million acres irrigable.

These developments have brought about far-reaching agricultural changes, including the cultivation of much more wheat, cotton, sugar cane, rice and winter vegetables. In the Gulf Coast Lowlands the major irrigated area is the Rio Grande-Matamoros district, where cotton, maize, fruit and vegetables are grown. In the upper reaches of the Rio Grande in the state of Chihuahua, the areas downstream from Cuidad Juarez and in the middle Conchos Basin are particularly important. On the lower Rio Grande the completion of the Falcon Dam in 1953 made about 500,000 acres irrigable on the Mexican side of the international boundary in the vicinity of Camargo.

CENTRAL AMERICA AND THE WEST INDIES

In Central America and the West Indies, irrigation is limited in extent, totalling little more than one million acres in all (Table 13). This is so partly because the amount of cultivable land is

TABLE 13

Central America		The West Indian Islands	
Guatemala	99	Dominican Republic	334
Honduras	82	Haiti	161
El Salvador	49	Cuba	148
Costa Rica	37	Puerto Rico	96
Panama	35	Jamaica	54
Nicaragua	30		
Total	332	Total	793

Central America and the West Indies: Major Irrigated Areas, Early 1960's
('000s of Acres)

(Based on estimates cited in *Farmers' World*, U.S. Department of Agriculture Yearbook, 1964, p. 77.)

restricted by unfavourable soils and terrain, partly because there is an adequate natural rainfall in most areas, and partly because adequate capital and technical expertise are lacking. Nevertheless, there are possibilities for the development of irrigated agriculture which could help to increase yields, especially in the dry winter season, and so help to relieve the pressure of growing populations on inadequate agricultural resources.

The major irrigated crop in these areas is sugar cane, which is grown extensively in the southern plains of the Dominican Republic, in Jamaica and Puerto Rico. Several of these countries have projects for extending the irrigable land, including Haiti and the Dominican Republic, which were planning to increase their irrigated farmlands by more than 175,000 and 250,000 acres respectively. However, recent political upheavals may have interfered with these projects. Jamaica also plans irrigation developments, including the Rio Cobre scheme, the Mid-Clarendon scheme and the St. Dorothy Plains project.[2] In addition, many wells have been drilled in recent years to tap underground supplies.

SOUTH AMERICA

Agriculture in South America has, in general, undergone no great development in the last twenty years despite the fact that the rapidly growing population imposes a pressing need for increased output. There are many reasons for this unsatisfactory situation, such as the shortage of capital, the absence of suitable governmental policies, inadequate systems of land tenure and use, archaic labour and recruitment systems, the very low average-income level of the rural population, the growing gap between rural and urban incomes, the gap between the small group of large entrepreneurs with large incomes and the peasants at a minimum subsistence level, and the relative ignorance of modern agricultural techniques. Some areas suffer from long dry seasons when agricultural work comes to a virtual standstill. One of the most effective ways to improve this state of affairs would be to introduce and extend communal irrigation works to lengthen the work cycle. Elsewhere, in parts of the Andes and in the Amazon and Parana basins, there is too much rainfall, which renders the fields sodden and uncultivable for long periods; there, drainage would be the answer.

As a recent United Nations report emphasises, greater investment in irrigation works should be part of agricultural development programmes formulated for the countries of South America.[3] Such investment need not necessarily be very great, as considerable agricultural improvements can frequently be achieved locally on a small scale without a high input of capital and labour; for example, in some suitable areas, very little machinery would have to be imported to build irrigation systems with local labour and materials. Furthermore, in many areas, even though water is a scarce resource that is not properly utilised at present, were it to be applied scientifically to the land, it would be possible to irrigate much larger areas without greatly increasing the supply of irrigation water.

Irrigation at present is found mainly in the major arid zones. These lie in Chile, Peru and Argentina and together contain three-quarters of the irrigated land in South America. In 1963, approximately twelve million acres were under irrigation, representing about 6·4 per cent of the cultivable area (Table 14).

TABLE 14

Chile	3,370	Ecuador	425
Peru	2,995	Bolivia	168
Argentina	2,772	British Guiana	148
Brazil	865	Uruguay	64
Venezuela	642	Surinam	35
Colombia	544	Paraguay	30

South America: Major Irrigated Areas, 1963
('ooos of Acres)

(Based on United Nations estimates cited in *Farmer's World*, U.S. Department of Agriculture Yearbook, 1964, pp. 77-78.)

Some extension of the irrigable area has taken place in recent years, but development has tended to be very gradual and slow, and many countries have failed to provide regular and continuous financing for the few irrigation projects on which construction has been reported. More than thirty million acres of potential arable land could be irrigated if capital were available and firm governmental support and encouragement were assured. Mexico has provided an example in this respect, and in the last few years there have been encouraging indications that other Latin American countries, like Chile and Peru, will follow Mexico's lead.

Chile has more than three million acres under irrigation, representing some three-quarters of the cultivated land, and has suitable land and water resources for developing at least another

WGI Q

two million acres. The major sources of water for irrigation are the westward-flowing streams which rise in the Andes and flow into the Pacific Ocean. In the arid area of northern Chile, these streams create irrigated oases which provide foodstuffs for mining settlements like Copiapo and Vallenar and ports like Arica and Antofagasta. In the south of this area, in Atacama Province, vine-yards are important, especially in the Huasco and Vallenar districts. Irrigation is most important in the Central Valley, whose Mediter-ranean climate of summer drought necessitates a continuous supply of Andean meltwater to promote the cultivation of such crops as tobacco, hemp, maize, wheat, sugar beet, vines, vegetables and citrus fruit on more than two and a half million irrigated acres. Fortunately, the mountain streams provide ample silt-laden water, and the westward slope of the land makes irrigation fairly easy by means of gravity canals. Cultivation is carried on in a few large estates by somewhat inefficient methods, and as large areas of potentially fertile land are uncultivated and ample water is avail-able, this region has considerable possibilities for the extension of irrigated agriculture.

Irrigation in Peru dates back to the Incas, whose highly developed system of aqueducts and canal networks fell into disuse after the conquest of the country by the Spaniards. Today, Peru has almost three million irrigated acres, based on rivers which flow westwards from the Andes across the narrow coastal belt, as in northern Chile. Along many of the streams the demand for water is so great that little is allowed to reach the sea and go to waste. But elsewhere, especially in the south, Andean meltwater causes floods and occasional disastrous landslides during the summer. Among the oasis towns of northern Peru are Piura and Chiclayo, which together produce a large majority of the country's rice. Piura relies partly on the Quiroz irrigation scheme, whereby water is brought by pipeline through the mountains from the headwaters of Andean streams. Farther south is Trujillo, which specialises in the production of sugar cane, while in central Peru the irrigated area around Lima is served by the Rimac River and produces cotton, sugar cane, vines and market-garden produce. Similar ribbon oases are found south of Lima, notably at Ica, Moquegua and Tacna (Fig. 53).

In recent years, the government of Peru has begun a programme to extend the irrigated area by transferring water from the eastern side of the Andes to the arid coastal lowlands by diverting river courses through mountain tunnels. Included in this programme is the Marcapomacocha water diversion project, whereby a trans-Andean tunnel brings water from lakes on the Atlantic side of the Andes into the Santa Eulala and Rimac rivers south of Lima. In the Tinajones project near Chiclayo in northern Peru, irrigation

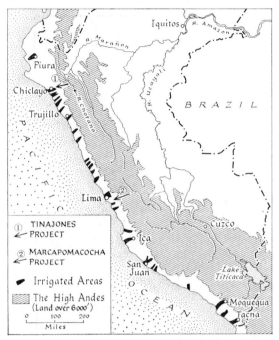

FIG. 53.   Irrigated areas in Peru.

depends on the annual flow of the Chancay and Chotano rivers. As eighty per cent of this flow occurs between December and April and there are no storage facilities to hold the water, much of it is wasted. The Tinajones Dam and a number of secondary dykes will enclose the waters of the Chancay and Chotano, thereby creating a reservoir with a storage capacity of 360 million cubic metres. When completed, the dam will permit an extension of the irrigable land in the Chancay valley, at present 110,000 acres, to more than 200,000 acres. Moreover, as water will be available the year round, it will be possible to obtain two rice harvests instead of the present one a year, as well as greater yields of maize.

At least another dozen schemes of varying size and complexity are planned on the coast and a similar number in the Andean region. If and when they are completed, they will add approximately one and a quarter million acres to the irrigable lands of the country. There is also the tantalising possibility of tapping the waters of Lake Titicaca and leading them by canal to the arid lands

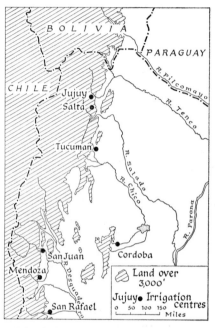

FIG. 54.   Major irrigation centres in north-west Argentina.

of southern Peru. Such a scheme, although apparently quite feasible from an engineering point of view, would be very expensive.

Irrigated agriculture in Argentina is almost entirely restricted to the arid north-west and Patagonia. The only cultivable areas in the north-west are oases, supported by streams which flow eastwards from the Andes (Fig. 54). Among the largest of these oases is Tucuman, where sugar is grown on large plantations and where maize, alfalfa and wheat are cultivated. In the San Rafael area, viticulture is particularly important, and the San Juan, Mendoza and San Rafael oases form the major wine-producing region of Argentina. In recent years, large extensions of irrigated lands have been made in the Mendoza area, using water from the Mendoza River, and alfalfa and temperate fruits are grown in large quantities. By contrast, Patagonia is sparsely populated sheep country, and irrigated agriculture is restricted to limited strips in the northern valleys of the Colorado and Negro rivers, where cereals, alfalfa and vegetables are grown for local consumption.

Irrigation in Brazil is largely restricted to the north-eastern section of the country. It is particularly important along the coast, where it promotes the growth of cotton, sugar and rice. For some time, there has been increasing emigration from the Sertão, the dry interior plateau country, to the coastal cities of Rio de Janeiro, Sao Paulo, Salvador and Recife, largely due to the climatic hazards of the Sertão in the form of poorly distributed rainfall and periodic droughts. In an attempt to halt this drift of population to the towns, the Brazilian government has made sporadic but largely ineffective attempts to lessen the effect of climatic vagaries by constructing dams and irrigation works. In the nineteen-thirties a number of important dams were built in the 'drought polygon' of north-east Brazil, but unfortunately no accompanying irrigation networks were added, partly because the construction of dams was an easier and more attractive engineering task and partly because, as Dr. Butland puts it, 'the individualism of the Sertão dweller does not take kindly to anything of a co-operative nature, which is the essence of water development'.[4] A similar programme was attempted in the nineteen-fifties when the government built more than a hundred dams, and private individuals built other smaller ones. But the pattern of the nineteen-thirties was repeated, and once more dams were built without adequate prior planning for irrigation and farming. As a result, despite the considerable agricultural potential of the area, fewer than 17,500 acres were irrigated there in 1961.[5] However, the recently completed multi-purpose São Francisco Valley scheme in Minas Gerais, based on the Tres Marias Dam on the Indaia River, holds out hope for a considerable extension of irrigated agriculture.

Irrigated agriculture in Venezuela, dating from the nineteen-forties, is found mainly in the central ranges and along the southern side of the western range of the Andes. In 1963, Venezuela had approximately 650,000 irrigated acres, chiefly supporting large farms and estates, of which some forty-five per cent was irrigated from rivers, forty-five per cent from wells and springs and only ten per cent from reservoirs. The area irrigated by reservoirs has increased in the last two or three years and will further increase as a result of large-scale schemes already under construction and currently being planned. Since 1950 the Venezuelan government has spent a great deal of money on large-scale irrigation schemes

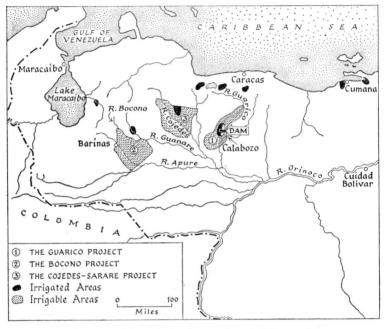

FIG. 55.   Major irrigation projects in Venezuela.

to open up new land, particularly on the southern slopes of the Andes and in the Orinoco Basin (Fig. 55). The Guarico project, intended to mitigate extremes of drought and flood, is based on a rock and earth dam built across the Guarico River upstream of Calabozo. Official sources claim that this scheme has been a great success and that more than 250,000 acres have been made irrigable, though this is probably a very optimistic estimate. The Bocono project on the river of the same name in Barinas State and the Cojedes-Sarare scheme ninety miles north-east of Bocono in Portuguesa State together provide about 75,000 irrigable acres, and it is hoped that the development of the latter scheme will eventually make a further 150,000 acres available. It is difficult to judge the success of such schemes, but official optimism notwithstanding, there is reason to doubt that they have greatly increased Venezuela's agricultural productivity. In some marginal areas, irrigation facilities have not been used by the farmers, who have judged their cost too high for the yields obtained. Elsewhere, especially in the area of the Guarico project, irrigation has been extended to areas of poor soils, and limited crop yields have resulted. A recent report issued by a mission of the International Bank for Reconstruction and Development opposes the expansion of investment in large-scale irrigation schemes on a number of grounds: there is abundant good land waiting to be taken up on which large-scale irrigation is not required; farmers need much more experience in using irrigation on small projects; and any programme for greatly extending irrigated agriculture must be based on careful research into suitable crops and soils.[6]

The only other South American countries with appreciable areas under irrigation are Colombia and Ecuador, with about 550,000 and 425,000 acres respectively. Most of these lands are in the Sierra regions and have been developed by private enterprise. Elsewhere in South America, irrigation is limited, which accounts in part for the low level of agricultural productivity. In Bolivia and Uruguay, large areas would benefit from irrigation, but development projects are primarily at the planning stage and existing schemes are small. Guyana (British Guiana), however, has recently implemented a number of irrigation schemes, including the Tapakuma project west of Georgetown in Essequibo County, and the Coventyne drainage and irrigation scheme in the coastal lowland between Coventyne and Berbicer, where it is hoped that 50,000 acres of ricelands and 78,000 acres of pasture and drained lands will eventually come into use.

Bibliographical References

1. *Economic Bulletin for Latin America, VIII, No. 2, October 1963* (United Nations, New York), 1964, p. 162; *Farmer's World* (U.S. Department of Agriculture Yearbook, 1964), pp. 76-77.
2. *Jamaica, 1961* (Her Majesty's Stationery Office, London), 1965, pp. 397-400.
3. *Economic Bulletin for Latin America, VI, No. 2, October 1961* (United Nations, New York), 1962, pp. 22-25.
4. Butland, G. J., *Latin America* (Longmans, London), 1961, p. 308.

5. Hirschman, A. O., *Journeys towards Progress: Studies of Economic Policy-making in Latin America* (Twentieth Century Fund, New York), 1963, p. 43.
6. International Bank for Reconstruction and Development, *The Economic Development of Venezuela* (Oxford University Press), 1961, p. 57.

Additional Sources

Cline, H. F., *Mexico* (Oxford University Press), 1962.

Galbraith, W. O., *Colombia* (Oxford University Press), 1953.

Owens, R. J., *Peru* (Oxford University Press), 1964.

Robinson, H., *Latin America* (MacDonald & Evans, London), 1961.

Scobie, J. R., *Argentina* (Oxford University Press), 1964.

Simpson, L. B., *Many Mexicos* (University of California Press, Berkeley). 1962.

AUSTRALASIA

Australasia has a total irrigated area of about 3,600,000 acres, of which by far the greatest proportion is in south-east Australia and in the Canterbury Plains of New Zealand.

The total acreage and use of irrigated agriculture in Australia in 1966 is shown in Table 15. This represents an increase of more than seventy-five per cent since 1959, when just over 1·9 million acres were under irrigation. There is some scope for further extension, but probably only to a limited degree. In the near future the only major increase is likely to be in existing areas along the Murray and Murrumbidgee rivers in the south-east interior lowlands, using water from the Snowy Mountains scheme, and along the Darling River.

Only a small fraction of Australia's total land area is irrigated because of the lack of suitable supplies of water over vast areas. The main irrigation schemes are along the country's only major river, the Murray, and its tributaries, and consequently Victoria and New South Wales contain eighty-three per cent of the total irrigated area. There are numerous rivers along the northern and eastern coasts of Australia, some of which are used for irrigation and others which will be developed sooner or later. Unfortunately, along most of the coastlands the terrain is rugged and unsuitable for large-scale irrigation. The Murray-Darling Basin has the most favourable conditions with graded plains like the Riverina and deeply etched gorges suitable for large dams like the Burrinjuck on the Murrumbidgee and Sugarloaf on the Goulburn.[1]

Schemes controlled by state governments involve approximately ninety per cent of the total irrigated area, and an even higher percentage involves headworks and other structures financed from public funds. In the last fifty years, state governments like Victoria have encouraged intensive irrigation schemes to promote settlement and develop resources. Consequently, the irrigation pattern reflects a highly centralised control of water allocation and land division. This policy contrasts sharply with the United States, where irrigation has developed with minimal public control.[2] As irrigation in Australia is controlled by state government departments and not by the federal government, practice varies somewhat from one state to another. In general, however, Australian irrigation is characterised by close co-operation between the farmers and a number of official and semi-official organisations, including irrigation commissions, state departments of agriculture, co-operative marketing establishments and the Commonwealth Scientific and Industrial Research Organisation (CSIRO).[3] In Victoria and New South Wales a distinction is made between those areas which have been designated full irrigation areas and which are entirely dependent upon irrigation, and those in which farmers can irrigate only part of their lands. In both states, there are two major types of area subject to irrigation: large areas using relatively small amounts of water for pastureland, and small areas using large amounts of water for intensive cultivation. The latter areas are considerably more important to the Australian agricultural economy.

The principal irrigated crops are orchard fruits, grown mainly in the south-east; sugar cane, which is limited to the Queensland coast; vegetables in a number of states; vines, grown mainly in the south-east; and rice, which is almost entirely restricted to New South Wales. In 1966-67, land devoted to these and other crops such as fodder crops, and fallow land, made up about forty per

TABLE 15A

States	'ooos of Acres	Percentage of Total
New South Wales	1,441	43
Victoria	1,314	39
Queensland	344	10·3
South Australia	139	4·2
Western Australia	70	2
Tasmania	47	1·5
Northern Territory	1	—
Australian Capital Territory	1	—
Total	3,357	100

Australia: Acreage of Irrigated Land, 1966-67

(Based on figures cited in *Bureau of Census and Statistics Statistical Bulletin*, No. 24, 'Rural Land Use and Crop Production', 1967.)

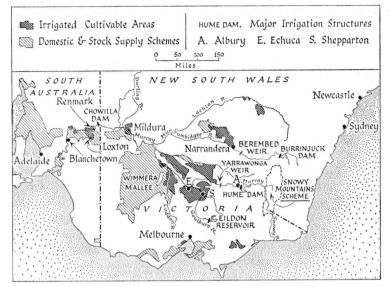

FIG. 56.   Irrigation in the south-east interior lowlands of Australia.

cent of the total irrigated acreage, with the remaining sixty per cent being devoted to irrigated pasture (Tables 15A and 15B).

The major areas of intensive cultivation based on irrigation are shown in Fig. 56. The Murrumbidgee irrigation areas are a few miles from the river on the semi-arid plains of the Riverina.

TABLE 15B

Crops	'ooos of Acres
Orchards	143 (Victoria 47, N.S.W. 36, S.A. 32)
Sugar cane	142 (All Queensland)
Vegetables	118 (Queensland 39, Victoria 27, N.S.W. 17, Tasmania 13)
Vines	94 (Victoria 47, S.A. 28, N.S.W. 18)
Rice	74 (All N.S.W.)
Cotton	42 (N.S.W. 22, W.A. 12, Queensland 8)
Tobacco	12 (All Queensland)
Hops	1 (All Tasmania)
Other crops, including fodder and fallow land	709
Total	1,335 = 40 per cent of total irrigated area.

Australia: Acreage of Irrigated Croplands, 1966-67
(Based on figures cited in *Bureau of Census and Statistics Statistical Bulletin*, op. cit.)

Water is stored in the Burrinjuck Dam, forty miles north-west of Canberra. It has a capacity of about 850,000 acre-feet, and during the irrigation season, which usually lasts from August or September to April, it feeds water down the Murrumbidgee to be diverted into a main irrigation channel by the Berembed Weir near Narrandera. From there, it flows by gravity canals onto the farmland, where grains, including rice, vegetables, vines and pasture are grown. As the water supply is limited, only about 100,000 acres are intensively irrigated, though a number of irrigation districts also use supplementary irrigation for the extensive cultivation of wheat, oats and lucerne. This area suffers from the usual problems of waterlogging and salinity and is also liable to occasional droughts which reduce water storage and to occasional heavy rains which deluge farmlands already supplied with irrigation water.[4]

The Murray valley irrigation areas are spaced out at intervals along the valley. The key structure is the Hume Dam, about nine miles upstream from Albury, which feeds water into the river during the irrigation season. At present, it stores almost one and a half million acre-feet of water and this is now being increased to two and a half million. Forty-five miles downstream from Hume Dam is the Yarrawonga Weir, which raises the water sufficiently to divert it into main canals on either side of the river. Between Yarrawonga and the mouth of the Murray, a series of weirs and locks helps to maintain local water levels, especially between Mildura and Blanchetown. Five barrages across the mouth of the river prevent the encroachment of salt water.

Intensive irrigated arable farming flourishes in two main districts: west of Echuca, where pastures for dairy cattle and fat lamb production are most important, and around Mildura, which specialises in vineyards and also produces citrus fruits and vegetables. Extensive pastoral irrigation is important in the Wimmera-Mallee area of Victoria, where water collected in storage dams from various sources is supplied to farmers once a year in winter by a stock and domestic water supply scheme.

The Goulburn valley, with about one and a half million acres, has the largest irrigated area in Australia and is supplied with water mainly from the Eildon Reservoir, which has a capacity of two and three quarters of a million acre-feet. East of the river, especially around Shepparton, orchard crops including pears and apricots are most important, and west of the river, dairying and the production of pigs, fat lambs and cereals predominate. In addition to these three main areas, there are a number of smaller, intensive irrigation settlements in the south-east, including Renmark and Loxton in South Australia, which specialise in fruit, grapes, sultanas and currants.

The areas under irrigation in the south-east interior lowlands could undoubtedly be extended if more water were made available,

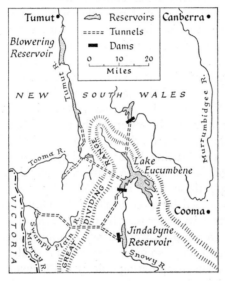

FIG. 57.   The Snowy Mountains scheme.

and a number of schemes have been implemented to provide additional supplies. The most important of these is the Snowy Mountains scheme (Fig. 57). The scheme is intended to utilise fully the water resources of the Snowy Mountains area for generating hydroelectricity and increasing the flow of the Murray and Murrumbidgee rivers for use in the inland irrigation areas. This is being accomplished by diverting the Snowy River and its tributaries (which presently flow wastefully eastwards into the sea) northwards and westwards by a series of tunnels through the mountains to water the semi-arid inland plains. The main storage unit of the scheme is Lake Eucumbene with a capacity of more than three and a half million acre-feet. Water is led from it by tunnels into the Murrumbidgee and its tributary the Tumut

River. The Snowy River itself is being diverted through a series of tunnels into the headwaters of the Murray. When the scheme is completed, an extra 800,000 acre-feet of water a year should be added to the Murray River and about 1,120,000 to the Murrumbidgee, sufficient to irrigate well over 600,000 acres, mainly in New South Wales and Victoria.

Construction has also begun on the Chowilla Dam on the Murray River twenty miles above Renmark. The three-and-a-half-mile-long dam will cost over eleven million pounds and will create the largest reservoir in Australia, with a storage capacity of more than four and a half million acre-feet. It will bring security from drought to many irrigation farmers along the Murray River, and although it will be more vital to South Australia, whose agricultural development is being hampered by lack of water, it will also benefit Victoria and New South Wales by enabling them to make increased use of the waters of the upper Murray.

A recently completed scheme is the Menindee Lakes project (Fig. 58) on the Darling River. Costing just over three million pounds, it consists of seven separate, normally dry, shallow lakes, or billabongs; these have been linked by channels and their capacities increased by levee banks. The Darling itself has been dammed so that its water may be diverted into the lakes through a regulator. In the past, when heavy summer rains occurred, the Darling brought down so much water that it spilled over its banks and went to waste, evaporating quickly in the heat. Now it can be retained, and in dry years the water stored in the lakes will be allowed to re-enter the river. The total capacity of the project is more than one and a half million acre-feet, which will make possible a good deal of local irrigation for raising fat lambs and for growing citrus fruit, vines and vegetables. By means of a channel from Lake Tandou, the great anabranch of the Darling, which normally flows only once in ten years, will be regularly filled to be used for watering stock. The scheme will have more than merely local significance: by regularising the flow of the Darling, it will enable South Australia, which is now guaranteed a minimum supply from the Murray each year, to draw more water from this alternative source, thereby allowing Victoria and New South Wales to use more water from the Murray. It is hoped that the successful completion of the Menindee Lakes project will mark the first stage of a much larger scheme to conserve water along the

Darling by constructing up to forty weirs along the 1,335 miles of the river above Menindee.

Queensland has about 300,000 acres under irrigation, of which almost a half is devoted to sugar cane. Irrigation based on the pumping of ground water is particularly important in the lower Burdekin valley, because the rainfall there is unreliable and less

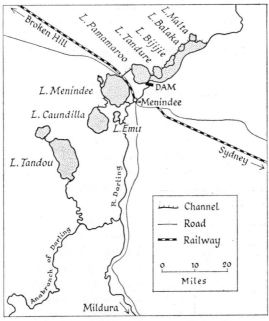

FIG. 58. The Menindee Lakes project.

than forty inches a year. Supplemental irrigation is also used for growing sugar farther south in the lower Burnett valley around Bundaberg. Other irrigated crops include tobacco in the Ross River delta, citrus fruit around Gayndah and Mundubbera along the upper Burnett valley, and vegetables near Brisbane.

Western Australia's small irrigated area, about 70,000 acres, is mainly on the subcoastal plain between Perth and Bunbury and is largely based on high-level dams on rivers like the Harvey and Collie, which store the winter flow. In addition, individual farmers raise ground water by wind-pumps and diesel pumps to support dairy cattle and the cultivation of vegetables and fruit (Table 16).

TABLE 16

| Crops | Irrigation Districts | | | |
	Waroona	Harvey	Collie River	Total
Pasture	3,371	13,274	12,095	28,740
Fodder Crops	210	221	609	1,040
Potatoes	9	84	333	426
Other vegetables	279	51	34	364
Orchards	—	178	45	223
Totals	3,869	13,808	13,116	30,793

Irrigation in South-west Australia, 1965-66
(Acres)
(Based on figures cited in *The Official Year Book of Western Australia*, No. 7, 1968, p. 255.)

There are also smaller irrigation areas in the north at Carnarvon on the Gascoyne River, where bananas and vegetables are grown; at Liveringa on the Fitzroy River in the Kimberleys, where rice is cultivated; and at Kununurra on the Ord River. The Ord River irrigation scheme is one of Australia's most interesting new agricultural projects (Fig. 59). Situated in the extreme north of Western Australia, the valley of the Ord River is being developed for cotton-growing and agricultural activities once thought impossible in those latitudes. It is hoped that the scheme will eventually support a population based largely on agriculture and settled in the growing township of Kununurra. The dam across the Ord River, about sixty-five miles inland from Wyndham, provides water for about 12,000 acres of cotton. At a later stage, it is hoped to build a larger dam thirty miles farther upstream with a storage capacity of three and a half million acre-feet, which will provide for the irrigation of a

FIG. 59.
The Ord River project.

further 150,000 acres and also generate hydroelectricity for new industries. The entire scheme will take fifteen years to complete at a cost of about twenty-five million pounds.

The farms in the scheme are all between 600 and 700 acres in size, and the farmers pay only one pound per acre for their land and thirty shillings per acre-foot for water. The cotton crop receives a government subsidy, and it is hoped that the cotton seed can be sold as protein for beef-cattle feed. Experiments to develop strains of sugar cane suitable for growing in this area are being carried out. A model township has been laid out at Kununurra, and the farmers live there and drive the few miles to their farms. As the near-by Kimberley plateau is scenically one of the most attractive and unspoilt areas in Australia, Kununurra may well develop into a flourishing tourist centre. As yet, secondary industry consists of little more than a cotton-ginning plant, but considerable development of ancillary industry should become possible if and when hydroelectricity becomes available from the larger dam. Meanwhile, the Western Australian government hopes that the Ord River scheme, if successful, will be one of the keys to opening up the hitherto undeveloped northern part of the state.

The only other state with even a small amount of irrigation is Tasmania, with 47,000 irrigated acres. These are mainly located on the rich alluvial soils of the Derwent valley, about thirty-five miles upstream from Hobart, where hop-growing is important.

Irrigation in New Zealand is much more limited than in Australia, being largely restricted to the Canterbury Plains and central Otago (Fig. 60). The Canterbury Plains are relatively dry, usually receiving under thirty inches of rain a year. As many of the soils there are gravelly and porous and the area is liable to occasional hot, north-west winds, which have a desiccating effect on the vegetation, irrigation is desirable in many parts of the plains. The irrigated acreage has risen from just over 200,000 in the early nineteen-sixties to 255,000 in 1965.[5] The main irrigated area lies between the Rangitata and Rakaia rivers, with Ashburton as its market centre. Pastureland for sheep occupies the greatest acreage, and grain is the most important field crop. In addition, hay, turnips and alfalfa are grown as fodder crops. The water is conveyed from the upper Rangitata by a 'head race' or main channel, from which it is distributed through smaller channels to

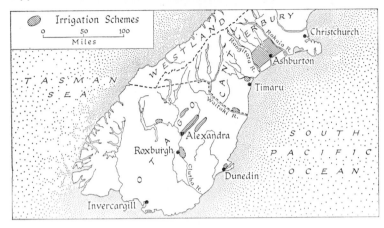

FIG. 60.   Irrigation schemes in South Island, New Zealand.

the fields. In central Otago, water for irrigation is obtained from the Clutha River for the cultivation of fodder crops, mainly grass, clover and lucerne hay. Irrigated orchards of cherries, apricots and peaches are also important, notably around Roxburgh and Alexandra, which are served by water-races and a network of distribution channels. In all, there are thirteen government irrigation schemes in central Otago capable of supplying an area of more than 50,000 acres.[6]

Bibliographical References

1. Taylor, G., *Australia* (Methuen, London), 1959, pp. 270-1.
2. Rutherford, J., 'Interplay of American and Australian Ideas for the Development of Water Projects in Northern Victoria', *Annals of the Association of American Geographers*, LIV, 1964, pp. 105-6.
3. Tweedie, A. D. and Robinson, K. W., *The Regions of Australia* (Longmans, London), 1963, pp. 161-62.
4. Robinson, K. W., *Australia, New Zealand and the Southwest Pacific* (University of London Press), 1962, pp. 173-75.
5. Cumberland, K. B. and Fox, S. W., *New Zealand, A Regional View* (Whitcombe & Tombs, Melbourne), 1963, pp. 216-17.
6. Olivier, H., *Irrigation and Climate* (Edward Arnold, London), 1961, p. 166.

Additional Source

Commonwealth Scientific and Industrial Research Organisation, *The Australian Environment*, 3rd ed. (Cambridge University Press), 1960.

INDEX

SUBJECT REFERENCES

Acre-foot, 16
Alluvial fan water, 133, 179
Appropriation doctrine, 19
Aqueducts, 106, 115, 216, 228
Aquifer, 5, 8, 40, 43, 45, 53, 88, 148, 191
Arab Development Society, 144
Archimedes' screw, 15; Plate 2A
Artesian water, 40-1, 49, 63, 146, 152, 179
Artificial precipitation, 6-7
Association of Landowners, 150-1
Associations of Land Betterment, 151
Atmospheric water, 6-7

Barrages, see Dams
Basin irrigation, 16, 30, 132, 181
Bilharziasis, 54n, 67
Billabongs, see Lakes
Border irrigation, 30; Plate 6B

Canal linings, 50-1
Canal systems, 27-8, 37; Plate 15
Cascina, 77
Cassa per il Mezzogiorno, 151, 153
Chains-of-wells, see Kanats
Chainan irrigation system, 109
Check structures, 27-8
Chemical spraying, 54-5
Computers, 37-8
Cone of depression, 43
Connate water, 6
Contour ditch irrigation, 30; Plate 6A
Controlled irrigation, 11, 69, 116, 139
Corrosion, 51
Corrugation irrigation, 32-3

Crop yields, 48-9, 68, 84, 101, 151

Dams, 13, 23, 79, 88, 104, 113, 122, 124, 126-7, 136, 138-9, 181, 192, 238
Denkli, see Shaduf
Dew conservation, 59
Ditch lining, 50-1
Diversion dams, 23
Doabs, 73-6
Double cropping, 84, 102, 109, 110, 114, 116, 117, 128, 136, 144
Drawdown, 43
Dry farming, 75, 79, 81, 86, 146, 193
Dry streams, see Wadis

Electrodialysis, 141
Equitable distribution, 19
Erosion, 56, 57, 88

Family farming, 86
Farm storage, 58-9
Farms, model irrigation, 89, 112
Fertilisers, 48, 121, 168
Fish breeding, 105, 107, 127
Flash distillation, 7
Flood control, 113, 120, 136
Flood irrigation, 11, 30-2, 136, 148, 153
Foggara, see Kanats
Fontanili, 152
Fossil water, 5-6
Frost protection, 168-9
Furrow irrigation, 32-3, 132, 151, 153, 199; Plate 7A

Gravity dam, 25

Ground water, 5-6, 40-5, 123, 132, 140, 179-80, 187, 191, 192, 193, 200, 207-8, 216-17, 241

Harat, see Sakia
Hexadecanol, 52
Hortas, 163
Huertas, 78-9, 157, 159
Hydrologic cycle, 1-2, 9

Incas, 13, 228
Indus Water Treaty, 121
Intercropping, 144
International Commission on Irrigation and Drainage, 105
Inundation canals, 15, 117
Irrigated pasture, 82, 84-5, 236, 243
Irrigation, capital costs of, 87
  co-operatives, 91, 135, 146, 150-1
  economic aspects of, 83-95
  Field Service Stations, 91
  functions of, 38
  history of, 11-14, 77
  human landscapes of, 62-82
  labour requirements of, 83-4
  origin of, 11-12
  societies, 85, 102
  total extent of, 99, 101

Jheel, see Tanks
Juvenile water, 6

Kanats, 12, 17, 63, 106, 132, 133, 146, 148
Karez, see Kanats
Kharif crops, 73
Korag, see Kanats

Lakes, 83, 240
Land consolidation, 91
Land subsidence, 44, 207-8
Laterals, 27, 66
Latifundies, 79-81, 160
Locusts, 195

Mekorot, 141
Mineralisation, 43, 48, 49
Monsoon, 107, 127

Moors, 14, 159
Multiple cropping, 102

Nile Waters Agreement, 188-9
Nilometer, 12
Nitrogen, liquid, 156
Noria, see Water-wheels

Oases, 41, 62-4, 106, 132, 138, 140, 145, 146, 179, 191, 193, 216, 228, 230-1
Octodecanol, 52
Organic irrigation, 168
Overcropping, 181

Perennial surface irrigation, 19, 22-39, 84, 181, 182
Persian wheel, *see Sakia*
Phoenicians, 13
Phreatic surface, *see* Water table
Phreatic water, *see* Ground water
Phreatophytes, 53-5
Picottah, see Shaduf
Pilot projects, 112, 134, 146, 196, 222
Pipelines, 28, 142
Pond-irrigation system, 107
Property rights in water, 18-20
Protective films, 52
Pumps, 24, 41, 128, 136, 183, 187-8

Rabi crops, 73
Rahats, 113
Rainfed irrigation, 11
Reverse osmosis, 7
Rice, 47-8, 69-71, 84, 102-3, 106, 108, 109, 111, 112-13, 115, 116, 121, 122, 124, 129, 134, 136
Riparian doctrine, 19
River regimes, 23
Rotation pasture, 77-8, 81

Sakia, sakiyeh, 12, 14, 18, 42, 63, 65, 117, 146; Plate 1B
Salination, 35-7, 125-6, 136-7, 145, 146, 155, 180-2, 191, 238; Plate 8

Sand-dune water, 179
Sawahs, 69
Sedimentation, 23, 55-8, 88
Seepage, *see* Water leakage
Shaduf, shadoof, 12, 14, 18, 63, 65, 163; Plate 1A
Silt, *see* Sedimentation
Silt-trap, 56
Siphons, 28
Slurry, 168
Small Dams Organisation, 127
Snow-ridging, 58
Soil Conservation Service, 91
Spray irrigation, *see* Sprinkler irrigation
Springs, 69, 132, 140, 145, 146, 148, 152, 163, 192, 232
Sprinkler irrigation, 33-4, 92, 140, 151, 153, 165, 166, 167, 168-9, 199, 219n; Plate 7B
Strip irrigation, 30; Plate 6B
Subirrigation, 34
Subsand dam, 180
Subsoil irrigation, *see* Subirrigation
Subsurface water, *see* Ground water
Subterranean water, *see* Ground water
Supplemental irrigation, 34, 43, 45, 81, 92-3, 99, 127, 151, 169, 215, 218, 241
Surface water, 5
Swamps, 179, 184

Tambour, *see* Archimedes' screw
Tanks, 12, 13, 16-17, 70-3, 105, 114, 117, 121, 122, 123, 146; Plate 10B
Tayouan irrigation system, 109
Terrace irrigation, 17, 69, 102, 108, 109, 115, 132, 140, 144, 205; Plate 3B
Traditional irrigation, 10-21, 62-5, 73-4, 99, 103, 106, 113, 117, 136, 163, 181; Plates 1, 2 and 3
Transplantation, 102
Treadmill, 69, 103, 106; Plate 3A
Tube wells, 37, 42, 73, 121, 123, 125-6, 146

Tunnels, 17, 115, 145, 214, 229, 239-40

Uncontrolled irrigation, 11, 84, 103, 110, 111, 205
Underground water, *see* Ground water
United Nations, ECAFE, 112
    FAO, 54, 103, 197

Wadis, 144, 146, 179, 191, 192
Water, application of, 29-34
    conservation of, 19, 50-60, 105, 141
    degradation of, 49-50
    desalination of, 7-8, 141, 143
    desedimentation of, 56-8; Plate 9B
    distribution of, 26-9, 88-9
    drainage of, 34-8, 88, 181-3
    evaporation of, 27, 51-3, 140, 172, 174, 186-7
    harvesting, 58-9
    leakage, 27, 50-1, 63, 121, 125
    measurement of, 28-9
    pollution of, 49
    quality of, 48-50
    reclamation of, 44, 50, 141, 222
    requirements, 47-8
    storage and diversion of, 23-6
    temperature of, 43, 48-9
    transpiration of, 53-5, 140; Plate 9A
    underground storage of, 52-3
    See also Mineralisation, Salination, Sedimentation
Water hyacinth, 53-5
Water table, 5, 34, 88, 126, 140-1, 145, 180, 187, 207-8
Water Tribunal, 159
Water vapour, *see* Atmospheric water
Waterlogging, *see* Salination
Water-meadow, 153, 155, 157, 167
Water-spreading, 53
Water-wheels, 15, 79, 113, 115, 148, 163; Plate 2B
Weirs, *see* Dams

Wells, 17-18, 73, 78, 87, 92, 103,
105-6, 117, 123, 133, 134-5,
137-8, 140, 145-6, 153, 163,
165, 166, 196, 217, 226, 232;
see also Tube wells

Wildlife, 155
Windmills, 15, 148, 165, 241
Wind-pumps, *see* Windmills

Zone of saturation, 5

REGIONAL REFERENCES AND PLACE NAMES

Aden, 146
Afghanistan, 20, 131, 132
  Helmand Valley project, 132
Africa, 101, 178-206
Algeria, 56, 64, 192
Angola, 200-1
Arabian peninsula, 62, 145-6
Argentina, 222, 227, 230-1
Aruba, 7
Asia, 99, 100
Australasia, 101, 235-44
Australia, 51, 52, 59, 84-5, 92, 235-43; Plate 20A
  Goulburn valley, 238-9
  Menindee Lakes project, 240-1
  Murray valley, 86, 235, 238, 239-40
  Murrumbidgee area, 47-8, 235, 237-8, 239-40
  Ord River project, 242-3
  Snowy Mountains scheme, 235, 239-40
Austria, 169

Babylonia, 12
Bahrain, 146
Bali, see Indonesia
Belgium, 45, 169
Bolivia, 233
Brazil, 231
  São Francisco Valley scheme, 231
Bulgaria, 29, 169-70
Burma, 107, 116-17
  Kyetmauktang Dam project, 116-17

Cambodia, 107, 109, 111
Canada, 20, 101, 218-20; Plate 18A
  South Saskatchewan River scheme, 220
Central America and the West Indies, 225-6
Central Asia, 101

Ceylon, 16-17, 70-3, 101, 122-3; Plate 10B
  Gal Oya project, 123
  Jaffna Peninsula, 123
Chad, 196
Chile, 10, 13, 222, 227-8; Plate 19B
China, 12-13, 17, 36, 69, 100, 101, 103-7
  Dzungarian Basin, 106
  Hainan, 108
  Huai River Plan, 105
  Hwang-Ho River, 12, 104
  Imperial Canal, 13
  Manass Basin, 106-7
  Miyun Dam project, 105
  San Men project, 104
  Yangtse River, 70, 104, 105; Plate 3A
Colombia, 233
Congo, 179, 184
Cyprus, 17, 148

Denmark, 45, 169
Dominican Republic, 226

East Africa, 197-8
Ecuador, 233
Egypt, 10, 13, 15, 16, 18-19, 20, 22, 23, 36, 37, 41, 51, 54, 64-5, 84, 180-8, 189; Plates 11A and 17A
  Aswan High Dam scheme, 20, 23, 54, 83, 185-7
  Qattara Depression scheme, 187-8
  See also Nile Valley
England and Wales, 81, 87, 92, 151, 166-9
Ethiopia, 184, 198
Europe, 150

Formosa, see Taiwan
France, 10, 14, 86, 153-7
  Languedoc scheme, 156; Plate 16A
  Rhône Valley, 153, 155

Ghana, 196
Greece, 15, 163, 165-6
Guernsey, 7
Guyana, 233

Haiti, 226
Hungary, 169

India, 13, 15, 16, 22, 37, 42, 51, 69,
    70-1, 73-4, 84, 87, 89-90, 91,
    100, 101, 117-22; Plate 13
  Bhakra-Nangal project, 118
  Chambal project, 118
  Damodar Valley Corporation
    project, 120
  Gandak project, 120
  Hirakud-Mahanadi delta pro-
    ject, 90, 119-20
  Indo-Gangetic Plain, 37, 42,
    73-4, 117
  Kakrapar scheme, 120
  Kangsabati scheme, 120
  Kosi Dam scheme, 122
  Mayurakshi scheme, 120
  Nagarjunarsagar scheme, 118;
    Plate 13B
  Punjab, 120-1; see also Pakistan
  Rihand scheme, 118-19
  Tawa scheme, 120
  Tungabhadra project, 89, 120
  Ukai project, 120
  Upper Kistna project, 120
  Uttar Pradesh, 73-4, 119, 121
Indochina, 109, 111-12
  Mekong River project, 111-12
  See also individual countries
Indonesia, 69-70, 85, 114-15
Inter-Calary Continental Albienne
    Nappe, 45, 191
Iran, 17, 20, 131, 132-5
  Greater Dez project, 134
  Muhammed Reza Shah Pahlevi
    Dam, 134
  Plain of Khuzestan, 133-4
Iraq, 45, 132, 135-8; Plate 15A
  Derbendi Khan Dam, 136
  Dibbis Dam project, 137
  Dokan Barrage, 136

Eski-Kalak project, 137
Gharraf project, 137
Habbaniya scheme, 136
Wadi Tharthar scheme, 136
Israel, 45, 58, 59, 140-3
  National Water Carrier, 142-3;
    Plate 15B
Italy, 10, 14, 76-8, 83, 86, 151-3
  North Italian Plain, 10, 76-8,
    151, 152

Jamaica, 226
Japan, 44, 47, 102
Java, see Indonesia
Jordan, 20, 142, 143-5
  Great Yarmuk project, 139,
    143-4
  Jordan Valley Plan, 142-3, 144

Kenya, 197
  Tana River project, 197
Korea, 102-3

Laos, 109, 110-11
Latin America, 222-34
Lebanon, 140, 142
  Litani project, 140
Libya, 64, 192-3

Madagascar, 203, 205
Malawi, 199, 200
  Shire Valley project, 200
Malaya, see Malaysia
Malaysia, 115-16
  Trans-Perak River scheme, 116
Mali, Niger River project, 194-5
Mauritius, 205
Mexico, 13, 20, 50, 101, 222-5, 227
  Papaloapan project, 223
  Raudales Malpaso project, 222
Monsoon Asia, 10, 69-76, 102-30
Morocco, 20, 45, 180, 191
Mozambique, 199, 200
  Limpopo valley project, 200
Muscat, 146

Near East, 101

Nepal, 122
  Chandra Canal, 122
  Judha Canal, 122
Netherlands, 45
New Zealand, 243-4
  Canterbury Plains, 243; Plate 20B
Nigeria, 179, 196
Nile Valley, 10, 12, 15, 16, 18-19, 53-4, 64-7, 178, 179, 180-7
North Africa, 191-3
North America, 207-21
North Vietnam, 15, 69, 70, 84, 109-10
  Tonkin delta, 109-10
North-western Europe, 166-9

Oman, 146

Pakistan, 10, 12, 37, 42, 51, 74-6, 100, 101, 123-9
  Chaj Doab, 126
  Ganges-Kobadak scheme, 128
  Indus Basin, 12, 123, 125, 126
  Indus Basin Plan, 124-5
  Khairpur project, 126
  Mangla Dam, 124; Plate 14B
  Sukkur Barrage scheme, 125, 126-7; Plate 14A
  Tarbela Dam, 124
Persia, 12
Peru, 10, 13, 222, 227, 228-30; Plate 19A
  Marcapomacocha project, 229
  Quiroz scheme, 228
  Tinajones project, 229
Philippines, 17, 69, 107, 109, 129
  Magat Dam, 109
  Pampanga River valley, 109
Poland, 169
Portugal, 163
  Alentejo Irrigation Plan, 163
Puerto Rico, 226

Qatar, 146

Rhodesia, 199-200
  Sabi-Limpopo Irrigation Project, 199-200
Rumania, 150, 169

Sabah, see Malaysia
Sahara Desert, 5, 17, 41, 45, 62-4, 179-80, 191; Plate 11B
Saudi Arabia, 45, 131, 145
Senegal, Richard Toll project, 195
Somalia, 198
South Africa, 198, 201-3
  Makatini Flats project, 203; Plate 17B
  Orange River project, 202-3
  Vaal River scheme, 202
South America, 101, 226-33
South Arabia, see individual states
South Vietnam, 109, 110, 111
South-east Asia, 11, 69-70, 84, 101, 107-17
Southern Africa, 198-205
Southern Europe, 151-66
South-west Asia, 10, 15, 131-49
  Tigris-Euphrates Valley, 131, 134, 135, 136
Soviet Union, 10, 20, 34, 36, 37, 50, 51-2, 58, 101, 170-6
  Caucasia, 51-2, 174-5
  Central Asian republics, 50, 58, 170-1, 172-4; Plate 5A
  Ukraine, 175-6
  Volga River, 174
Spain, 10, 14, 78-81, 83-4, 86, 151, 157-63
  Badajoz Plan, 79-81, 160-2; Plate 16B
  Murcia, 78-9
Sudan, 20, 53-4, 179, 183-5, 188-91
  Gezira, 24n, 54, 65-7, 85, 184, 188-9
  Jonglei scheme, 184-5
  Kenana project, 189
  Manaqil project, 66, 188-9
Sumatra, see Indonesia
Swaziland, 199, 203
Switzerland, 169
Syria, 15, 131, 138-40, 142, 143
  Damascus oasis, 138
  Orontes valley, 138-9
  Roudj project, 139
  Youssef Pasha project, 138

Taiwan, 91, 107, 108-9
Tanzania, 184, 197-8
  Pangani River project, 198
Thailand, 107, 111, 112-14
  Greater Menam project, 113;
    Plate 10A
  Yan Hee project, 113-14
Tibet, 107
Trucial Oman, 146
Tunisia, 45, 192; Plate 11B
Turkey, 20, 91, 131, 132, 146-8
  Keban dam and project, 148

Uganda, 183, 184, 198
United States, 7, 10, 13, 19, 20, 33,
    36, 40, 44, 48, 49-50, 51, 52,
    55-6, 81, 83, 101, 207-18,
    235-6
  California, 10, 43-4, 87, 207, 208,
    209-13; Plates 5B and 18B
  California Water Plan, 210-12
  Canadian River project, 216
  Central Arizona project, 213
  Central Valley project, 209;
    Plate 5B

Colorado-Big Thompson pro-
    ject, 214-15
Colorado River Storage Project,
    213
Columbia Basin, 25-6, 83, 85-6,
    214; Plate 4
Imperial Valley, 36, 48, 57, 67-8,
    212; Plate 12
Missouri Basin project, 217-8
Uruguay, 233

Venezuela, 231-3
  Bocono project, 232
  Cojedes-Sarare scheme, 232-3
  Guarico project, 232, 233

West Africa, 193-6
West Germany, 45, 151, 169
Western Europe, 10, 34, 81, 93

Yemen, 146
Yugoslavia, 166

Zambia, 91, 179